CD START INSTRUCTIONS

1 Place the CD-ROM in your CD-ROM drive.

2 Launch your Web browser.*

3 From your Web browser, select Open File from the File menu. Select the CD-ROM drive (usually drive D for PCs and the Desktop for Macs), then select the file called Welcome.htm.

* We have included the Microsoft Web browser Internet Explorer on this CD in case you do not have a browser or would like to upgrade or change your browser. Please review the Appendix of this book for more information on this software as well as other software on the CD.

MINIMUM SYSTEM REQUIREMENTS

The CD-ROM is designed to work on both Macintosh and Windows operating systems.

Macintosh System

- Computer: 68020
- Memory: 4 MB of RAM
- Software: System 7.0 or higher
- Hardware: 2X CD-ROM drive

Windows System

- Computer: 386 IBM PC-compatiable
- Memory: 4MB of RAM
- Software: Windows 3.1, NT, or 95
- Hardware: 2X CD-ROM drive

D1501493

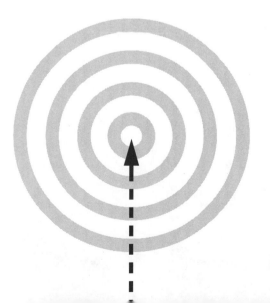

internet
GAMES
directory

Lycos Press
An Imprint of Macmillan Computer Publishing USA
Emeryville, California

internet GAMES directory

BY
MARC A. SALTZMAN

AND
SEAN MCFADDEN

Publisher	**Stacy Hiquet**
Publishing Director	**Cheryl Applewood**
Acquisitions Editor	**Kenyon Brown**
Development Editor	**Renee Wilmeth**
Copy Editor	**Debi Anker/Creative Solutions**
Production Editor	**Ami Knox**
Proofreader	**Joe Sadusky**
Cover Illustration and Design	**Megan Gandt**
Book Design and Layout	**Bruce Lundquist**

Lycos Press books are developed as a joint effort of Lycos and Que. They are published by Macmillan Computer Publishing USA, a Simon and Schuster Company.

Lycos ™ is a trademark of Carnegie Mellon University

Activision is a registered trademark of Activision, Inc. © 1996 Activision, Inc. MechWarrior, BattleTech, BattleMech and 'Mech are registered trademarks and NetMech is a trademark of FASA Corporation. ©1996 FASA CORPORATION. All rights reserved.

Lycos Press imprint books are produced on a Macintosh computer system with the following applications: FrameMaker®, Microsoft® Word, QuarkXPress®, Adobe Illustrator®, Adobe Photoshop®, Adobe Streamline™, MacLink®Plus, Aldus® FreeHand™, Collage Plus™.

Lycos Press, an imprint of
Macmillan Computer Publishing USA
5903 Christie Avenue
Emeryville, CA 94608

ISBN 0-7897-1055-2

Manufactured in the United States of America

10 9 8 7 6 5 4 3 2 1

This book is dedicated to **STAN AND HONEY SALTZMAN** for their support and encouragement.

This book is also dedicated to **IAN ELLIS** in acknowledgment of his superior gamesmanship.

Collectible Card Games 80

THE authors would like to express their appreciation to the great folks at Lycos Press and Ziff Davis Press, in particular: Ken Brown, Ami Knox, Renee Wilmeth, Lucresia Ashford, Debi Anker, and Carol Burbo.

Sean McFadden would also like to thank Katharine English for her professional encouragement and his family for their continuing support.

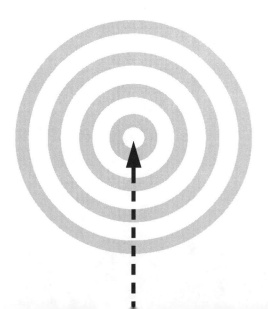

THIS book was written to serve as an introduction and guide to game resources that can be found online. We have attempted to choose sites that reflect the richness of the material available and to organize these selections in a logical, easy-to-use manner. Our hope has been to provide a tool that offers both quick reference and useful insight into how and where to mine the Internet for its abundant deposits of game-related treasures.

The Web directory section of this book, Part 2, breaks up each gaming genre into Action/Arcade, Adventure, Role-Playing, Strategy, Sports, Simulation, War, and Classics/Puzzles. To help you more easily navigate this section, we wanted to briefly define the classifications of games to be clear about our gaming categories.

Action/Arcade games are those which rely more on hand-eye coordination rather than story or strategy. These are often called *twitch* games and are generally faster paced and reflex-oriented. **Adventure** games involve the player in a journey of exploration and puzzle solving. The games usually entail a linear storyline in which you, the protagonist, set out to accomplish a goal or purpose through interaction with other characters and various objects.

Role-playing games (or RPGs) are similar to adventure games but rely on character development (usually involving statistics), conversation, and strategic combat more than puzzle solving. Huge epic quests and fantasy worlds are common and storylines are not always linear as in traditional adventure games.

Strategy games are a wide-ranging gaming genre but emphasize logical thinking and planning. They often stress resource and time management, which takes precedence over fast action and character involvement. **War** games are a subset of Strategy games that re-create historical battles or made-up conflicts between at least two parties. Strategic tactical direc-

tion and organization are necessary, and the game creators usually place the decision-making skills and execution of commands in the player's hands.

Sports games artificially simulate a single player or team's game from an instructional or playing perspective. Realism of the game is significant as fast action and strategy are often both necessary. **Simulation** games (or Sims) endeavor to realistically simulate a given animate or inanimate object. Most often Sims place the gamer in a first-person perspective and recreate machinery such as planes and tanks. There are, however, examples of Sims that attempt to mimic even the animal kingdom such as the Sanctuary Wood's game *Wolf or Lion.*

Lastly, **Puzzle or "Classic"** games include usually older leisure games such as card, trivia, word, tile, or board games. Chess, checkers, backgammon, Mahjongg, and Klondike Solitaire are perfect examples. They have also been known to describe more "simple" computer games as in older arcade favorites or games that may lack a deep story or player commitment; *Tetris* and Sid & Al's *Incredible Toons* are good examples. It is important to mention that some games may overlap categories but we have sorted them as suitably as possible (is Papyrus's *NASCAR Racing* a sports game or a racing simulation? Well, both, but you'll find it in our Sports section because, after all, it is a sport. You get the picture!).

As many of you are aware, the Web is in a constant state of dramatic change. You may find that some of the Web sites we've covered here have since changed their addresses or closed their doors entirely. This is a fact of Internet life, so don't be disappointed. Simply recheck the URL, try again later (there may be a network or server problem), or zip over to Lycos and find another site related to your interest. This minor obstacle may even result in some fun surfing and the discovery of other cool sites!

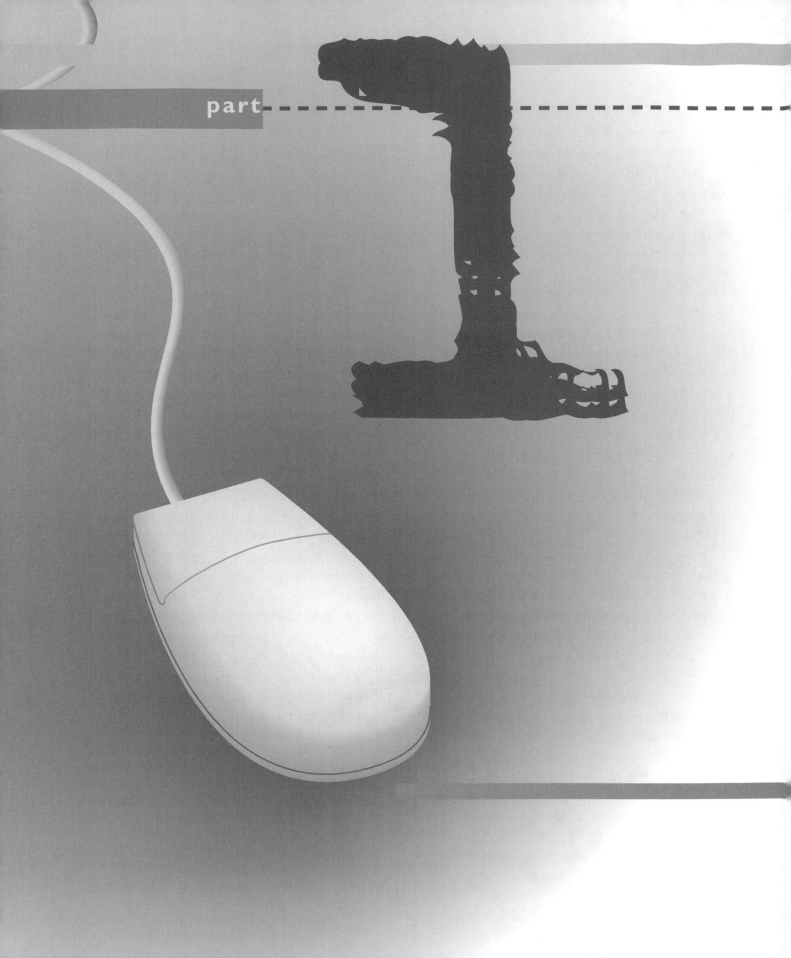

INTRODUCTION TO INTERNET GAMING

THE INTERNET DOES GAMES

SEARCHING THE INTERNET FOR GAMING RESOURCES

HOW DOES THE INTERNET PLAY?

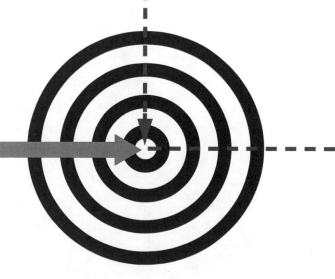

THE INTERNET
DOES GAMES

I remember as a child my grandfather bought me a book entitled *50 Card Games for Children* (by Vernon Quinn). I can still recall the awe of having so many *choices* of what to play—all with a simple deck of cards and this magical book. A few years later, at age 12, the same feeling returned while I sat with this warm black Colecovision unit on my lap and a mountain of game cartridges at my side. Little did I know then, that something would come along and bring the entire *world* of gaming to my fingertips—the Internet.

This international assembly of interconnecting networks has taken the accessibility of knowledge to new exciting levels never before imagined. Due to the Internet's overwhelming size and prowess, the world of gaming has grown so fast, and in so many directions, that we need to analyze and organize its rapid development. This book is designed to introduce what computers and cyberspace have to offer the gamer—what exactly there is out there, how to find it, and how to use it.

First, let us take a brief chronological look at the history of gaming as a whole—this way we can put the Net's presence and impact into perspective. From there we will discuss the young history of gaming on the Net itself and the various styles of gaming available to satisfy all tastes.

MAHJONGG TILES TO PINBALL ISLES

The oldest game in history dates as far back as 3,000 B.C. The tile game of UR originated with the Sumerian people located in the region of the Tigres-Euphrates valley (or, by modern maps, only 100 or so miles from the Persian Gulf). As early as 2,000 B.C., one century later, we find a wall painting in an Egyptian tomb depicting two people playing a game of pieces later to be identified as Senet, a predecessor to Backgammon. However, the ancient Chinese board game Mahjongg is possibly the best documented and most widespread multi-player game that dates back between 3,000–3,500 years ago. Four players would collect engraved tiles to make matched sets before their opponents did.

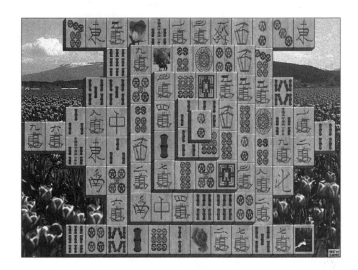

In years to follow other tile and wood games such as variations of checkers, dice, and dominos became prevalent in many other Eastern societies. Chess was said to have been introduced to Persia as early as 531 A.D.

Internationally recognized card collector Ben Bornstein maintains that Persian, German, and Italian royalty would pay artisans to hand-paint wooden cards since they were the only ones that could afford such a luxury. But it wasn't until the 15th and 16th centuries, when manufactured paper became widespread, that playing cards would become available to the common man.

The 20th century gave birth to cardboard and plastic board games such as 1935's Monopoly, which has sold over 160 million copies since its debut. More importantly for our discussion, the first coin-operated pinball game also emerged out of the 1930s. Starting with Gottleib's historical debut of Humpty Dumpty, the pinball industry continued to boom into the 1950s and 1960s and became a multimillion dollar industry. The rise of electric and magnetic pinball machines opened the doors to modern day gaming rooms, or arcades.

This was the calm before the storm, for just around the corner was the first of the two most exciting turning points in the history of interactive entertainment—electronic video gaming. This revolution in the 1970s occurred simultaneously in both arcades and home systems where games could be played right on your television.

FROM PONG TO DONKEY KONG

Pong was invented in 1972 by Atari corporation's Nolan Bushnell.

This simple game—with "paddles" and a white "ball"—led to the video arcade explosion of the late 70s and early 80s that etched a place for itself in the annals of pop culture. Before fighting games ruled the digital scene, arcade faves—like Space Invaders, Missile Command, Galaxian, Asteroids, Defender, Centipede, Frogger, Zaxxon, Q-bert, Robotron, Donkey Kong, and of course, the megahit PacMan—swallowed millions of quarters from red-eyed teenagers. These instant classics soon became household words and could only be rivaled by other types of games in the 80s such as Rubick's Cube and Trivial Pursuit.

ON THE HOME FRONT

Pong was released for home use in 1974, and over 100 variations were cloned and distributed by companies such as Coleco, Radio Shack, and Magnavox. But the breakthrough was the Atari 2600. With hundreds of cartridges to choose from, Atari modified the way we looked at gaming by offering a wide selection of titles right at our fingertips. In the years that followed, 1979's Intellivison and 1982's Colecovison dominated living room floor space. Both the arcade and home gaming industry suffered from a mid-decade dry spell until the advent of the 16-bit Nintendo and Sega gaming systems in the latter half of the 80s.

Compactibility (Nintendo Gameboy vs. Sega GameGear) and 32-bit capability (Sega Saturn, Super Nintendo, 3DO, Sony PlayStation) laid the groundwork for TV gaming units in the 1990s. These gaming consoles remain popular today, but 64-bit newcomers are edging their way into homes slowly, proving the preference for superior quality graphics and fast 3D rendering.

It wasn't until the past couple of years that our home computers could be used as *advanced* gaming systems. Many text-based and graphically weak games came from computers in the late 80s and early 90s, but they just couldn't compete, or excel, against TV gaming consoles. That is, until now.

The rise in the presence of computers in the home allowed for bigger budgets for computer entertainment manufacturers, which ultimately

meant better games. The processing speed of PCs improved, as did graphic quality (CGA and EGA to VGA and SVGA); hard disk space and RAM increased; and digital sound became the mainstay.

Then, in 1992, a small, little-known Texas company by the name of id Software released a breakthrough game entitled Wolfenstein 3D. This radical new gaming engine put the player in a completely 3D environment so it appeared as if one was looking out of the soldier's eyes. To this day it remains the biggest *shareware* hit (the try-before-you-buy software philosophy originated from the mind of developer Jim Knopf). Shareware is based on the honor system—the user is expected to send the company money if he or she continues use of the product or wishes to request the full version. Shareware, or freeware, marks an important echelon in our look at Internet-related computer gaming. One year later the folks at id Software did it again with Doom—another momentous game for yet two other reasons. First, this was the first game of its genre where the player could play head-to-head against others who had the same game. Computer artificial intelligence (AI) could now be replaced with real human strategy and discernment. Secondly, gamers could create and exchange their own levels, so the possibilities for gameplay were endless. Many subsequent "3D perspective" games followed in the footsteps of Doom by supplying level editors for free to their players.

In the years to follow games became much bigger, supporting more graphics, better quality sound, and eventually full-motion video. CD-ROMs (which held up to 500 times more information) soon replaced floppy diskettes as a means of holding all this data, and Compact-Disc-quality audio also enriched the gaming experience. Games were soon programmed to support multiplayer activity involving network play, direct PC-link, modem-to-modem, and eventually Internet play.

Although the latest trend in computer gaming includes Virtual Reality (VR) headsets and 3D acceleration cards, these new toys are microscopic in comparison to the impact of how this new global communication has changed the face of gaming.

GAMING AND THE INTERNET

As previously mentioned, the integration of electronics was the first of two key turning points in the history of modern gaming. The second, of course, was the emergence of the online world; Bulletin Boards, online services, and the Internet.

Before the Internet was what it is today, localized online Bulletin Boards (BBS) offered text-based chat groups, electronic mail, and minimal file-transfer. These systems were based on a single PC or Macintosh attached to one or more modems, which allowed people to call in via their phones and computers. In 1978, Roy Trubshaw, a University of Essex student in England, wrote the game Mazewar, which became the first multiple-user dungeon (or domain) game (MUD)—see Chapter 12 for a look at this genre of game. It was a multiplayer version of the text game DUNGEN whereby players would type in commands and try to find, and kill, other players trapped in the same maze. MUDs are still popular today and are widely available. Non-real-time e-mail games (mainly

war games and trivia) were also played regularly and still have a small but faithful following.

Around the same time BBSs became more prevalent, Usenet groups, or discussion forums, were used by students at Internet-linked universities to communicate to one another. Soon after games appeared, but it wasn't until the late 80s and early 90s that more advanced, larger services were offered on a national, then international scale. Online pay-networks such as the Imagination Network, America On-line (AOL), Genie, CompuServe, and Prodigy all offered their own exclusive games. These companies varied in prices and services and they still remain popular today, although the continued growth of the Internet (primarily, the World Wide Web) has been giving them a run for their money. Why *pay* when you can PLAY!?

The Internet, in its infancy, was primarily a text-based web of information including smaller networks like Usenet newsgroups, FTP (file transfer protocol) archives, Gopher, and Archives sites—all of which are still around today and are discussed later in this book.

The dawn of the World Wide Web (WWW or Web) really opened up the world of gaming on a global scale. The WWW is the universe of hypertext servers (HTTP), which are the servers that allow text, sound, graphics, animation, and video to be mixed together. The Web did to the Internet what Windows did to DOS—it added a user-friendly graphical interface whereby clicking on colorful icons executed a given action or command. Internet application software, or *browsers,* are the Web surfer's window to the online world. Mosaic was the first successful graphical browser developed by the National Center for Supercomputing Applications (NCSA), responding to a growing demand for a user-friendly point-and-click interface. Popular browsers today like Netscape Navigator or Microsoft Internet Explorer share one of the most recent additions to hit the Net for gamers—free *plug-ins* to add to your existing software. Popular add-ons to date are Java and Shockwave (interactive animation and sound), Real Audio and Crescendo (sound and music), and Quick-Time and VDOLive (video). A visit to a Web site equipped with any of these plug-ins enhances the surfer's overall multimedia experience. What this means to gamers is that they can now play games, in real time, without downloading first to their hard drive.

These two Web sites provide most of the browser add-ons:

Netscape Navigator 'Plug-Ins':
http://home.netscape.com/comprod/ mirror/navcomponents_download.html

Microsoft Internet Explorer 'Add-Ins':
http://www.microsoft.com/ msdownload/

There are many ways an online subscriber can use the Internet as a tool to satiate his or her gaming needs. However, two main distinctions must be made first. Single-player games are games for one person only that can either be downloaded and played off the hard drive or played in real-time online. Multiplayer games include head-to-head gaming with one other or many other players (either online or with your favorite CD-ROM game, but also in real-time), or non-real-time games such as e-mail games.

The newest and most exciting trend on the Web are multiplayer gaming networks such as The Entertainment Network (TEN) or M-Player, where one can play a favorite CD-ROM against others anywhere in the world. Even graphically intense games such as Duke Nukem 3D, Command & Conquer, Warcraft II, or Quake are now coded by their manufacturers to allow head-to-head Internet play. Multiplayer play is also available if the game supports it, whereby hundreds of players can take part in the same virtual environment. As with Doom, the spontaneity and diversification of *real* human opposition can now replace programmed artificial intelligence—an important step in the continuing evolution of computer gaming.

Statistics predict that by January 1, 1998, there will be approximately 3,500 CD-ROM titles released that will be able to support Internet multiplayer action.

Modem speeds are continuing to increase with the presence of Integrated Services Digital Network lines (ISDN) and Cable modems promising up to 400,000 bps (bits per second). With these lightning speeds on the horizon we may witness yet another exciting turn for the future of Internet gaming, including real-time video and faster real-time online games with even better graphics and sound.

There are, of course, also sources on the Web where one can access information about non-Internet games, including hints, walkthroughs, patches/upgrades (program fixes), add-on levels, discussion forums/chat groups, and FAQs (frequently asked questions files). Up-to-the-minute reviews and free downloadable demos are also available to game enthusiasts to assist them in their future purchases.

The *Internet Games Resources Directory* is an exhaustive roadmap to finding the most comprehensive gaming resources on the Net. This book is designed to illustrate the many facets of gaming available online, encompassing both the various single-player and multiplayer games worldwide. Gigantic archives containing thousands of free game demo sites will be provided in the pages to follow, along with online magazines (or *e-zines*), discussion forums and chat groups, gaming manufacturing directories, and game strategies and tips for all the hottest titles today.

Think of this book as your manual to a tremendous adventure game with many possibilities and outcomes. Like slowly peeling off the layers of an onion skin, you will unravel this massive Internet playground. Enjoy your journey—you have the entire world at your leisure!

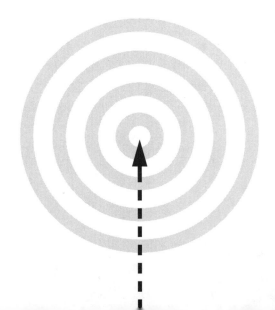

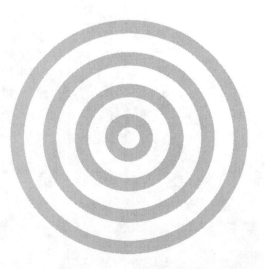

2

SEARCHING THE INTERNET FOR GAMING RESOURCES

SOMEWHERE, right now, a game fan is hard at work on what to his mind is "the most awesome" Web page devoted to his favorite game. Somewhere else, another gamer is posting answers to queries she's run across in her favorite newsgroup. Still, at another computer screen in another part of the world, two players are hunched over working out code for a new Java applet, a new game level, or even new gaming software they plan to share with the whole Internet community. Daily, new sites, new information, and new games are appearing on the Internet for the enjoyment and amusement of all.

With the Internet's gaming environment as dynamic as the play it generates, newbies, or those new to the Internet, sometimes find it hard to stay abreast of the latest goings on. In fact, some even find it difficult to uncover the resources that have been online for quite awhile. But no one need be lost in cyberspace nor feel overwhelmed by the growing volume of information available online if they know how to search for what they're seeking. And the key to effective searching is using the best search tools that are available.

WELCOME TO LYCOS: COME PET THE WOLF SPIDER

Based in Marlboro, Massachusetts, Lycos, Inc. began in 1994 with a simple realization: As the Internet grew, users would need more and more efficient tools for locating the resources available online. It was then that Lycos set about the task of "cataloging" the Internet and created what has become the company's top-rated search engine, an electronic query system that allows users to find Web, FTP, and gopher sites by subject and then link to those sites with a simple click of a mouse.

The first step toward developing this manageable search system required that Lycos build a database in which users could search. This need led to the development of the company's powerful spidering technology. The Lycos spider actively roams the Internet in search of Web, FTP, and gopher sites, pursuing its quarry much like the *Lycosidae* family of spiders for which the company is named. At the time of this writing the number of unique Uniform Resource Locators (URLs), or Internet site addresses, captured by the spider had topped 59 million, and by the time this book is printed, the number will probably exceed 60 million.

Imagine it! Every day, the Lycos Wolf Spider, as it is affectionately known, prowls the Internet looking for new site addresses to capture and bring home to feed the Lycos database. But new addresses aren't the only information the spider retrieves. The spider also collects keywords that will help distinguish each site from all the others and by which users can search for a site's address.

ALL ABOARD THE LYCOS SEARCH ENGINE: THE BASIC SEARCH

Once the database was of sufficient size to be of use, Lycos then put in place the easy-to-use interface which allows anyone from anywhere in the world to search through the continually expanding database free of charge. Here's how it works:

Let's say I want to find something on games.

1   I go to the Lycos home page at http://www.lycos.com/.

2   I type the word "games" into the text entry box.

3   I mouse-click the search initiator button. What I get in return is the listing for every

document in the database that has the word "games" as a keyword.

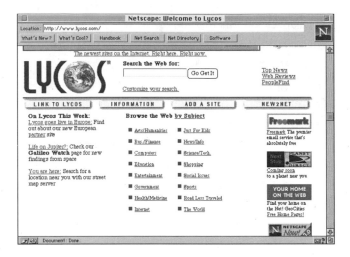

Easy enough, right? Well, yes and no. Today there are over 130,000 documents—these could be HTML files, image files, sound files, or anything else that can be linked to via a URL—with the broad-meaning keyword "games" in their listings. Tomorrow there will probably be even more. That's too much information to go through. I need to narrow my search and be more specific. If I knew which game I were looking for, I could enter its name and find the URLs of the sites offering information on that game. But let's say I don't know the game's name. Let's say I'm not even looking for a specific game, but rather a type of game—card games, for instance.

If I were to input the words "card games" into the text entry box and initiate a search, my results would still include the thousands of documents I found with my first search; however, because there is a second keyword, the listings would be sorted such that the ones that appear first will be the ones which the search engine "thinks" are most likely what I'm after. Now that's progress, but the above example could also return a variety of new documents and add them to my search results as well.

The reason for this is the search engine is set to return the listing for every document which has "card" or "games" as a keyword. Think of it as an "OR" search. So even though sites discussing computer cards have nothing to do with games, they could turn up in my results. By the same token, even though sites discussing video games have nothing to do with cards, they could be in the search results as well. So how do I refine my search to look for only those documents which contain both keywords at once?

To limit my search results in this manner, I need to visit the Lycos Search Form screen. There, I can fine-tune searches so that the results that are returned will meet more exact criteria. To get to the Search Form screen, simply mouse-click the hyperlink below the data entry box on the Lycos home page, or link to http://www.lycos.com/lycos-form.html.

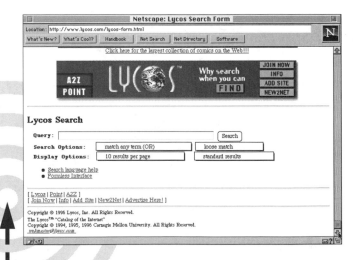

TINKERING WITH THE SEARCH ENGINE: WHAT DOES THIS BUTTON DO? SEARCH OPTIONS

There are two Search Options available that allow users to manipulate the parameters of a search. The first option changes the "match" criteria the search engine uses in comparing keyword strings to the database. In other words, it allows users to change the search from the default setting, "match any words," to the more particular "match all words" setting and to tell the search engine to return only those documents with keywords that match all the keywords entered in the data entry box. Consider this an "AND" search. By refining a search in this manner, users can eliminate from their search results many of the irrelevant documents that are returned by an "OR" search, and produce results more keenly focused on the subject at hand.

In my case, by changing to the "match all words" setting, I can ask the search engine to eliminate from the search results all the companies selling computer cards, which have nothing to do with games, and all the varieties of game sites that fall beyond the realm of cards. To change the match setting, simply mouse-click the default setting, "match any words," and a pull-down menu will appear. Then, move the highlight to the match setting desired.

Other "match" settings are also available. The search engine can also be set to match specific numbers of keywords, from three to seven. These options could come in handy, especially if a keyword has an alternate spelling. For instance, let's say I'm interested in collectible card games, but I know that the word "collectible" has a commonly used alternate spelling, "collectable." I could enter the keywords "collectible collectable card games" into the data entry box, change the match setting to "match 3 words," initiate the search, and feel confident the results will include sites with both collectible and collectable card games.

The second Search Option allows users to set the selectivity of the search engine in determining match results. Settings include *loose, fair, good, close,* and *strong.* Obviously, when the search engine is left on its loose setting (the default), searches return the greatest number of entries, or "hits," because the search engine casts a wide net to include all documents with any relevance to the keywords queried. Conversely, when the setting is changed to strong, a search will return the fewest number of hits, including only those documents with a strong relevance to the keywords queried. It's best to experiment with this setting to better understand its effect on searches.

The Search Form also provides Display Options, which allow users to change the format in which the search report is presented. If less information is wanted than is presented in the standard report, users can request a summary only. Or, if more information is desired, a detailed report can be requested. The number of hits listed per page can also be changed from the standard 10 hits to 20, 30—even as many as 40 hits per page.

KEEPING THE SEARCH ENGINE ON TRACK: WILD CARDS

Sometimes when conducting searches, situations arise that require the use of "wild card" characters in order to get the results desired. For example, let's say I want to search for collectible card games, but want to make sure the search engine isn't too particular about the spelling or misspelling of the keyword "collectible." In this case, I could use the "$" character to convey that command to the search engine and enter "collect$" as the keyword. The search engine would then look for any word variation built upon the root word "collect."

Conversely, if I want to limit the search engine from looking for variations on keywords, I could add a "." (period) to the end of the word. So if I were to enter "game." as the search word, any site with "games" as a keyword would be passed over.

Finally, let's say I want to look for card games, but am not interested in collectible card games. By attaching a minus sign or hyphen to the search word, "-collectible," I can tell the search engine I'm not looking for those sites, and though they will appear in the search results, they will be sorted to appear down the list so that the games I'm interested in, such as hearts, spades, bridge, and poker, appear first.

OTHER LYCOS SEARCH TOOLS: POINT AND a2z

As a dynamic company geared to serving the changing needs of its customers, over the past few years Lycos has added additional online search tools to complement its star performer, the Lycos search engine. First came the Point catalog of top Internet sites, and soon after, the a2z directory.

Unlike the Lycos search engine, which allows users to effectively search the whole of the World Wide Web, the Point catalog is limited in its size and scope. The sites available at Point represent what are considered the "Top 5%" of everything posted on the Web and are organized by category. Rather than 130,000 documents dealing with games, Point catalogs about 100 sites. These sites

have been selected for their presentation and content, and for the joy of the experience they provide. Each site is rated and reviewed, so Point readers can get a feel for a site before they link out. Point offers gamers a general reference—a place to sample the variety of play that can be found online.

The a2z directory, on the other hand, offers a more extensive resource. It features the most linked-to sites on the Internet, organized by category and subcategory. Under the category of games, the dozen or more subcategories include general indices, company home pages, and individual game sites. The directory offers gamers an easy way to track down some of the more popular gaming sites online.

SITES TO SEE, THINGS TO DO

Gaming resources are available via every Internet protocol, not just the Web. Web pages offer interactive gaming, documents that introduce and detail the finer points of games, and indices that serve as gateways to voluminous topical resources. Newsgroups offer gamers a venue to discuss topics of interest, aid one another, and meet new folks with similar interests. FTP sites are often a gold mine of downloadable game demos, shareware, and freeware; while a telnet connection can gain players admittance to online, real-time playing areas, including MUDs, where fantasy worlds are built through the ingenuity of the players who inhabit the realm.

When it comes to games on the Internet, there's no shortage of things to do and see. But not every game is for everyone, nor should that be the case. Cyberspace is a vast environment with plenty of room to accommodate most every taste. It is then up to each of us to seek our own level of excitement and entertainment. We should leave those games that do not appeal to our personal preferences to those who find them worthwhile.

Always remember, especially when viewing a game fan's page or an interactive gaming site posted by an apprentice programmer, that someone invested his or her time to create that page. And they did it for free, for the love of doing it. This is the spirit that makes the Internet as dynamic as it is. It should be encouraged, not diminished. So appreciate and recognize these efforts for what they are: someone's attempt to share their enthusiasm and to communicate fun.

3

HOW DOES THE INTERNET PLAY?

THIS chapter is designed to illustrate the many ways to use the Internet as a tool to fulfill all your gaming needs. There are literally thousands of resources, whether your preference is to download games to play off your hard drive, play real-time games online (single- or multiplayer), or to get information to assist you (or add to) your existing games. Strap yourself in as we have a lot of ground to cover first, before we start on our digital journey…

ARCHIVED SITES AND RESOURCES

The most common means of gaming on the Internet is to find the game you are looking for and download it to play off your hard drive. At this point in time your internal hard drive, or hard disk which stores the data, is faster than your modem connection through a server. For this reason alone it is beneficial to copy the game first to your own computer. Another purpose of doing this is to eliminate the time you are online for the obvious cost concerns, notwithstanding the amount of Internet traffic we would all experience if we just played our games in real time off the Net. The games that we download are not full commercial releases but are shareware, freeware, and game demos.

Based on the honor system, shareware games are free to play and distribute, providing the gamer with a unique opportunity to "try before you buy." However, a small *donation* to the author is expected if continually used (information on how to contribute is usually stored in the *readme.txt* or *order.txt* file). Freeware, although some consider it to be the same thing, has taken on a slightly different meaning over the past few years. Freeware are games that are free to play, and a fee is not neces-

sary (but most often welcome, of course); and they are usually made by independent authors willing to give out their work for recognition. Most often, freeware derives from college or university students designing games as a hobby or to gain programming experience. Game demos are similar to shareware in the sense that they may only contain part of the full game and are expected to give you a taste of what the gist of game is all about. No donation or fee is required—these companies are banking on you getting hooked on their games so you will go out and pick up the full copy. (For example, seven levels are free to download although 35 levels are found in the full version of the game.) Once downloaded, these can either be single-player or multiplayer games (networked or modem-to-modem play but not on the Internet); but the key is, you have to play them off your hard drive.

There are thousands of places online that house these shareware, freeware, and game demos—they are most often found in FTP archives or on the World Wide Web.

FTP or File Transfer Protocol Sites

File Transfer Protocol is just what it sounds like—a common way of moving files across the Internet. By logging onto an FTP site you can send or retrieve files. These publicly accessible repositories of material are known as "anonymous FTP servers" as you ID *anonymously* as a temporary visitor on their computer. FTPs contain vast indices, and gaming manufacturers often make their product demos accessible to the public by having them stored on these FTP sites ready for download. For example, the EA (Electronic Arts) FTP server is ftp://ftp.ea.com/, where the EA games are available with a mouse-click in the Demos section (see Figure 3.1).

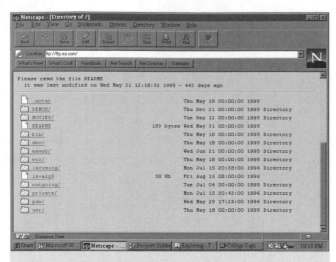

Figure 3.1
FTP site for Electronic Arts

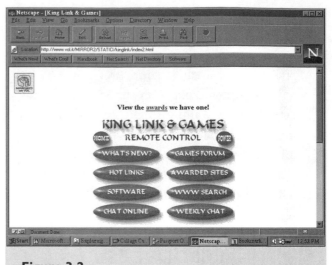

Figure 3.2
Example of a Web page—King Link & Games page

Other prevalent FTP sites are huge archived lists, such as ftp://ftp.cdrom.com (72GB of hard drive space on their system!), or ftp://ftp.sunet.se (Swedish University Network), where thousands of games from different companies are obtainable. The World Wide Web is fast becoming a common front door for these FTP sites, so you may not need to visit a raw FTP site often.

World Wide Web

The World Wide Web (WWW) exploded over the past few years as an exciting hypertext server application by which, through *browsers,* we access text, sound, and images. Instead of plain text as on FTP sites, the WWW browser uses a user-friendly graphical interface to help you navigate through the Internet easily, with big colorful clickable buttons (see Figure 3.2).

The majority of games covered in this book are available on the World Wide Web. These Web site addresses, or Uniform Resource Locators (URLs), house these games on their server for download,

or their page is a graphical front door to a FTP archive. There are three main types of Web sites to get games: gaming manufacturer Web sites, personal or fan-related pages, and larger independent mega-sites.

Gaming company Web sites are either the developer or publishers of a computer game you are interested in playing, such as Interplay (http://www.interplay.com/) (see Figure 3.3) or 7th Level (http://www.7thlevel.com/).

Personal home pages or fan-related sites are usually specialized into genres of games or one game in particular, such as Grendel's Gaming Lair (http://www.grendelslair.com/), or Tom's Doom Page (see Figure 3.4)—a tribute to the game Doom (http://www.cs.tulane.edu/www/Ward/doom.html).

These sites are made by everyday people of all ages that would like to share their gaming interests with the online world. The game-related Web sites that receive the most *hits* (number of people to visit the page) are definitely the huge sites, such as Happy

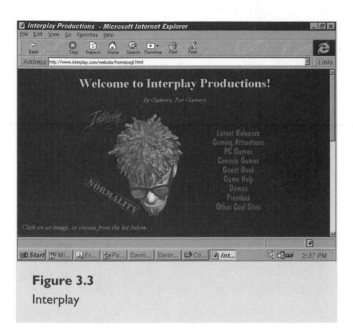

Figure 3.3
Interplay

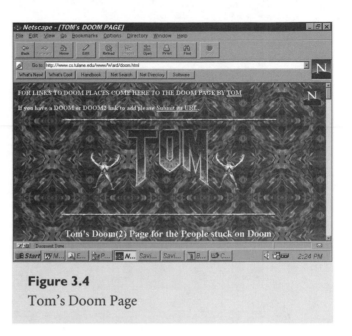

Figure 3.4
Tom's Doom Page

Puppy (http://www.happypuppy.com/) and Games Domain (http://www.gamesdomain.com/), that house thousands of shareware and demo games under one "roof."

These mega Web pages can afford to offer such services because they are supported by advertisements, some sites may contain an online store to purchase games by mail.

Besides downloading games, all of these Web sites discussed also contain useful gaming news, strategy tips and hints, patches (updates that fix bugs in a computer game), Frequently Asked Questions (FAQs), add-on levels, chat groups, and discussion forums.

ONLINE GAMING: SINGLE-PLAYER, HEAD-TO-HEAD OR MULTIPLAYER GAMES

Another way to enjoy games on the Internet is to actually play online in real time. Single-player or multiplayer games are available in many formats

on the Net that do not require you to download the game first.

SINGLE-PLAYER REAL-TIME GAMES

Real-time online games on the World Wide Web are fun and convenient because there is little or no waiting involved. More and more Web sites are featuring games to play while you are there, but keep in mind they are considerably slower and probably less detailed than the games you would be playing off your hard drive.

Refreshed Frames

In your Web travels you will come across some game pages that allow you to play games online in real time by using refreshed frames—the Web site reloads the screen to a new related page based on your clicked or typed decision. Sites such as the Net Noose game of hangman (see Figure 3.5) (http://www.netscape.com/people/nathan/net-noose/index.html), the 80s server's Who Can It Be

Now? musical trivia game (http://www.80s.com/who.html), or the Cindy Crawford Concentration game (see Figure 3.6) are perfect examples (http://www.Facade.com/Fun/concentration/).

There are, of course, more in-depth, free, epic-like role-playing game pages that you can play in real time as well, such as CyberDungeon: The Game (http://www.cyberdungeon.com/game/game.html) and S.P.Q.R. (http://pathfinder.com/@@ThtPtAcAPgvo5BTO/twep/rome/#cont).

Plug-Ins

Plug-ins are exciting new additions for World Wide Web browsers—namely Netscape's Navigator and Microsoft's Internet Explorer. Unlike refreshed frames, you can now experience games with real-time interactive animation and sound. These plug-ins, or browser add-ons, such as Sun Microsystem's Java, Macromedia's Shockwave, and FutureWave's FutureSplash are available for free on the Net or may already come equipped with your newest browser version. For example, *WebFrog,* a Frogger clone (see Figure 3.7), can be played at The Internet Arcade (http://www.rocketsci.com/interarc.html), or try your luck with Broderbund's Mudball Wall (http://www.broderbund.com/studio/activemind/mudball.html) (see Figure 3.8).

Figure 3.5
Net Noose Game

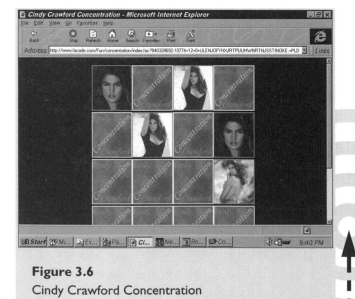

Figure 3.6
Cindy Crawford Concentration

Figure 3.7
Shockwave WebFrog game

Needless to say, these plug-ins have brought real-time gaming on the Web to new levels, examples of great Java applets/scripts and Shockwave games will be given throughout this book.

MULTIPLAYER REAL-TIME GAMES

If solo play isn't your thing or artificial intelligence just doesn't challenge you enough, then take advantage of the Internet's awesome head-to-head or multiplayer games. There are many types to play and most have their own chapter later in this book, but here is a brief overview of multiple-user dungeons (MUDs, and MUSHs, MOOs, MUXs, MUSEs), Commercial Online Services, Game Networks, and other real-time multiplayer games.

Multiple-User Dungeons/Dimensions/Dialogues (MUDs)

These real-time multiplayer role-playing games embrace the gamer in combat, strategy, and adven-

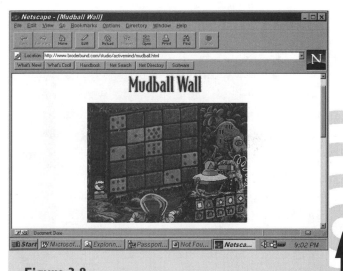

Figure 3.8
Shockwave Mudball Wall game

ture scenarios with many others around the world. Most often these games are text-based, and an online avatar or alias (a *virtual* representation of you) explores a huge world involving a large cast of characters and puzzles. These are the oldest (and probably still the most popular) games played on the Internet, as there are thousands of variations of MUD-type games. The best place to start is a MUD Index—a list of what's out there on the Net, such as The MUD Catalogue of Catalogues (http://www.educ.kent.edu/mu/catofcat.html), MUD Links (http://shsibm.shh.fi/mud/muds.html), or The MUD Connector (http://www.mudconnect.com/).

See Chapter 12 for more information about these games.

COMMERCIAL ONLINE SERVICES

Before the WWW's "Big Bang," major online services offered gamers text-based and graphical head-to-head games, which still remain strong despite the fierce competition from the Web. Well-known online pay services—America Online (AOL), The ImagiNation Network (INN), Prodigy, CompuServe, and especially Genie (with over 25 multiplayer games)—(which are really just big bulletin boards) have fairly good multiplayer games. These commercial online services carry an exclusive line of games and charge roughly $10.00 a month for five free hours and $3.00 per extra hour to be part of their online community. See Chapter 13 for more information.

Entertainment has always been a priority for these companies, but recently they have been having problems keeping up with the new generation of online networks using the Internet as a platform for multiplayer computer games.

GAME NETWORKS

Enter the newest and best thing to hit the Internet for gamers since the onset of the World Wide Web—online dial-up networks allowing you to play your favorite CD-ROMs against anyone, anywhere. Companies such as DWANGO, The Entertainment Network (TEN), XBAND PC, and M-Player GameWay are paving the way for head-to-head or multiplayer gaming as if you were playing through a networked or basic modem connection. By downloading these companies' software first at their Web site (it may also be bundled with newer store-bought CD-ROMs), the gamer can play titles such as Quake, Duke Nukem 3D, Command & Conquer, and Warcraft II in a fast real-time environment.

As this book goes to press, these gaming networks are offering free software and access, but they do mention that prices will soon be announced. Game companies such as Blizzard Entertainment (developers of Diablo and the Warcraft series) have also begun to start their own multiplayer pages for their games. "Battle.net" is Blizzard's free gaming arena, where all you need is your usual TCP/IP access Internet account (http://www.blizzard.com/bnet/bnet.htm).

See Chapter 13 for more information about these sites and other free Internet gaming networks, such as Kali and IHHD, where you can use your current Internet account and existing CD-ROM games.

OTHER MULTIPLAYER GAMES

As in the single-player section, there are also refreshed-screen Web pages that offer live real-time multiplayer games. One such popular site is The Bingo Zone (http://www.bingozone.com/) (see Figure 3.9).

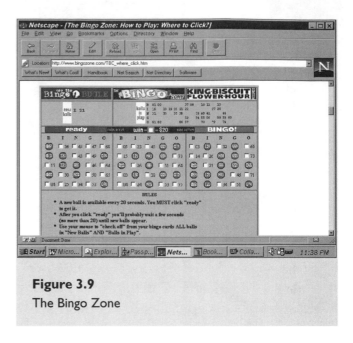

Figure 3.9
The Bingo Zone

A new ball is shown every 20 seconds as you compete worldwide for cash prizes, but you have to click to reload the screen when ready. Another example of a refreshed real-time multiplayer game is Legends of Kesmai—an interactive graphical SVGA role-playing game (http://www.kesmai.com/).

E-MAIL GAMES AND NON-COMPUTER GAMES

A small but dedicated group of gamers enjoy non-real-time e-mail games or play-by-mail games (PBMs). People have been playing Diplomacy since the 1960s via snail mail, but the onset of the Internet has made e-mail games not only faster, but more convenient and more exciting. These include various role-playing and Dungeons and Dragons games, mysteries, online scavenger hunts, wargames, trivia, and other strategy games such as Chess. See http://www.pbm.com/~lindahl/pbem_magazine.html and http://www.pbm.com/~lindahl/rgp.faq.html for your various choices. Chapter

11 will also provide more information and a deeper look into these types of games for all parties interested.

Let's not forget that the Internet can also be used to aid in other electronic gaming endeavors such as TV console video gaming systems (Nintendo, Sega, Sony PlayStation) and arcade and pinball games. Non-electronic amusements such as sports, card, tile, and board games can also benefit from the information attainable online. Many strategy guides, FAQs, and specific posting forums, or *newsgroups* (see Figure 3.10), are located on the Net and offer specialized interactive information on your favorite pastime.

For example, do you need the fighting codes to beat Sega Saturn's *Virtua Fighter 2*? Then visit The Virtual Times International WWW site at http://virtualtimes.com/vidgames/satvlfr.htm. Not having much luck at your weekly poker game with your buddies? Then roll on down to RGT Online at http://www.RGTonline.com/ for some useful tips. Do you want to see who may own a nostalgic pinball game you have always wanted to buy for your basement? Then zap to the rec.games.pinball newsgroup and post your request. Get the picture? The Internet can be used in so many ways to satisfy

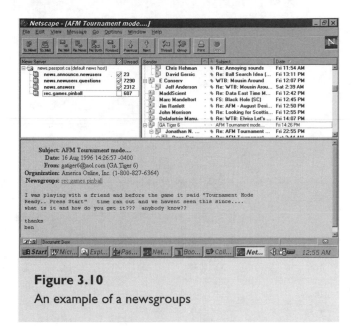

Figure 3.10

An example of a newsgroups

all your single-player or multiplayer gaming needs. We are now ready to dive into thousands of exciting gaming sites on the Net, which are outlined and categorized for you in the pages to follow. Don't forget—if you like what you see at a particular Web page, save it as a "favorite" or "bookmark" it for future visits. Enjoy your online expedition, and happy surfing!

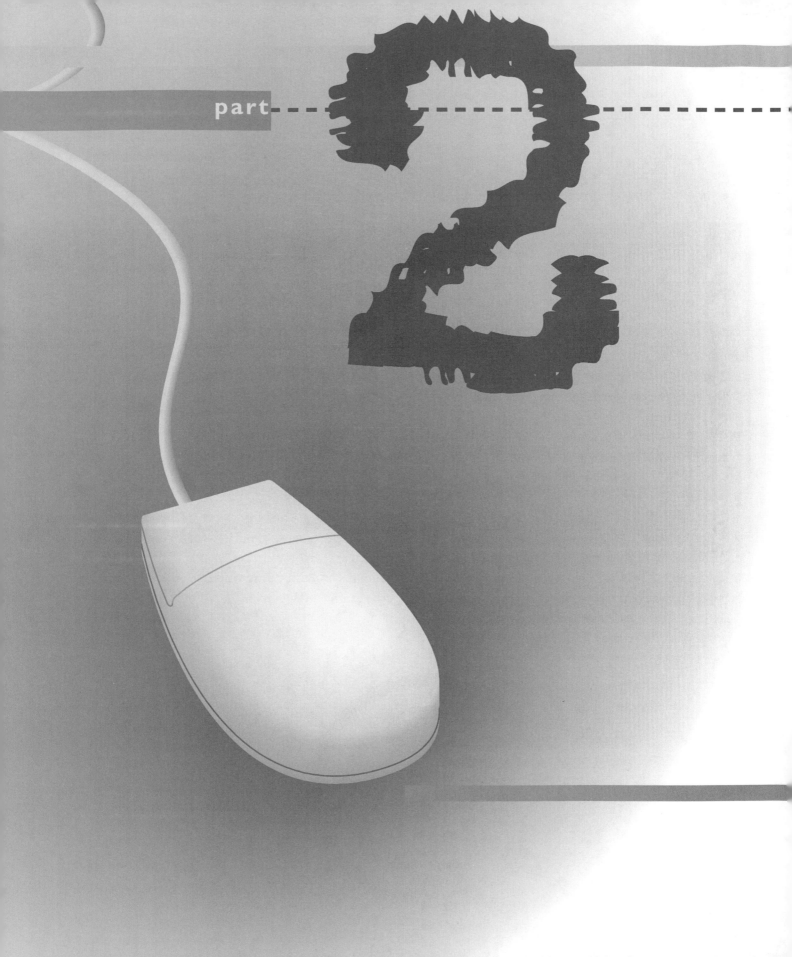

part 2

WEB DIRECTORY OF GAMES

ACTION GAMES

ADVENTURE GAMES, COLLECTIBLE CARD GAMES, AND ROLE-PLAYING GAMES

SIMULATION GAMES

STRATEGY AND WAR GAME SITES

SPORTS GAMES

BOARD GAMES, CARD GAMES, AND PUZZLES

4

ACTION GAMES

3D Games Page

http://www.techline.com/~musickl/
nigel.htm

A Web site dedicated to 3D favorites Doom I, Doom II, Heretic, Hexen, Duke3D, and Dark Forces. Shareware, cheats codes, WADS (custom-made levels), and a long list of links are provided here. Essentially one long page with hot-linked icons to the game company's FTP site.

3D Gaming Scene—Dark Forces

http://www.pol.umu.se/html/ac/split/
darkforces.html

A links-happy page connecting the Dark Forces fan to various Web sites and FTP archives around the world. Cheats and mission codes to use during play are also given. This is part of the 3D Gaming Scene mega-site set out to provide gaming-action fans with links and services to enlighten your gaming encounters. The main page is at http://www.pol.umu.se/html/ac/spel.htm.

@dver@ctive's Shocked Games and Diversions

http://www.adveract.com/shkgames.htm

Five games that require the multimedia plug-in Shockwave are featured here: Plaque Attack, Frenzy!, Shockwave Bowling, Darkroom Game, and Tooth Time. Some of the games are a massive 640 x 480 in size (opposed to the usual small Shockwave window in the middle of the screen), so adjust your browser accordingly. @dver@ctive has developed these titles as part of their interactive business card lineup.

Ackbar's Dark Forces & Jedi Knight Page

http://www.muzik.com/ryloth/

This Netscape 3-enhanced site gives you Dark Forces (DF) and Jedi Knight (JK) news, previews, screen shots, sounds, FAQs, patches, links, and many files (mainly DF levels and other utilities). Crescendo music from the games chaperone your stay here, and Ackbar's site is constantly updated with all the latest gossip and even a Quick-Time movie page (see a CNN JK scene!). An impressive page.

A Larger World

http://hubcap.clemson.edu/~pranks/
swmain.htm

This is primarily a Star Wars fan site but contains some useful files and information about the game Dark Forces. Pete Rank's page covers add-on levels, patches, editors, utilities, links, and toys. A framed split-screen design is used here to access what you want more efficiently. Note: Check out the middle right panel for a screen-shot slide-show of all the highlights of the Dark Forces universe.

Alienvasion!

http://www.LooseJocks.com/littlealien/

A very cute (and tiny 10K!) Shockwave game to play in real-time. A Mothership releases little green aliens that run around this Web page. Click on them with your mouse to make them splatter! It gets tough as they multiply, so keep your trigger-finger ready. This page also hot-links you to the super-extended version of Alienvasion, with music, scoring, and messages. Funny URL name too!

All Marathon Zone

http://studwww.rug.ac.be/~tklskns/
Marathon.html

A page dedicated to Bungie's 3D-action hits Marathon and Marathon 2: Durandal. Download the demos, the Marathon cheater, spoilers, strategies, and the Universal Patcher (save anywhere, plus more...). This page has some great links to other Marathon-related sites; check 'em out.

Andy's Duke Nukem 3D Homepage

http://www.empnet.com/andy/duke3d/

Andy Gerlicher's page provides cheats, maps, FAQs (including a FAQ file for editing .CON files), patches, and other files for the Duke enthusiast. Download either the full shareware version v1.3d (5.7 MB) or six diskette-sized split files. A link to 3D Realms page is also provided.

AUTHOR'S PICK

Applet Arcade, The

http://members.aol.com/shadows125/arcade.htm

An award-winning collection of over 50 Java-based games to play in real time. No downloading to your hard drive is required. From Air Assault to Xcogitate, everything is here, including Centipede, Asteroids, Missile Command, Pinball, Pool, and many more. The Frogger and Pacman were particularly worth playing. Some are at this Web site while others are linked to the corresponding page. All of these games loaded very fast, and there is a wide assortment to choose from. Enjoy!

Asterix's Game Page
http://members.tripod.com/~game29/

This ambitious and fairly successful page received quite a few hits this past summer. Asterix contains an easy-to-use graphical engine to help you decide what you want out of this gaming site. This Web page is most deserving in its online gaming composition, including forty or so links around the world for fine online real-time games. All game sections of this site including 3D action

games, Mac titles, and gaming utilities are presented in alphabetical format with handy brief descriptions.

Baal's 3D Gamer's Arena
http://www.net1plus.com/users/baal/

This is a site strictly devoted to Doom, Doom2, Duke Nukem 3D, Heretic, and Hexen. It's a frames-enhanced site with an intro, FAQs, shareware, and cheats for each 3D game. I found something out just by fooling around with the monster animation. Click on the demon and he stops running; click again and he starts!

Battle Beast—J. Mateo Baker's Page
http://www-scf.usc.edu/~jmbaker/battlebeast/

Cool page on the ultimate cartoon fighting game from the folks at 7th Level. Graphics, sounds, cheat codes, hints, and "taunts" are downloadable or readable online. Check out the intro title page shot or the New Scores area—a point-by-point structure for each Battle Beast move.

Blex's Killer Duke Nukem 3D Page
http://mrnet.com/blex/killer.htm

Yellow frames, Metallica midi music, and wavy blue wallpaper? Cool! This Duke page is best viewed at 1024 x 768 pixels, with Netscape version 3.0. Download or access a Duke Nukem live chat, cheats, screen shots, FAQs, links, and a massive file list (mainly user levels and RTS files). Surfing Duke stuff listening to "One" is quite cool (especially that middle part with the double-kick bass drum!). Grab the zipped-up wallpaper collection while you're here—it contains thirty or so backgrounds.

Blue's 3D House of 3D Carnage
http://www.panix.com/~sheaslip/3d/

Choose your Deathmatch poison: Quake or Doom 2. This site is a tribute to the multi-player angle of both hot 3D games. Read Blue's helpful tips on keeping alive, or download the multitude of levels to try out. Tons of FAQs and other worldwide sources of hot-links make this page an all-inclusive nest for blast-fest fun. The Doom 2 page asks, "Tired of getting your ass kicked?" so study Blue's Deathmatch Strategy Guide—there are over twenty HTML pages!

Brad Wernicke's Duke Nukem Web Site
http://www.bwernicke.com/games/duke/

Almost five hundred user maps are here for your downloading pleasure. One of the most respected places on the Net for up-to-date news and files for 3D Realm's monster hit, Duke Nukem 3D. Other utilities, cheats, FAQs, and a message center are here, or download Aapogee's shareware, Death Rally, for a change of pace. If Quake is your thing, visit Brad's page at http://www.bwernicke.com/quake/quakfram.htm.

Bryan's MechWarrior 2 Page
http://www.lookup.com/homepages/69636/mw/mech2.html

One of the better Mech sites to hit on the Web, containing information on all Mechwarrior 2, Ghost Bear's Legacy, NetMech, and Mercenaries. Bryan's site is well-designed and uses Web technology, including animations and frames. Hints & tips, utilities, reviews, news, cheat codes, and more are all used here for the right reasons: to present the gaming content of this

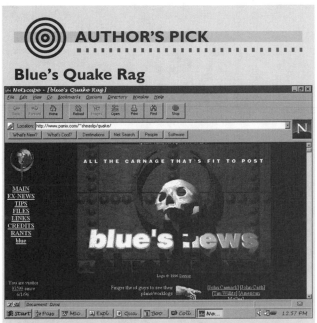

AUTHOR'S PICK
Blue's Quake Rag

http://www.panix.com/~sheaslip/quake/

News and files for id Software's 3D game of carnage, Quake. This is one of the best sources on the Net for Quake stuff (along with Quake Command and Scary's Quakeholio). Keep up-to-date with current news and industry happenings (such as new Quake utilities). Download maps and other files. Make a note of his helpful tips to fine-tune your single-player or multi-player game. Bookmark the useful Quake links, or read Blue's unique and opinionated "Rants" section. There is also a hot-link to "finger" the guys at id to see what they're working on next (John Carmack, John Cash, Tim Willits, and American McGee). Extremely popular page (almost 100,000 hits in the three months since its inception).

Web page in an attractive and engaging manner. If time is on your side, go to Bryan's home page at http://www.lookup.com/homepages/69636/home.html to shoot over to other gaming sections such as Warcraft II, Command & Conquer, Tie Fighter, and Dark Forces.

Bust Out!
http://www.tiac.net/users/pschwarz/ bustout.html

A Shockwave clone of the old arcade hit, "Arkanoid." Move the paddle back and forth with your mouse and don't let the ball hit the ground. Try to remove as many of the colored tiles as you can and advance to more difficult levels. Neat sound effects and fast load time make this game an enjoyable diversion.

Byron's Duke Nukem 3D page
http://www.geocities.com/TimesSquare/ 1956/

A fan-related Duke Nukem 3D page offering custom-built maps, screen shots, reviews, and links. On the opening page, there's a great picture of Duke with one of the major beasts from the game. Download the sequel to "Outpost"—a single or multi-player user map (Outpost 2.zip) made by Byron himself and very cool! Visit Byron's Cyberdemon page (Doom 2 and Hexen levels) at http://www.geocities.com/TimesSquare/2598/.

Chris's Duke Nukem 3D Homepage
http://www.burgoyne.com/pages/chriss/

Join a live Java chat or download Duke secrets, cheats, maps, or the latest shareware version. The best part of this site are the files available for free: Build FAQs (on how to make your own user levels), various front-end map shells, Internet-play programs, icons, RTS sound clips, a new music utility, a Duke Nukem 3D screen-saver, and other cool stuff.

Chris's Hexen Page
http://www.healey.com.au/users/thornton/

A myriad of Hexen resources including tons of down-loadables (demos, editors, levels), links, and a very big HTML Hexen guide, written by Chris Thornton himself. The downloads page will please any Hexen fan that likes to create, exchange, or try out custom-built levels. A job well done.

Classic Video Games Index
http://users.colloquium.co.uk/~fraser_gj/ page3.htm

A page dedicated to all that is late 1970s and early 1980s. The video game revolution touched the hearts of many of us, and the beeps of Galaga and chomping of Pacman makes me feel nostalgic. Broken into six zones, The Classic Video Games Index provides share-ware or freeware PC clone games of past favorites: Defender, Frogger, Space Invaders, Q-bert, and the like. Many related links are also available. Love the *Comic Sans* font.

Classic Video Games Nexus
http://iquest.com/~lkseitz/cvg_nexus.html

Opposed the Classic Video Games Index, this site caters more to the home invasion of video game consoles. Units such as Pong, Atari, Intellivision, and Colecovision are attended to. There is some coin-operated info, but the TV units dominate here. There is also an impressive list of links to other related sites (emulators, collectors, etc.).

Claw Marks
http://www.jade.se/wc/

The online Wing Commander (WC) Magazine is another thorough counterpart to Origin's popular space series. The surfer is accompanied by WC music upon landing on this page, which serves as a good background while browsing the various sections. These separate areas are broken out effectively using frames and clickable graphic images. News of a rumored WC movie and game sequels are discussed in detail. Also available here are WC history, pilot profiles, strategies, and more.

Also see:

The Official Wing Commander Web Site at
www.ea.com/origin/english/prod-info/pc-cd/
current-titles/wing-4/index.html

and its Unofficial counterpart Terran Confederate

Underground at
www.tcu.why.com

Other good fan-related pages:

God's Backyard: Ext. Privateer
http://www.teleport.com/~daberle/god/priv.htm

The Axuis System
http://www.geocities.com/SunsetStrip/2367/
wingm.htm

Phoenix Chronicles—Wing Commander
http://falcon.jmu.edu/~schollks/wing.html

AUTHOR'S PICK
CleverMedia's Shockwave Arcade

http://clevermedia.com/arcade/

Web guru Gary Rosenzweig created this fantastic arcade boasting fourteen adventures for all gaming tastes. Clean and attractive Web design allows the gamer to experience real-time fun with games such as Pretty Good Bowling, Scamper!, The Jazz Thinger, and Space Pirate. Make sure you try out either of the two golf games, which feature multiple courses and cool sound effects that make for great re-playability. Shockwave is one of the best plug-ins available for Netscape or Internet browser.

Evan's Wing Commander Homepage
http://www.icenter.net/~eadnams/

My Wing Commander Page
http://www.geocities.com/TimesSquare/4570/
wcpage.html

Calisto IntraNews
http://www.calisto.com/

The Terran Outpost
http://greatbasin.net/~madman/topage.html

Wing Commander on IRC
http://www.calisto.com/bearcat/wcirc.html

Combined Duke 3D and Quake Page
http://www.ipswich.gil.com.au/~andrewm/

Brought to you by Australia's infamous "InFaMOuS" is a combo page dedicated to the top two action titles of 1996. The Duke Nukem 3D section has demo downloads, links, and other stuff (FAQs, cheats, maps, and patches). Quake has pretty much the same (a shareware version to download, links) as well as cheat codes, a pak-to-wad utility, and various maps for single-play or QuakeMatches.

Complete Gaming Headquarters
http://www.netwrx.net/macgyver/

A Links, FAQs, and cheats site heavy on action titles: Descent I & II, Doom, Duke Nukem 3D, Heretic, Hexen, Mechwarrior 2, One Must Fall, Primal Rage, Quake, Rise Of The Triad, Strife, Terminal Velocity, and more. Click on your game(s) of choice and The Complete Gaming HQ will give you a long list of relevant Web sites to check out, strategy files, and more.

Computer Gaming World's Dark Forces Tips
http://www.zdnet.com/gaming/print/9506/features/doc2.html

One of my beefs about Dark Forces is that you can't save your spot during the game, and since the fourteen levels are so big, it's frustrating to have to start all over—even if you're near the end. Thank heavens Computer Gaming World magazine (one of the world's leading authorities on computer games) has provided helpful hints and strategies to beat the game by Jason Kapalka. Select which mission you're having difficulty with and it'll bring you to the appropriate help page along with screen shots.

Craig's Unofficial Abuse Website
http://members.tripod.com/~ABUSE/

Craig's site offers news, levels, FAQs, cheats, shareware, and links—all related to Crack Dot Com's smash game Abuse. The success of this side-scrolling game came as a surprise, considering most computer

action titles use the first-person 3D perspective engine. Lots to download and read here if you're a fan of the game or want to see if you are.

Crusader: No Regret
http://www.ea.com/origin/english/prod-info/pc-cd/coming-soon/no-regret/

The official site to EA/Origin's sequel to Crusader: No Remorse. In Crusader: No Regret, you're still a renegade silencer out to settle a score with the powerful World Economic Consortium, using up to twenty-one fast-action individual maneuvers and fifteen devastating weapons. At time of visit, all that was available here was a game description, system requirements, and product screen shots.

Crusader: No Remorse—official page
http://www.ea.com/origin/english/prod-info/pc-cd/current-titles/crusader/

At Electronic Arts/Origin's U.S. site, grab Crusader screen shots (makes cool wallpaper); "meet" the designer/director, Tony Zurovec; download and view two movies (both AVI and MOV); play the demo; read the system requirements and game description; or play the MOD music files. Info on ordering the official strategy book is provided as well. Before you buy the official strategy guide, see if these sites help you out: http://www.pcentertainment.com/games/Dec95/tip/crusader-tip.html, http://www.pcgamer.com/s_crus.html, or http://www.happypuppy.com/hleukart/crusadercheat.html.

Crusader: No Remorse—Welcome to the Resistance
http://www.intac.com/~thatguy/crusader/crusader.htm

After your introduction to and mission debriefings for the Resistance, you get to the heart of the site: cool cheats and hints to Origin's hit game, Crusader: No Remorse. Brought to you by "That Guy," this page also gives away a secret at the end of Level 2. Check out the five game-character animations.

Cursed to Crawl

http://users.aol.com/benupies/index.htm

A creepy page offering Quake clan listings, related sites, and QuakeMatch information. Benu's page on Doom II (including WAD levels and other utilities) is also just a click away. Read the Napalm Death quote at the top of the page, or if you're curious, go through Benu's "Esoteric Stuff" area.

Cyberdemon's Page

http://www.geocities.com/TimesSquare/ 2598/

This Web site includes Doom2 and Hexen levels, screenshots, and map previews. A great title pix greets you upon your arrival, and from there you can download Webmaster Byron Collins' own levels or other uploads to his page. Sounds, Utilities, Links, Reviews, Comments, and Coming Soon sections are listed in the framed sidebar. Visit Byron's Duke Nukem page as well at http://www.geocities.com/TimesSquare/1956/.

Duke Nukem 3D Page at Gamelords.com

http://www.gamelords.com/

Part of the terrific Gamelords Web site now (see the mega-sites chapter), it isn't often that a page can actually contribute to the appreciation of an existing game. However, visiting Damian August Holmberg's frames-happy fan site breathes new life into an already awesome action game. There are literally hundreds of worthy all-inclusive Duke Nukem 3D sites around the globe, but few have managed to offer what is found here. This Web site is as rich in content as it is in design. A chat group, level maps, and a boundless library of add-ons to really get more bang out of your buck are available.

Dark Forces Cosy Nook

http://userwww.service.emory.edu/ ~anoviko/nook.html

A very cozy Web page designed to give its visitors Dark Forces goodies. Editors, converters, and other

AUTHOR'S PICK

Dark Forces Homepage, The

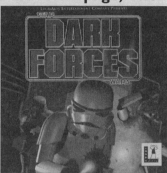

http://www.best.com/~dalton/DarkForces/

This is probably the most popular Dark Forces Web site on the Net, with more than a quarter of a million hits and counting. Everything is here, including custom-made levels (and editors to make your own), screen shots, news, sound clips, cheat codes, FAQs, Mac files, and affiliated links. Also noted are enemy, weapons, and item pictures with descriptions. Visit the related Dark Forces Newsgroup at alt.games.dark-forces or visit the official site at the Lucas Arts http://www.lucasarts.com/.

utilities are available for download to create new levels, characters, and backgrounds in your existing Lucas Arts Star Wars game. Links to related sites around the globe are also offered.

Dark Forces GOBs Page

http://www.pncl.co.uk/%7Eidries/dark_ f.html

Since Dark Forces doesn't support multi-player play (hiss, boo!), at least there are some creative folks out there making their own levels and refining the ones given with the original game. This page provides the utilities to make your own GOBs (levels like Doom WADS, Warcraft PUDs...) and gives away a few, too.

Dark Forces Midi Page
http://www.tiac.net/users/carr/darkmidi.htm

You know a game is well done when you're whistling the tunes well after turning off the computer. Or when a theme song played during a game pumps you up to a point where you're ready to blow up anything in your way. You know anything to do with Star Wars has good tuneage, so why not collect and play the songs when you're surfing the Web? This page houses almost fifty midi tunes from the game broken up into handy levels and enemies. If time isn't on your side, download a zipped-up version of all forty-six tunes available in one whole swoop (only 490KB!).

Dark Forces Page, The
http://www.wpi.edu/~ss/DF_index.html

Fans of the Star Wars universe and Lucas Art's Dark Forces (DF) alike retreat to this site, featuring a walk-through, speech upgrades, editors, patches, art packs, and other miscellaneous information. The Web design is very frugal but the neat DF utilities make it a beneficial stay. The hypertext version 2.6 of the FAQ deserves recognition. It's compiled and maintained by Karsten A. Loepelmann.

Dark Forces WDFUSE Home Page
http://www.ping.be/~ping4087/wdfuse.htm

WDFUSE is a Windows-based editor exclusively designed for creating new Dark Forces worlds. The shareware program allows the gamer to edit existing game levels or add-ons built by fans, or to generate new levels from scratch. Besides downloading the program, this Web page discusses features and tips in using WDFUSE along with updates, news, and other related utilities. To save time and frustration, check out the known problems and bugs area before diving into WDFUSE.

Death of the Duke Page, The
http://152.160.53.241/Duke/

A very different Duke Nukem 3D tribute site specializing in midi tunes and the "first and largest automated player listings." Grab Duke utilities and editors, maps, RTS and CON files while you listen to thirty-plus Duke

songs available on the sidebar jukebox. Nice dark feel to this page.

Definitive Duke Nukem 3D DukeMatch Repository, The
http://nukem.apk.net/

The folks here take their Duke 3D multi-player gaming SERIOUSLY. What they offer to you, for free, are the absolute finest DukeMatch maps that the Duke community has to offer—they will not post a DukeMatch map on their site that doesn't meet the highest of standards. Let's face it—there are tons of places on the Net to grab DukeMatch user maps, but it's good to know there's some discretion out there (I've seen some pretty bad levels). Try out BlockWar, Trenches, and City @ War.

Descendarium: An Illustrated Guide to Descent I & II
http://www.gamesdomain.com/moonglow/

No stone has been left unturned while creating this colorful and often animated guide to one of the best PC action games to date. Parallax Software and Interplay have taken Doom's 3D engine to new heights by implementing a complete six-degree-of-freedom rotation to your spacecraft (up, down, right, left, or complete somersaults front or back). Joerg Riebert's Descendarium is a very good supplement to Descent and Descent II and contains secret and bonus levels, cheat codes, strategies, screen shots, downloadable demos, and much more. A very modern and useful site.

Descent 2: Vertigo Overload

http://www.atw.fullfeed.com/~jkrutke/des-main.htm

This is a 21-gun salute to Parallax and Interplay's computer action title, Descent 2. Download the demo, video clips, and cheat codes, or view gameplay screenshots, words from the authors, features, and links. A page on music from the game is also highlighted. Nice animation and graphics at this site.

DMU Duke Nukem 3D Page

http://www.cms.dmu.ac.uk/~hc2jb/
Duke.html

Nice-looking frames-enhanced Web site dedicated to all that is Duke. The knockout game of the year gets more royal treatment with strategy tips, screen shots, news, and neat downloadables: the shareware game, patches, editors, FAQs, user custom-built maps, and other utilities. There's also a cool links section and message area.

Don's Hexen Pages

http://www2.awinc.com/users/dgronlun/
hexen/hexen.html

A more graphically impressive site than The Wacky Hexen Page, and it probably has more hits than John Olerud! Don's fan site is also a contender for the most comprehensive assortment of Hexen files and add-ons found anywhere. This gorgeous Web page, along with Don's own Duke Nukem 3D site (http://www2.awinc.com/users/dgronlun/duke3d/duke3d.html), continues to serve as a template for many other successful personal gaming pages. There are access hints, walkthroughs, stats, inventory and beastiary guides, WADS, e-mail, FAQs, links, and a guestbook.

Also see:

The Official Hexen Page at GT Interactive
http://www.gtinteractive.com/hexen/

and the

Official Hexen Page at Raven Software
http://www.ravensoft.com/html/hexen.htm

AUTHOR'S PICK

Digital Nostalgia

http://www.umich.edu/~Webspin/games/

Marc Sakey's award-winning page was created as a high-tech memory lane, a moment of digital nostalgia. Game console emulators such as Commodore 64, Atari, or Colecovision are given for your PC, or download and play the best clones for arcade classics. Try out excellent remakes of Donkey Kong, Dig Dug, Galaxian, Ms Pacman, Lunar Lander, and more. A tutorial on how to zip and unzip a game is offered here for beginners. This Web page also has a hearty Links section to related sites around the Web, or check out the cool utilities available like Mo'Slo (to slow down older games that just cook on your current Pentium!). All in all, a great page for us Generation Xers that have a sentimental slant toward arcade games and early TV console systems.

Don's Duke Nukem 3D Pages

http://www2.awinc.com/users/dgronlun/
duke3d/duke3d.html

One of the more popular Duke Nukem sites (and let's face it, there are LOTS of them). The midi version of the theme song keeps you company while you peruse through the files, cheats, links, FAQs, and of course... levels. These pages are now mirrored at GamePro magazine online at http://www.gamepro.com/. Also check out Don's Hexen Page at http://www2.awinc.com/users/dgronlun/hexen/hexen.html.

Don Sielke's Home Page: Dark Forces
http://interoz.com/usr/dsielke/dforces.htm

If you have completed Dark Forces but are not ready to shelve the game just yet, try out these custom-built add-on levels and components. Many to choose from, including *Reclaiming Cloud City, Emperor's Gambit* and *Operation: Just Cause* are from Don's personal collection; or try creating your own with use of the free utilities available here. After sifting through what may be of interest, go through the related links to continue your DF conquest around the Web.

Doom I, II, Heretic, Hexen, Duke3D, and Dark Forces Page
http://www.techline.com/~musickl/nigel.htm

OK, so the name of this Web page isn't too creative, but there is quite a lot to get here. There are other games than those listed above that also have informative cheat codes and hacks: Quake, Descent I and II, and Warcraft II. Although extra levels were mentioned—I couldn't seem to find out quite where they were!? A nice-looking page nevertheless, with cool graphics from the various 3D action games.

Doom II Deathmatch Level WADS and Other Cool Stuff
http://www.island.net/~idendy/

Ian Dendy and Clint Bowick (the guys at Rogue Enterprises) bring you a collection of home-grown Doom II Deathmatch WADS, The Deathmatch Database, and other neat utilities for DOOMing (modem strings, ed.itors, FAQs, etc.).

Duke 3D Highlight Zone
http://www.cris.com/~darkman/

Informative page for the die-hard Duke Nukem enthusiast. Join the Elite e-mailing list to have the hottest map levels sent to you automatically, or download the ones provided on this site. Keep your speakers cranked because you're also in for an auditory treat with MIDI and WAVs playing simultaneously. Other utility files are also available. This site is maintained by Darkman (level creator extraordinaire) and is hosted by the Concentric Network.

Duke Nukem 3D User Maps
http://www.bayserve.net/~mike/duke/maps.html

Part of Mike Miller's Duke Web site, this section/URL takes you right to the custom-built user levels. This is one of the largest-rated collection of single-player and multi-player maps on the Net (especially multi-player DukeMatch levels). You can search for a desired level via the search engine by name, by date, or by the number of players it's designed for.

Duke Nukem on the Wildman Rudeboy Website
http://ourworld.compuserve.com/homepages/jonathan_wildman/duke.htm

This is Jonathan Wildman's answer to the 3D Realms game Duke Nukem 3D. There are over sixteen departments here, such as "Doom vs Duke: The Dispute Continues," "The DukeMatchers Forum," user maps and RTS sound files, and links to official Duke Nukem news, FAQs, and the Aapogee live-cam. There are a few of Wildman's own user maps to choose from, as well (including Neighborhood Rumble and Oasis of Chaos). As the Duke says, "Come Get Some!".

Duke Nukem RTS Distribution Site

http://www.cyberhighway.net/~srogers/
duke/index.html

This specialty Web site's name says it all—an archived collection of RTS sound files to use with your Duke Nukem 3D or Rise of the Triad games. RTS files, or Remote Ridicule Files, were designed by Aapogee in 1995 when Rise of the Triad was released. They are used to ridicule your opponent during multi-player gaming, and it has become quite an art to create your very own RTS sound bytes. If you think yours are good enough, you may want to upload or exchange files with your online peers here. The hundreds of free RTS's are well organized for your indulgence.

Duke Versus Duke

http://w3.gwis.com/~doomboy/

Put up your Dukes! This is Doomboy and Roland's Duke Nukem 3D page, providing DukeMatch and single-player maps to download and try out. I like the idea of them having a separate icon for solo play or multi-player games, because I know from experience about craving a great single-player game in the middle of the night but having a directory with the games all mixed in together. There's nothing worse than starting a new user level and finding out you're the only one in the game! Cool maps with descriptions.

Earth Academy

http://www.calisto.com/academy/

Jump Point recently joined this mega-force honoring the Wing Commander (WC) galaxy. Missions, cheat codes, FAQs, trivia, pilot tips, and other informative files are here for your disposal, whether you're interested in the first or last in the Wing Commander series. A section on the off-shoot WC game Privateer is also included here.

AUTHOR'S PICK

Duke Nukem 3D Rodeo Shootout

http://www.cyberrodeo.com/duke/

The Rodeo Steakhouse restaurant/bar in downtown Fort Worth, Texas has been attracting quite a crowd lately and it ain't for their beef. It so happens they now house the CyberRodeo—a place to surf the Net and chow down. This Web site is dedicated to the networked multi-player competitions between eight Duke Nukem 3D players. These DukeMatch battles occur every few months and carry a complete itinerary including food, drinks for all, and hefty prizes for the winners. View photos from past competitions or download the user map used for the fight. Sponsors include *3D Realms Entertainment* (the folks who brought you Duke Nukem 3D) and *TEN* (the exclusive carrier of Duke Nukem 3D on their Internet-based gaming network). A cool idea and Web page...let's face it, what goes better with Duke than beer and steak?!

Earthworm Jim Official Page

http://www.activision.com/ewormjim/
ewjim.html

Top-selling console and computer-game Earthworm Jim has even spawned its own TV cartoon show. Download demos to see why this charismatic soil-crawler is a hit, or preview the "Slimy Screenshots" section. Earthworm was one of the first native Windows 95 games to hit PCs.

Electric Pancake, The
http://users.aol.com/johnjankow/ epframe2.htm

3D action and real-time strategy games are highlighted here: Doom 2, Warcraft 2, Command & Conquer, Heretic, Hexen, and Descent. Download levels, editors (to make your own), Deathmatch pics/screen shots, and front-end utilities. Area of note: the Map Room is a central area where Deathmatch players can see where everyone was in the level at that moment (created by John Jankowski, the designer of this Web page, and his brother Jim). Visit Jim's own site, The Pit of Ultimate Darkness, at http://members.aol.com/jw-janko/index.htm.

Eradicator
http://www.accolade.com/products/ eradicator/acerspla01.html

The official site to the hot 3D action title Eradicator, by Accolade. This Doom-style game allows you to view your world from a first-person or third-person perspective, and you can choose between three characters, each with their own battle style, special weapons, unique abilities, and unique levels. At this site, download the 7 MB demo, view screen shots, match to make sure your system specs are up to par, get tech support, and more.

Erick's Duke Nukem 3D Page
http://www.geocities.com/TimesSquare/ 4185/

A Netscape 3+ or Microsoft Internet Explorer 3+ enhanced site. This page is updated frequently with maps, CONs, RTS, and links additions. This page is most noteworthy for its DukeMatch strategy tips, donated by Erick and other Duke players around the globe. Also available: a guest book, cheat codes, and other utilities.

Fury3
http://www.cnet.com/Content/Reviews/ Cdrom/Reviews/0,50,311,00.html

C-Net's six-page review of Microsoft's Fury3. We've seen this game engine in 3D Realms/Terminal Reality's Terminal Velocity game—an action flight-sim combat game with many worlds to fly through. Screen shots, system requirements, and an extensive look at the native Windows 95 CD-ROM game.

Galaxian
http://www.worktechs.com/space/ space.html

You won't need any hard drive space to play this real-time animation space game. Galaxian is loosely based on William's early eighties classic arcade game of the same name. By using your mouse skillfully you are in control of a ship equipped with deadly arrows. Cool sound effects and a neat hit-and-miss ratio counter. Fun for all ages.

Gamer's Alliance
http://www.proaxis.com/~rowell/doom/

A hang-out place for Quake and Doom fanatics. Looking for editors, multi-player info, or levels for Doom, Doom2, Ultimate Doom, and/or Quake? Well, you came to the right place. Many pages make up this site, including their WAD and Utilities corner. Enhanced for Netscape 3—neat music and wallpaper, too.

Gamers Realm
http://www.Websolutions.mb.ca/realm/

A Canadian site for DOS and Windows games. Download a shareware game or demo you've head about or grab a cheat from their long alphabetical list. Each game is rated, and talk about interactivity—if there's a game or a cheat for a game you want that isn't already on this site, you can request it and Webmaster Graeme Skinner will try to get it to you ASAP.

Gamers.org

http://www.gamers.org/

This is former home of well-renowned DoomGate. Piotr Kapiszewski and Steve Young are the designers and hosts to one of, if not *the* one, most popular Doom Web site in the world. There is so much to do here it has its own search engine! This site really is a tribute to 3D action gaming as a whole, and most other popular shareware titles, such as Strife, Quake, Hexen, and Abuse, are accessible here also. Doom fans worldwide can peruse through the vast WAD area, where you can download the online community's picks for the best add-ons around. Graphically the site is not much to write home about (it has an FTP feel to it), but it is extremely rich in content and organization.

Heretic Levels Mega-Page
http://pages.prodigy.com/SC/hereticlevels/

A no-frills site but chock-full of gaming goodies for id/ Raven's Heretic. Tons of levels (I mean tons), cheat codes, shareware, FAQs, a 4-level Hexen beta, Death-Match tips, screen shots, patches, and a rumor mill. Heretic WADS are this site's key asset, so point your browser this way if you've finished the game but are still itchin' for more.

Holy Quake Site, The
http://www.abc.se/~m10013/quake/ quake.htm

A relentless look at 1996's most anticipated game from the creators of Wolfenstein 3D and Doom. This Web page is an all-inclusive overview of Quake information and files. Whether you're a beginner or pro, this site caters to your Quake needs, with sections on how to play the game in Windows 95, a monster guide, playing tactics, and a sweeping Links area. Make note of the immense Quake Console Commands list also available at http://www.trader.com/quake.htm.

Home Fries Software
http://www.oberlin.edu/~mblecher/hf/ hf.htm

Welcome to Home Fries Software, creators of fine Marathon 2: Durandal scenarios and products to supplement Bungie's hit game. This frugal site is fairly resourceful, though, with sections on Bungie's solo maps, Netmaps, Physics models, and Home Fries products with screen shots and description.

Husk's Duke Junk
http://www.magna.com.au/~husk/duke3d/

A frames-enhanced Web site with a very fast page-load time. Find out how to crack the "parental lock" in the Australian version of the game or hot-link to the Alien-phobia site (also in Australia) and see what maps they're creating for Duke Nukem 3D. Other sections include "Filez" (shareware goodies), Cheats (more than twenty-two codes), and "DukeMatch" (find other players to play head-to-head with—in Australia).

InterARC—The Internet Arcade
http://www.rocketsci.com/interarc.html

This Shockwave arcade has clones of late 70s and early 80s arcade classics like Frogger, Asteroids, and Space Invaders. The Frogger remake, in particular (WebFrog!), is highly addictive. Memories of quarter-filled pockets run through my mind as I try to get my little amphibian friend across a busy road and snake-filled swamp.

Introspection Wing Commander's Home Sector
http://home.cdsnet.net/~akkbar/
wclinks.html

A sleek and informative Wing Commander site (WC) that brings you news, articles and rumors (past and present), press releases, links, previews of other up-coming WC games, and a "listening post": new WC fiction twice a month by Craig Lampert. Introspection's page is more like an e-zine, with their up-to-date columns and knowledgeable staff.

Invisible Knight's Jedi Knight FAQ Page
http://www.nucleus.com/~dlovejoy/jedi/
jktoc.htm

A large HTML FAQ covering Lucas Art's Dark Forces II: Jedi Knight (JK). Frequently asked questions are answered regarding game descriptions and features, multiple players, levels and level editors, Mac news, weapons (lightsabers!), the story, characters, the game engine itself, screenshots, movies, and more. Acknowledgments and references are provided and updated often.

Java Games
http://www.whidbey.com/bodo/
javagame.htm

The games here are either arcade-style or small-strategy brain-teasers. All programs can be played in real-time right on your screen with little or no load time. The remakes consist of Tetris, Missile Command, Pong, Tic Tac Toe, Blackjack, Zoop, Connect Four, Magic 8-Ball, Rubick's Cube, Java-Script casino, Yahtzee, and Duke Hangman.

Jedi Knight Outpost, The
http://www.3dg.com/JediKnight/

In anticipation for Dark Forces II, or Jedi Knight, this page by Tola Dalton provides hot news, screen shots, official press releases (from Lucas Arts), game details, and more. This Windows 95-only sequel is a 3D first-person perspective game set in the Star Wars universe, once again with Kyle Katarn as the protagonist.

Jose's Tekken 2 Page
http://home.earthlink.net/~joseanibal/
index.html

Check out the main title graphic when you get to this page—cool! Jose provides the Tekken fan with special moves, characters, PlayStation codes, Tekken 3 info, and links. In the *moves* section, each character is highlighted, or you can write down, or print out, the general codes to assist you in the game.

Josh's Gaming Page
http://www.azstarnet.com/~duke3d/

A Web site honoring games Duke Nukem 3D, Descent, and SimCity 2000. Josh Barr's main page is quite plain but once inside (especially the Duke page) there is quite a bit to see and download here. Plenty o' maps, cheats, tips, and pictures for your discretion. Make sure you join the "Elite Duke 3D Mailing List"—a free e-mail service devised to send you the latest Duke Nukem maps played on TEN and elsewhere.

Justin's Game Page
http://www.connections.w1.com/justin/

Justin has rounded up the finest in demo and shareware versions of the top PC games to download. Each game is listed alphabetically, with file size and brief description in the framed sidebar. Not a very big collection, but Justin's Game Page hosts most of the top names from the last few years in all genres.

Kano's MK Page
http://gee.cs.oswego.edu/~keith/
mkstuff.html

Mortal Kombat (MK), MK 2, MK 3, Ultimate MK, and MK 4 are examined here at Kano's Web page. Click on the color graphic to choose which game you want for cheat codes, moves, tricks, or view screen shots. Hot link to the associated CookieMan's Lair to read more on MK and hear MIDI tunes by Queen, Smashing Pumpkins, or even the BattleStar Galactica song.

Keymaster's Doom, Doom2, Duke 3D, Heretic, and Hexen Site
http://www.geocities.com/SiliconValley/
Park/5616/index.html

As the name indicates, these 3D games each have their own section offering a WADS list (some levels created by the Keymaster along with others), utilities, patches and other files, games, Deathmatch tips, cheat codes, links, and more. Bonus: Cool wallpaper to copy for your own, and I like the Top Ten WADS area.

Killer Tips for Mechwarriors
http://piggy.ucsb.edu/~jones/tips.html

This Web site provides Mechwarrior 2 tips on weapon usage and configuration, combat movement, controller configurations, and useful tricks against particular enemies (thirteen of them, plus a dozen from the expansion pack). A tips exchange virtual cork board is a new feature here.

Le Quake
http://www.worldnet.net/~edwin/quake/
quake.htm

A French Web site dedicated to id Software's Quake. An introduction, FAQs, editors, levels, screen-shots, and a links section are all provided here. Le Quake is nicely arranged with frames and graphics from actual screen grabs. Surf this site and download the various files or find a gaming partner for some head-to-head action in France or Quebec, Canada.

Lou's Mechwarrior Info Page
http://www.computer.net/~louish/
mech.html

A bare-bones page dedicated to Activision's gaming sensation Mechwarrior 2 and its expansion pack Ghost Bear's Legacy. Downloadable demos, patches, cheat codes, and FAQs are contained within these walls. Lou's tribute site has two endearing sections: the gaming registry for head-to-head destruction and the history of Mechs. Unfortunately, not much else is here that a discerning surfer couldn't find elsewhere.

Mad Dog's 3D Games
http://www.cybercomm.net/~iceman2/
3dgames.html

System requirements, downloads, cheats, and strategies for games The Need For Speed, Descent, Doom, CyberMage, and Quake are here for your disposal. One cool thing about this site is you can sign up to get a free biweekly cheats newsletter by e-mail.

Marathon
http://www.bungie.com/
BungieProducts.html

The official page to Marathon, Marathon 2: Durandal, and Marathon Infinity (the new scenario Blood Tides of Lh'owon, plus other goodies). These highly successful 3D action games from Bungie Software originated on the Mac but have been recently ported over to the PC.

Get a thorough overview of each game, view screen shots, download the demos, get a full version (with a valid credit card), and more.

Marathon 2: Durandal
http://www.ctnet.com/marathon/

Basically a page of custom-made maps for Bungie Software's Marathon 2: Durandal. There is a brief introduction, features of the game, and relevant links. Many of the maps created here by Drew or Chet are for multi-player games. Their maps are stored as *Stuffit* archives, so you will need to decompress them with Stuffit Expander, which is available online at Aladdin Systems at http://www.aladdinsys.com/aladdin.html.

Marathon Magazine on the Web
http://general.amug.org/~marathon/
maramag/

Marathon Magazine is the premier free electronic magazine for fans of Marathon and Marathon II, 3D action games created by Bungie Software for the Mac and PC. Download the mag or the Marathon software catalog to read offline, or pore over the related links on the Web.

Other Marathon and Marathon 2 Sites:

Marathon New Magazine
http://www.wco.com/~eriksale/News.html

Marathon!!!
http://www.ames.net/marathon/

Marathon 2 Web
http://www.amug.org/~marathon/slurpee/
marathon2/index.html

Matt's Mechwarrior 2 Page
http://www.deter.com/mw2/

Matt Deter's Mechwarrior page at his Web site offers screen shots, undocumented key sequences, patches, cheat codes, and links for Mech 2 and Ghost Bear's Legacy. I particularly liked the Sounds page hot-linked to http://www.cae.wisc.edu/~choon/eugene/audio.htm— very different. It's good to know that when you hear "critical meltdown imminent," it's not the game speaking!

Max Game Page
http://www2.passagen.se/max/

Pure PC action with the likes of Eradicator, Doom, Duke Nukem 3D, Road Rash, Hexen, Z, Fire Fight, Quake, Heretic, and more. Each game has the story/background, system requirements, screen shots, the demo and other news, and information. An uncluttered, fast, and attractive page designed with scrolling animation, boxes, and a refreshing format. Hot links to the adjoined FTP sites and newsgroups are listed for each game to get bonus levels, cheats, and FAQs.

Mechwarrior 2 High Octane Info Site
http://www1.clarku.edu/~rmohns/mw2/
highgraph.html

Cool page that takes advantage of the Shockwave and Java plug-ins. Besides all the animations, sound, and music, there is some substance here. An overview of the game is provided first, then cheats, hints, Q & A, stats, editors, and the infamous Mechwarrior 2 crack (that allows you to play the game without needing the CD-ROM in the drive!). A noteworthy section is 'New on the Target Range,' a news page and public bulletin board to keep up-to-date on all the BattleMech happenings. Download the Mech 2 Theme Pack for Windows 95 to give your desktop some punch. If you don't use Netscape 2.0+, don't have the Shockwave plug-in, or are running less than 14.4 bps, then turn your browser to http://www1.clarku.edu/~rmohns/mw2/lowgraph.html.

Mechwarrior 2: The Clans, From Activision
http://rom.oit.gatech.edu/~willday/mw2/
index.html

Will Day's Mechwarrior 2 site pays homage to one of the best computer games of our day. Many screen shots, reviews, movies, patches, hot links, and FAQs (text and HTML version) are submitted for your perusal. Download a great Mech picture for your Windows wallpaper or read various strategies on conquering the game. Besides the logo on the main page this is a plain site to look at, but the various sections make it a worthwhile visit.

Mechwarrior 2 Unofficial Strategy Page
http://users.aol.com/sphere200/mech2.htm

A very large, comprehensive Web page that offers strategies to Mechwarrior 2 and Ghost Bear's Legacy gamers. A stats breakdown of each Mech, cheat codes, playing tips, and general and mission-specific guides to help you kick some 31st century butt!

Also see:

Official Mechwarrior Page at Activision
http://www.activision.com/

Hot 100 Mechwarrior Page
http://www.100hot.com/mirrors/
mech2home.html

Mechwarrior 2 Infopage
http://arbornet.org/~lokety/mw2_index.html

Macintosh Mechwarrior Page
http://members.aol.com//mw2site/
MACMECH.html

MindHackers Home Page, The
http://www.domain.com.br/~olifiers/index.htm

Mike Miller's Duke Nukem 3D Site
http://www.bayserve.net/~mike/duke/

This is a relatively average fan-based site but has an interesting section called "Fun Things to Do and See." Here you will find secrets and bonuses inherent in the game that will make you laugh and prompt you to try them out for yourself. By the time you read this, many secrets in Duke Nukem 3D will be known but I guarantee you'll find at least a few neat ones here. This Web page also supplies the player with advice and strategies for a competitive and fulfilling multi-player game. The usual Map collections are also available here, donated by like-minded Web enthusiasts.

Mindwave's Duke Nukem 3D Site
http://www.cyberramp.net/~chowboy/
duke3d.html

A colorful page offering the Duke Nukem 3D demo, game overview, cheat codes, user maps (including Mindwave's own custom-built levels), and a comprehensive list of secrets for Episode's 2 and 3. Hot links are also covered (including the 3D Realms Live-cam). Download his "Mitch22.zip" map—it takes place in a hockey arena!

Modem Games Yellow Pages
http://www.azstarnet.com/~doomgod/

The Modem Games Yellow Pages (MGYP) were created to assist gamers in finding people in their area code to play computer modem games with. This is a great idea since many of us would rather play for free against someone in our area rather than spend online time playing with someone over the Net. Also, most of us don't have access to Networked stations. Add your name to the list or search the large database for locals. You may also download a selection of Doom WADS while you're here.

Monolith Systems: Heretic Archives

http://norden1.com/~bielby/heretic/heretic.htm

Designed by Brett A. Bielby, this site helps you conquer Raven Software and id Software's 3D gothic action adventure Heretic. It's all broken down here for you on how to beat the game: secrets, cheats, strategies, and weapons. This frames-enhanced site also has a cool Artifacts pictures and text area.

Mortal Kombat WWW Pages

http://www.cs.ucl.ac.uk/students/A.Espindola/mk/

Award-winning MK page full of animation and tons of text to bring information, characters, rumors, sounds, movies, screen shots, news, gossip, codes, and strategy tips to the computer screen. This site covers all three platforms of the game: arcade, computer, and TV gaming consoles. Read up on Mortal Kombat 4 scheduled for a spring or summer 1997 release.

Motaro's MK Page

http://greg.simplenet.com/mk/

This is another all-in-one Mortal Kombat source. Sections including The MK Story, Kombat Kode Central, Entertainment, Chat, MKI, MKII, MK3, UMK3, MK News, The Vault, Sites, Survey, Guestbook, and What's New. This frames-enhanced site contains multiple toolbars and makes for an enjoyable and easy navigational design. Motaro teaches MK moves and secrets for each of the various MK games.

Moves, Hints, Tricks, etc. for Popular Computer Games

http://pilot.msu.edu/user/chowdhur/cheats/computer/cheats.htm

Pages and pages of great tips, walkthroughs, cheats, codes, moves, and tactics for all kinds of computer games. Compiled from many sources over the Net, this is a good database regardless of your gaming genre preference. Hint: press CTRL and "F" to bring up the

"Find" menu—type in your game of interest, and ENTER, and it'll take you right there.

Mr. DooM's Quake Page

http://www.erie.net/~mrdoom/quake.html

A simple yet effective Web design breaks up Quake cheats, codes, news, links, tips, secrets, monsters, files, and up-to-the-minute Quake servers for your multiplayer needs. This page is part of the Mr.DooM's Web site—the id software game that started it all. The Quake Match screen shots are worth viewing (check out that bloody ax shot!). If Mr. DooM does to his Quake site what he did with his Doom/Doom 2 pages, look forward to an awesome Quake headquarters in the near future.

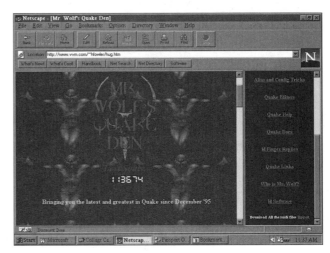

Mr. Wolf's Quake Den

http://www.vvm.com/~hfowler/hug.htm

This is a thorough fan-related site designed to give other Quake fans toys, tricks, and news to supplement the game. A nicely designed site created for easy use and navigation to its many sections and subsections. Quake editors, help, tips 'n secrets, many useful links, and id software company info are all attainable in the framed sidebar (and more), whereas the main screen documents day-to-day news on Quake and other 3D related computer game products. Self-pronounced *Quake-a-holic* Heath Fowler is 'Mr. Wolf,' a computer science major in Texas. Up-to-the-minute Quake-related news is this site's greatest attribute.

My Duke Nukem and Command & Conquer Web Site
http://www.geocities.com/SiliconValley/6971/index.html

By the sounds of this title you'd think the Webmaster was providing a bunch o' files pertaining to two of the hottest games of the decade. Well, nothing was found for Command & Conquer (at all!), but some cool Duke stuff was there: 100+ user maps provided alphabetically with rating and file size, a Duke Nukem Plus Pack for Windows 95, and related links.

My Favorite Duke Nukem 3D Site!
http://www.wesnet.com/kevinfin/game/duke3d.htm

Nothing like hearing the Duke Nukem theme song to pump you up while you're surfing! Kevin Fincel's page takes advantage of all the coolest plug-ins and is littered with maps, extra user levels, and RTS files (pre-recorded voice insults to use during Dukematch head-to-head play). Animated icons will guide you around this site so you can browse through various files to heighten your Duke experience. Kudos to Kevin for excellent Web page design and creative use of multimedia technology.

Nailhead's Presents...Duke Nukem 3D
http://www.virtualtimes.com/vidgames/duke3d/

A very dark, cool Netscape 3+ enhanced site. Creepy midi music welcomes and accompanies you on your travels here: the definitive Duke Nukem 3D user levels, cheat codes, downloadables (patches, utilities, RTS files, slide show, icons), and links. Nailhead's own maps are available along with the best of the Net.

Nando Net
http://www2.nando.net/nandox/shock.html

A Shockwave arcade featuring five different games. Both games "Space Battle" and "Nando Space Race" are a cross between *Space Invaders* and *Galaxian*. Cool

sounds on Space Race and quite small to load (45K). The other three games are puzzle-related.

Net Game Connection: Jedi Knight Preview
http://www.3dg.com/ngc/games/jk/

This is Tola Dalton's preview of the highly anticipated Dark Forces sequel. Lucas Arts blew us away with their *Doom*-style game set in a Star Wars universe. Here are the first screen shots available as well as game description, features, and differences between Jedi Knight and the original. This is part of the lager Net Game Connection Web site at http://www.3dg.com/ngc/index.shtml.

Oberlin 'Mech Lab
http://kellnet.com/harley/mechlab.htm

Any other Mech page that I have traveled to is pale in comparison to Oberlin's Web site. However, this is a specialized site for the advanced Mech gamer, so don't visit this page if you just need general information (patches, cheats, FAQs, etc.). The 'Mech Lab is just that—downloadable *.mek Mechwarrior 2 or Ghost Bear's Legacy designs complete with screen shots, specifications, and mission suggestions. The custom BattleMechs created by Stacy Harley (and others) can be selected by mission-specific variants, Mech weight, or general purpose (how about just to make the game harder?). Game editors, books, links, and game technique can be found at Oberlin's Mech Bay at http://kellnet.com/harley/btech.htm. As if this wasn't enough to keep you busy until the 31st Century, also visit the Mechwarrior 2 Battle Plans Page by Harley at http://kellnet.com/harley/battle.htm.

Truly an example of how far a ingenious fan-related Web site can stretch an already vast Mech universe. Activision, FASA, and Battletech must be proud.

One Must Fall 2097
http://www.epicgames.com/omf.htm

This is the official Epic MegaGames site devoted to the PC fighting game, One Must Fall: 2097 (OMF). Read review quotes, and notes about the game; view screen shots, features and system requirements; or download the shareware or patch. A new page on net/modem support is up and running. For more information on OMF head-to-head play, visit the One Must Fall 2097 Tournament Site is at http://www.geocities.com/SiliconValley/Park/5498/index.html or the Ogre-Wolf's One Must Fall 2097 Ladder at http://www.geocities.com/SiliconValley/1645/.

Outer Rim Gaming Sector
http://pages.prodigy.com/outer_rim/

This action game Web site offers tips, missions/levels, cheat codes, editors, and builders for games such as Descent, Hexen, Doom II, Heretic, and Tie Fighter. Nicely arranged sections keep everything simple. Note: Download and try out the Doom II WAD 'Farside of Titan' and the Descent level 'Ice Sewer' for a real challenge.

Pathways Into Darkness, The
http://www.mit.edu:8001/afs/ athena.mit.edu/user/d/c/dcoufal/www/pid/

In 1993, Pathways Into Darkness (PID) was the first 3D first-person texture-mapped multi-level game for the Macintosh (published by Bungie of *Marathon* fame). This Web page features the Mac PID demo and upgrades, the FAQ, strategy guide, leve-by-level walkthrough (with maps), and a PID cheater program.

Pit of Ultimate Darkness, The
http://members.aol.com/jwjanko/index.htm

Come here to get more out of your Doom 2, Duke Nukem 3D, Quake, and Warcraft II. Each of the four pages at this site offer levels/maps (made by Web page designer Jim Jankowski, plus others), level editors, front-end software, links, and more. Visit Jim's brother John's site "The Electric Pancake" at http://users.aol.com/johnjankow/electric.htm.

Putz Descent Page, The
http://www1.shore.net/~mpcd/descent.htm

First download the game (or patch) from this site or from the linked FTP servers. Then, read the FAQs, cheats and techniques before downloading new editors and bonus levels to try out. Once completed, scan the links area for some other cool Descent sites around the globe. And if you're REALLY good, then download the free Kali software to play a little head-to-head action.

Quaaaaake! The Quake Pages
http://www.quaaaaake.com/

Lots to do here including a pick-a-Midi contest, Deathmatch screen shots, news, editing software, and an interactive Java chat section. There is also a shrine to Sean "Redwood" Martin for his *savoir-faire* on the inside scoop at the Quake camp (see above). Various sound clips accompany the myriad of sections here, most notably the Play and Files pages. A comprehensive Links area is here broken down alphabetically and separated into Newsgroups, Web Sites, and FTP archives.

Quake Stomping Grounds, The
http://www.stomped.com/

This extremely popular Web page is designed by Guy Gustavson and his team of volunteers to bring you the most comprehensive and complete Quake-related news, files, multi-player play information, tips, editing software, and screen shots. Need help? No problem—take advantage of the Stomping Ground's Quake FAQs, Q & A section, and a Consoles Command page. Probably the largest Quake file collection found anywhere on the Web; if you prefer FTP, visit via FTP://ftp.stomped.com/pub/quake/. Happy stomping!

Quakeworld
http://www.magicnet.net/~jza/quakeworld/

A clean and relatively useful site for the Quake follower. With the abundance the numerous mammoth fan sites on the Web this may serve as a more simple, and less-heavy, Quake refuge. Orderly news, contests,

AUTHOR'S PICK

Quake Command

http://www.nuc.net/quake/

One of the most uniquely-designed, informative, and resourceful Quake sites on the net. This huge site is run by Steve Bond (a.k.a. Wedge) and John Guthrie (a.k.a. Choryoth)—infamous *QuakeC* Gods—one of 20+ Quake building or editing utilities around today that allow you to construct new weapons and monsters (even used by id software, too). Besides their outstanding Quake weapons (the nail grenade, the axe-throw, flares, and even banana peels!), they have also designed vehicles such as an aircraft and jeep! Quake Command also features common and little-known Quake secrets, levels, files, and links to only the BEST Quake sites around. Don't forget the up-to-the-minute news and Quake gossip, too.

servers, links, charts, pictures, files, tips, cheats, and chats are conveniently arranged. A handy 'sounds' option is given if you want to listen to music while surfing this site (Nine Inch Nails does midi). The files section is tidy and trim and organized with discernment. Spice up your desktop with Quake icons, fonts, animated cursors, screensavers, or wallpaper.

Rayman
http://www.daren.com/rayman/ray.htm

Who ever said platform side-scrollers were dead? With games like Crack Dot Com's Abuse, Sierra's Lode Runner On-Line, and Ubi Soft's Rayman, the 'ol left-to-right runners are still going strong. Especially with Rayman, which has been voted an incredible 8.14 out of 10 from Computer Gaming World's reader's poll (second highest Action game score next to Crusader: No remorse at 8.49). This Web site offers the Rayman story, notes about the game (plus features), hints, pictures, and a downloadable demo. This site is best viewed with Netscape 3.0 or Internet Explorer 3.0.

Visit the Official Ubi Soft Home Page at **http://www.ubisoft.com/**.

Realms of Darkness, The
http://academy.bastad.se/~tinman/trod/realms.htm

A positively creepy site specializing in Doom-related 3D games. The moment you arrive here haunting Crescendo music fills your ears along with a backwards welcome message (which of course you can play back the right way using your .wav player!). T.R.O.D. contains a huge picture gallery that you can save and add to your Windows desktop or personal image collection. Not very many Web sites can alter your mood, but this macabre page from Sweden is drenched in useful Doom WADS, Japanese anime, various lists, and cool links. On top of the rich content, beautiful graphics and animation grace this page, adding to the dark feel. Hey, where else can you sign the *Guestbook of Hell?*

Rebel Assault Resource
http://acm.cs.umn.edu/~slug/rebel/

This is a fan-related page honoring Lucas Art's Rebel Assault and Rebel Assault II. Info, tips, tricks, FAQs, cheat codes, and links make up the content of this Web site. There aren't too many places on the Web to get this kind of info, so if you're a admirer of the game, visit Doug the Slug's resource center.

Redwood's Quake Page
http://http.tamu.edu:8000/~stm9233/ quake.html

Another news-heavy Quake page, but one of the better ones. Up-to-the-minute news and gossip on the Quake and id Software front to satisfy any dedicated fan of this year's mega-hit. The second half of this site provides the visitor with links broken up into various sections, such as Quake server lists, editing software, FTPs, Help, and other fan-based URLs.

Also see these official pages:

id software main page
http://www.idsoftware.com/

id Official Mirror Site
http://www.idsoftware.com/mirrors.html

id Quake Update
http://ids.usnetworks.net/net2_0/hotquake.htm

More Cool Quake Sites

All in One Quake
http://www.sys.uea.ac.uk/~u9412476/quake1.html

Blue's Quake Rag
http://www.panix.com/~sheaslip/3d/quake.shtml

Buzman's Quake Page
http://www.netzone.com/~deckm/quake.html

Death Angel's Quake Page
http://www.igc.net/~dangel/quake.htm

Elgrande's Quake Page
http://members.aol.com/elgrande1/index.htm

Game Room at Gigabyte
http://www.gygabite.com/gameroom/

Grizzly's Quake Page
http://www.geocities.com/Hollywood/7710/quake.html

Predator's Quake Page
http://users.mwci.net/~predator/quake.html

Quake at the Mecca
http://www.mm.com/user/tcdmntia/wwd/quake/

Quake Clan Ring, The
http://www.clearlight.com/~iathycs/qcring.htm

Quake Heaven
http://www.execpc.com/~tduckles/rob/quake/

Quake Mania
http://www-home.calumet.yorku.ca/dcardoso/www/ quake2.htm

Quake Rumblings
http://www.geocities.com/SiliconValley/Park/3251/ quakep.html

Quake Seismograph, The
http://ww2.netnitco.net/users/porter/quake/

Shadow and Warrior's Quake Page
http://users.mwci.net/~shadow/quake.html

Shake N' Quake
http://www.canvasnet.com/quake/

Tremor
http://www.Webcom.com/psi/

Ventura's Quake page
http://www.computer-services.com/ventura/

Rich's Dark Forces Home page

**http://members.aol.com/dfmaverick/
index.html**

An interesting Web site dedicated to where Dark Forces left off. The contents of this page are separated into an online game, Star Wars: The Tie That Binds, and Crow Calls, a Dark Forces Fanzine. The Tie that Binds continues the adventures of Kyle Katarn, the hero from the Dark Forces CD-ROM game, in which the outcome is based on your choices as the hero. Crow Calls contains news bulletins, a Top Ten add-on level area, and letters from the editor. An unconventional and virtuous site for DF fans.

Rick's Mechwarrior Page

**http://billboard.emedia.com.au/chipster/
games/mech.html**

A page on Mechwarrior 2 and NetMech. Numerous sections include the usual (Tips, Cheats, Downloads, Links) and not-so-usual (Mechwarrior Screw-Ups, Enabling More Mechs, and Easter Eggs [tricks right from Scott Goffman, 3D Animator at Activision Studios]). Not a graphically impressive site but heavy on useful information on the Mechwarrior universe.

Ryan's Duke Nukem 3D Page

**http://www.geocities.com/TimesSquare/
5808/**

Not only has Ryan Graf, 8th grade student, designed his own resourceful Duke Nukem site, but he has also included his own custom-built maps! Download these bonus map levels (try his DukeMatch Motel or D House) along with cheat codes, links, RemoteRidicule ™ files, and more. Hear the main Duke theme via Crescendo and choose whether or not you want a frames-enhanced version of his site. Great job from a young aspiring Webmaster/programmer!

Saturday Shockwave Games

**http://www.imperium.net/~onedan/
Saturday/games/index.html**

A Windows-like page offering three Shockwave creations: Quatris (a Tetris variation), 'Stroids (Asteroids clone), and 'Sile Command (Missile Command). Play these games in real-time using the free Macromedia interactive animation utility.

Scary's Quakeholio

http://www.rockisland.com/~phook/scary/

One of the best Quake sites on the Net, along with Quake Command and Blue's Quake Rag perhaps. Tons of levels, demos (camera or first-person angles), CURRENT news, utilities (including a QuakeC page), stories, maps, screen shots, secrets, strategies, and more. This site is hosted by Gamesmania at http://www.gamesmania.com/ (see Chapter 15).

Scorpion's MK Page

**http://www.sunlink.net/~dadamsky/mk/
mortal.htm**

A remarkably fast-loading page chock-full of Mortal Kombat information. Each of the releases is given the same treatment: news, moves, stories, rumors, and links. Whether you prefer the arcade version or TV console variation, it's all here at this award-winning site.

Secrets of Dark Forces

**http://laser.klemp.com/DAWSON/
darkforces/df.html**

The name says it all about this page designed by Dawson Klemp. Find out how to beat or cheat the game, play without the CD, or download the patch to use a lightsaber instead of your fist. There are various tutorials and mission editors to help in your battles against evil. There is also a Mac section for those interested. Mac Addict? Visit:

Dark Forces for the Macintosh Stuff
**http://www.primenet.com/~bradman/
darkforces.html**

Sektor's Mortal Kombat Page

http://www.megatoon.com/~gpouliot/mortal.html

Computer, arcade, and TV console versions of the MK trilogy are covered here. FAQs (HTML or text-based) and links (almost one hundred) to the various related sources around the Net make up the bulk of this site. Sektor's own FAQ describes the moves and codes to beat your opponents.

Space Pirates!

http://clevermedia.com/arcade/pirate.html

An interactive real-time Shockwave game with neat animations and music/sound effects. View the galaxy from your spacecraft window and land on various planets. Trade goods, attack other ships, and pay your crew. Lots of options, all accessible with a mouse click. It took no time to load either—cool!

Stallion's Duke Nukem 3D Pages

http://www.geocities.com/TimesSquare/3488/duke.htm

Duke Nukem cheats, user maps, RTS sound files, shareware and demos (walkthroughs and secrets), utilities, registered screen shots, and links are all available here. The news section is well-laid out by date and Duke happenings around the globe. A simple and attractive tribute page.

Strife

http://www.velocitygames.com/games/strife/strife.html

The official site to Velocity's 3D, action/RPG game. Check out the cool screen shots; read a meticulous product description and game overview, including system requirements; or download the patch if you already own the game. For Strife cheat codes, see http://www.netwrx.net/macgyver/strifech.html. Or download the playable demo at http://www.gamers.org/~rogue/demo.html.

Submarine

http://www.nando.net/nandox/submarine.html

A cool Shockwave game where you have to launch torpedoes at submarines. Move your target up, down, right, or left and click on the torpedo button—let 'em rip! A small game to load, neat sound effects, and a simple yet effective point n' click design.

Technicolor's Index

http://ddi.digital.net/~ecarr/index.html

A collection of Duke Nukem 3D and Quake files. The Duke section includes custom-made maps, editors, build FAQs, strategies/cheats, links, and even user art. Quake's Clan news, links, and server info is useful, but the Quake file library was under construction upon my recent visit.

Tekken Web Project

http://metro.net/slikatel/tkprojct.htm

Constantly updated Tekken page with WAVs, cool graphics, and up-to-date news. Built as a one-stop resource center for fans worldwide, including a movie archive, special moves/codes, image gallery, FAQs, chat, and even a glossary of terms section. Designed for Netscape 3+ and Internet Explorer 3+.

Tempest's Duke Nukem 3D Page

http://www.wi.leidenuniv.nl/~cwong/duke3d.htm

Due to space limitations, most of Cho Yan Wong's Duke maps have been removed from this page, so only the BEST ones around have stayed. You can download and use these maps or read an updated news section, tutorials, and FAQs (build and game). Cho's own user levels are also provided along with useful links. Make sure you download these zipped-up level packs from Intrepid and Canadian designer Chris Redekop.

Terminal Velocity

http://www.3drealms.com/cgi/kds?$=pub/tv.htm

Get vertigo at 3D Realm's official site for Terminal Velocity (TV), their 3D vehicle shooter that's "partly Star Wars and partly Descent!" (*Computer Gaming World* magazine).

Download the TV shareware version, full version (with valid credit card), view screen shots, the official FAQ, utilities, patches, and a story overview. Warning: this single-player or multi-player flight action game, created by Terminal Reality, does not come with it's own barf bag! For cheat codes go to http://www.netwrx.net/macgyver/tvcheats.html.

Terran Federation, The

http://newport.thirdwave.net/~spyder/

An impressive fan-related Web site dedicated to Origin's Wing Commander series. This page is an all-out tribute to everything and anything to do with all four episodes of the most popular space game series ever created. Much time and effort went into developing the different facets of this site, including a Wing Commander fighter index, its own IRC chat group line, huge graphic archives, and related links worldwide. Information is constantly updated and presented in crisp color and detail.

The Best 3D Game Ever, Duke Nukem 3D!

http://prairie.lakes.com/~wrichard/duke/duke.html

A very large repository of Duke Nukem files, stories, pictures, music, walkthroughs, cheats, and more. Check out the graphical transition of Duke over the years and read cool articles on the game, or download the interview previewing the work on the making of Duke Nukem 4. A wealth of information here to sift through.

Time Commando

http://www.activision.com/timecommando/index.html

Activision's official page for the hot fighting game. Time Commando takes you through nine worlds and twenty levels, with forty-five lethal weapons and eighty fierce enemies. A new action-packed video preview is shown here each week, along with a thorough product description, reviews, screen shots; you can also enter the Time Commando "Choose Your Adventure Sweepstakes."

Tom's Doom Page

http://www.cs.tulane.edu/www/Ward/doom.html

One of many specialized fan-related Doom pages, but this one is catered more for the Mac enthusiast. Access hundreds of files from id Software's breakthrough game, including various single-player or Deathmatch WADS (add-on levels), game editors, Newsgroups, and FTP hot links. Aesthetically pleasing site with the ability to add your favorite relevant Doom Web sites, as well.

Also see:

The Mac Doom Park

http://www.gac.edu/~bgustafs/macdoom_park.html,

The Original Mac Doom Page

http://www.eecs.wsu.edu/~rkinion/macdoom.html

The Mac Doom 2 Territory
http://www.geocities.com/Broadway/2192/
DOOM2.html

Mac Doom Review Homepage
http://www.voicenet.com/~reeltime/mdr.html

Toru's Shockwave Arcade
http://sharedcast.hccs.cc.tx.us/toru.htm

A six-game Shockwave arcade, including Acrobats, Escape Balls, Cockroach Busters!, and more. What's unbelievable here is Venknown's intro page—you won't believe your eyes or ears. The games themselves are small but amusing (especially Sara-Mawashi; click on the acrobats so they don't drop their plates). This site is also available in Japanese at http://www.bekko-ame.or.jp/~uenknown/mmd/sw/index.html.

Unofficial Duke Nukem 3D Links Site, The
http://www.tornado.be/~firefox/index.htm

With more than two hundred links (and counting) all related to Duke Nukem 3D, you've got quite a few hours of adventuring here. The top ten sites are charted for your inspection, or you may vote for your favorites, as well. Hot link to the Elite e-mailing board to get user maps sent to you automatically. This award-winning page is a great archive collection of (worthy) Duke pages on the Net. Sink your teeth in.

Val's Mechwarrior 2 Game Page
http://rampages.onramp.net/~val/

Another well-done Web site packed with Mechwarrior 2 goodies to aid in your gaming experience. First things first: If you haven't bought the game yet, download the demo and FAQ files. If you already own Mech 2, then access the patch and cheat codes directories. If you've mastered the game, visit the Mech Registry, get a copy of an editor (to make your own levels), read up on the add-on games, or give your e-mail address to be updated with Activision and Mechwarrior info. A nicely polished page offering the latest on Mech 2, Ghost Bear's Legacy, NetMech, and Mercenaries.

AUTHOR'S PICK

Tribute to Duke

Before Ringo came on board with Beatles, Duke was the band's favorite stick banger. Unfortunately, John and Duke didn't see eye to eye on creative and world issues so Duke decided to split from the band.

http://duke.intersphere.com/

A very funny tongue-in-cheek look at how Duke Nukem 3D has infiltrated our current pop culture. Besides having the regular files available at many other pages (demos, maps, utilities), this site poses Duke as a presidential candidate, one of the Beatles, riding the wave of Hurricane Fran, an Olympic Gold winner, a disco dancer, and taking part in our favorite movies and TV shows (The Dukes of Hazzard!?). The many animations, sound clips, doctored pictures, and amusing articles are good for a laugh—any Duke fan should definitely NOT miss this Web page. An off-the-wall, creative, and entertaining site brought to you by Team Duke (a.k.a. Mark Farish, Jeffrey Erb, and Mike Oryl at Intersphere Communications Ltd.).

Valvoline Internet Racing
http://ww3.valvoline.com/game/

A game and contest sponsored by Valvoline. You must have Macromedia's Shockwave plug-in and Netscape Navigator or Microsoft Internet Explorer to play. This racing game is really fun, but the first time you visit, you may have to wait a bit to load up. The motor oil company adds some spice to their Web page with this cool, real-time action driving game.

Video Arcade Preservation Society
http://www.vaps.org/

Yes, this is an official organization maintained by Kevin Ruddy (although officially started in 1990 by Steve Ozdemir). The aim of the society is to collect and preserve classic Coin Op video games, and to become a member you have to own at least one game in good working order. It may interest you that the top games collected by the almost six hundred members are Tempest (111), Asteroids (65), Ms. Pac-Man (64), and Robotron 2084 (64).

Vittorio Longhi's 3D Gaming Page
http://www.intercom.it/~vlonghi/

All first-person perspective games, such as Eradicator, Quake, Marathon 2, Josephine: Portrait of an Assassin, Hellbender, and more. They're here with game info and descriptions, downloads, screen shots. An attractive page with cool wallpaper and animations. Lots of links also make up this Italian gaming venue.

Void, The
http://www.citicom.com/~jpratt/index2.html

The Void is a framed, dark Web site catering to the 3D action fan. Games such as Blood, Strife, and Unreal are the topic of discussion here, but this site mainly acts as a springboard to the various 3D game manufacturer sites, as well as other fan-related links. It seems that quite a few of this page's hot-linked icons were not set up while I was on my travels, as they did not serve any particular function. Perhaps when construction has been completed, there will be enough here to warrant another visit.

Wacky Hexen Page, The
http://www.zensoft.com/Raven/Hexen.shtml

Another award-winning site devoted to offering all Hexen fans the creme de la creme of extra levels, FAQs, cheat codes, finishing moves (cool!), and even

Hexen recipes encrypted and embedded in the game for each monster! Created on October 30, 1995, this site is used mainly for its Answer Wizard; enter your Hexen query in the box and the whole Internet will be searched for an appropriate answer.

Well of Games
http://www.cybernet.dk/wellofgames/

Brought to you by Kristian Kolstrup and Gert Braun, this plain but resourceful page offers many sections for all your gaming needs. Areas are: What's New (current industry info, rumors), Cheats (more than two hundred games), Walkthroughs (when you've REALLY had enough), FAQs (a big list), a Universal Hint System page (cool!), Downloads (tons), Reviews & Ratings, a link to The Top 100 Internet PC Games Charts, Patches & Fixes (hundreds of games), and Links. Need another reason to visit?

Whack-A-Mole
http://www.mindframe.com/tools/
shockwave/game.html

The old carnival game has been brought to the PC for a second time (the first was in Sam n' Max Hit the Road by Lucas Arts). By using Shockwave technology, you can whack the moles on the head with your mouse in real-time. No downloading to your hard drive is required. A fun diversion brought to you by the Mindframe.com Web site.

Yeoman's Home Page
http://www.geocities.com/TimesSquare/
3841/index.html

An awesome page with Doom, Quake, and Duke Nukem 3D all rolled into one. Appropriate gothic music accompanies your visit while you download the shareware versions of the games, cheats, FAQs, utilities, and custom-made user levels for all three games. You may also peruse the links list or send Yeoman your own maps and WADS.

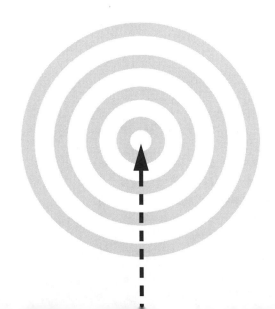

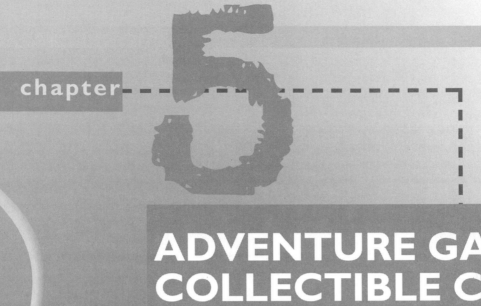

ADVENTURE GAMES, COLLECTIBLE CARD GAMES, AND ROLE-PLAYING GAMES

ADVENTURE GAMES

THE 7TH GUEST AND 11TH HOUR

The 7th Guest Hints

http://members.aol.com/UnclePita/
guest.htm

Find puzzle hints and solutions for the mind-benders found in The 7th Guest. Text and graphic representations aid players in finding their way toward a winning conclusion to the game.

Complete Walkthrough for The 7th Guest

http://www.algonet.se/~averpil/common/
solve/guest.html

This walkthrough of the puzzles found in The 7th Guest provides players almost all of the solutions. Where solutions aren't provided, hints are. Puzzles are featured in a hyperlinked directory and players can jump to the solution or hint for the particular puzzle that has them stumped. Along with the puzzle solutions, a floor plan of the house is also featured.

11th Hour Home Page

http://www.vie.com/prodinfo/11th/
home.html

Hosted by Virgin Interactive Entertainment, here's the official home page of 11th Hour, the sequel to The 7th Guest. Enjoy a background on the game as well as many promotional features that detail the work that went into this highly anticipated title. Enter the 11th Hour Challenge and vie for a place on the winners page. Or, search for game clues by digging through the vault for maps, hints, and narrative accounts.

11th Hour Hints

http://members.aol.com/UnclePita/
hour11.htm

Find useful game facts and a complete game walkthrough at this text-only site. Start at the beginning and move puzzle by puzzle toward winning the game. The walkthrough only points out the puzzles; players are left to their own devices to find the solutions, though some clues are offered along the way. This document could be a great help to anyone stuck in the 11th Hour with no apparent hope for success.

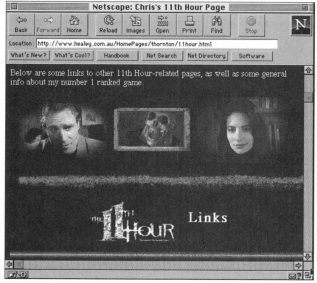

11th Hour Links

http://www.healey.com.au/HomePages/
thornton/11hour.html

When he authored this page, game fan Chris Thornton considered the 11th Hour his number one game pick, beating out Hexen. Read Chris' review to find out why the game rates as highly as it does for him. Also find a compiled list of links to 11th Hour-related sites, which include other fan pages, a non-playable demo, a walkthrough, updates and fixes, and general game information.

ALONE IN THE DARK I & II

Alone in the Dark
http://www.interplay.com/website/sales/
salealo1.html

Interplay hosts this official look at its chilling adventure game based on the writings of H. P. Lovecraft. Download a demo of the game and enjoy screen shots taken from the adventure. Also find a list of the game's awards and read the official line on what sets this spine-tingler apart from all the others. A link to the company's home page leads to product information and demos of other Interplay games.

Alone in the Dark 2
http://www.interplay.com/website/sales/
salealo2.html

Download a demo of the horror adventure that carries on where its award-winning predecessor left off. Hosted by Interplay, the site also offers an overview of the game illustrated with screen shots. A link to the company's home page leads to product information and demos of other Interplay games.

ANGEL DEVOID:
FACE OF THE ENEMY

Angel Devoid: Face of the Enemy
http://www.kalama.com/~magnus/
angeldevoid.htm

The Dogs D'Amour rate Angel Devoid: Face of the Enemy worth four out of seven shrunken gargoyles. Read the Dogs' review of this fast-paced, in-your-face action adventure or check out the walkthrough for hints. A link to Mindscape's official page is also featured.

Angel Devoid: Face of the Enemy
http://www.mindscape.com/msgames/
AngelDev/index.html

Mindscape promotes its cat-and-mouse action adventure game where players track the criminal mastermind Angel Devoid, but find the tables are turned. Read an overview of the game, check out system requirements, and enjoy a few screen shots. Those so inspired can order online, or read through other Mindscape product promotions.

Angel Devoid: Face of the Enemy
Click Through
http://www.gamespot.com/intmovie/
angeldev/hint4cc2.html

Take a tour, step-by-step, location-by-location through Mindscape's shoot-it-out-or-die action adventure Angel Devoid: Face of the Enemy. Playing options presented allow players (the good ones) to kill Angel or let him live.

BAD DAY ON THE MIDWAY

Review of Bad Day on the Midway
http://www.macweek.com/mw_12-04-95/
rev09.html

Read the MacWeek review for Bad Day on the Midway, a freakish carnival encounter where the object of the game is to emerge from the midway madness alive. Screen shots plus a brief explanation of the game and its most outstanding features are offered. The article appeared December 4, 1995.

Bad Day on the Midway
http://www.zdnet.com/complife/content/
960320/rev3.html

Computer Life weighs in with a "thumbs up" in its review of Bad Day on the Midway, a follow-up title from the same team that developed Freak Show. Read a brief description of the game and find out why the reviewer placed the game at the top of his play list.

Bad Day on the Midway
http://pathfinder.com/
@@FKKXcwQADhYHeeHL/inscape/BDM/
BDMHome.html

Explore the eagerly anticipated follow-up to the award-winning game Freak Show. Read an overview of the adventure game where the characters are like carnival rides, review the game's system requirements, find troubleshooting tips, and enjoy images taken from the game. For those who require help getting through the game, help is also available.

BAD MOJO

Bad Mojo Complete Walkthrough
http://www.algonet.se/~averpil/common/
solve/badmojo.html

Find out how the successful roaches maneuver through the maze of pipes, crevices, critters, and inconveniences toward uncovering the story and successfully returning to humanity in Bad Mojo. Walk through the whole game with the help of one who has gone before. The presentation is mostly text and offers only one graphic; however, descriptions are organized by rooms.

Bad Mojo Hints
http://members.aol.com/UnclePita/
badmojo.htm

Here's another copy of the same walkthrough offered above. Find the tips that make roach life livable, or at least fun, or ... well, it *is* just a game.

GameSpot: Bad Mojo at a Glance
http://www.gamespot.com/adventure/
badmojo/

The Pulse Entertainment title Bad Mojo falls under the spotlight at this site hosted by the GameSpot. Find a game overview, reviews, and answers to Frequently Asked Questions. Links lead to a demo and other downloads, technical information, and the personal home pages of players. For those who like a little help along the way, game hints and tips are also available.

BENEATH A STEEL SKY

Beneath a Steel Sky
http://www.revolution.co.uk/sky.htm

Revolution software hosts this official look at its popular adventure that takes players under the city streets and into the bowels of an unknown world. Review the awards won by this 1994 release, download a playable demo, check out the walkthrough for hints to game solutions, or enjoy a sampling of screen shots.

BIOFORGE

BioForge
http://www.ea.com/osi-old/bf-hm.html

Origin Systems promotes its role-playing adventure game where players explore an alien civilization and battle hostile forces, though they don't know who they are or where they are. Read a game overview, review system requirements, and check out the features that set this game apart. A series of screen shots are available to view, and a hint book is online to help those who can't help but help themselves to quick answers.

Bioforge—Complete Walkthrough
http://www.ozonline.com.au/gamesguide/
hints/pc/walkthru/bioforge.htm

Daniel Starr offers players general tips and a complete walkthrough for navigating the perils of BioForge. This text-only document offers no hyperlinks, but the steps players must go through are numbered to aid in navigating the page.

BioForge Technical Help FAQ
http://www.ea.com/osi-old/bftech/
bioforge.htm

Find solutions to most problems that could possibly keep you from enjoying BioForge. The menu of topics covered includes memory and configuration, sound, and the mouse. Also find out how to create a boot disk and access the game's readme file text.

BURIED IN TIME

Buried in Time
http://www.sanctuary.com/BITMenu.html

Sanctuary Woods Multimedia promotes its sequel to the Journeyman Project on this official page for Buried in Time. Find background details on the game, reviews, screen shots, and information for ordering demos and the full release version. A game of mystery, time travel, deception, and intrigue, Buried in Time features a non-linear story line. For those who need assistance, a walkthrough of the game contains tips and solutions.

Buried in Time 2 Hints
http://members.aol.com/UnclePita/
bury2.htm

Here's an attempt to walk gamers through the adventure known as Buried in Time. Find specific instructions and hints for moving through the game toward a successful conclusion. There are no hyperlinks to aid in navigating this site . Players must page through the whole document to find the solutions to the problems which have them stumped.

Journeyman Project 2: Buried in Time
http://darwin1.ucsd.edu:8000/connect/new/
products/presto/jp2.html

This page from ConnectNet, the electronic publication of a University of California business incubator, throws its spotlight on Buried in Time, the second game in the Journeyman Project series. Read about the game's background, premise, system requirements, and marketing support. Also find out what people had to say about the original Journeyman Project.

Walkthrough for Buried in Time
http://spoiler.et.ee/ADVENTURE/Presto/
buried.in.time.1.txt

Michael Beemer shares his three rules for adventure game playing: Look at everything, pick everything up, and save often. He also shares this walkthrough of Buried in Time. Prepare to spend some time with this text-only presentation. There are no hyperlinks, so users must page through the whole document to find the sections they're interested in reading. Sections include: General Notes, Introduction, Gage's Apartment, Farnstein's Lab, Chateau Gaillard, Da Vinci Studio, Chicken Itza, Culprit's Lair, Krynn Embassy, and Endgame Sequence.

CHRONICLES OF THE SWORD

Chronicles of the Sword
http://www.psygnosis.com/

Yet another attempt to cash in on the legend of King Arthur, Psygnosis' Chronicles of the Sword is promoted here. Read an overview of the game's premise and most outstanding features, and enjoy selected screen shots. Visitors can also look into other games by the same company, or access the company's support and e-clip pages.

Chronicles of the Sword Review— Kix TV

http://www.club10.com.au/kixtv/
gamereviews/chronicle/chronicle.html

Read this game review to find out why the folks at Kix gave Psygnosis' adventure quest to destroy the evil sorceress Morgana La Fay an 83.7% out of 100. Find a story line overview and screen shots woven into the text of the critical review.

GameSpot: Chronicles of the Sword at a Glance

http://www.gamespot.com/adventure/
chrsword/

Anyone interested in the Arthurian adventure Chronicles of the Sword may want to check out this Game-Spot spotlight. Read reviews, view screen shots, and check out the system requirements for the game. Also find a walkthrough and links to pages of related topical interest. Technical information online includes the game's readme file and a player discussion on the game.

CHRONOMASTER

Chronomaster

http://www.pcentertainment.com/games/
Mar96/chrono396.html

Shane Mooney grades Chronomaster as an average adventure in this March 1996 review. Read Mooney's critical review or link out for game tips and company information.

Chronomaster Review from Online Gaming Review

http://www.ogr.com/reviews/
chronomaster.shtml

Christopher Angel supports a different view of Chronomaster, rating it 8 out 10 in this May 1996 review. Read what's good about the game and what is bad about this

AUTHOR'S PICK

CNET Reviews - CD-ROM Central
http://204.162.80.5/Content/Reviews/
Cdcentral/cat.html

At $50.00 a game and up, playing around on the computer can get fairly pricey, fairly quickly. Anymore it takes a savvy, informed shopper not to get taken by the latest and supposedly greatest game to come down the pike—especially those games being driven by a promotions department that's hyped up and hungry for a sale. Sometimes it takes an objective eye to help tighten the focus and show things for what they are. That's why it's not a bad idea at all to check out how reviewers react to the new games coming into the market. As part of its search services, c/net offers a CD-ROM library of reviews, and "games" is one of the categories covered. Reviews are short and to the point, and links lead to supplemental material. If the reviewer feels the game is worth the expense, a recommendation to buy is given; if not, no recommendation is given and players are left to decide for themselves. The games reviewed are indexed alphabetically.

last project of famed science fiction writer Roger Zelazny. Links lead to the games vital statistics and to the Capstone's official Chronomaster home page.

GameSpot: Chronomaster at a Glance
http://www.gamespot.com/adventure/
chronoma/

Explore the adventure game where magic and science co-exist in a future time, Chronomaster. Hosted by GameSpot, this in-depth look at the game offers reviews, a game overview, and technical data. Also enjoy a sample audio file, screen shots, a click-through of the first five levels, and a complete walkthrough. Links to official, independent, and topic-related sites lead to a free demo offer, the complete story, and information about Chronomaster's writer and designer, Roger Zelazny.

COLOSSAL CAVE

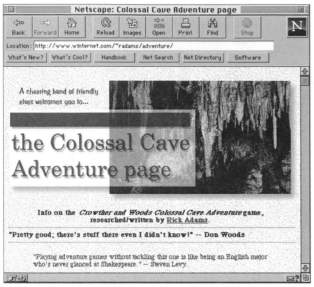

The Colossal Cave Adventure Page
http://www.winternet.com/~radams/adventure/

Rick Adams hosts this extensive look at the very old and very much still-enjoyed interactive-fiction adventure game Colossal Cave. Read a history of the game, download a copy to play offline, or link to the online version. Also find all kinds of cheats and hints including maps of the cave and a discussion of the magic word "XXZZY." Those who find they enjoy this kind of adventure game may want to follow the link to the Interactive Fiction archive.

Play Colossal Cave
http://www.biss.co.uk/~dbird/exec/advent0b.htm

Here's a "devilishly extended" online version of the game Colossal Cave. Page options include "start a new game" and "resume an existing game." Enjoy!

DAEDALUS ENCOUNTER

Daedalus Encounter
http://www.mechadeus.com/mecha/titles/daedalus/daedalus.html

Mechadeus promotes its interactive adventure movie starring Tia Carrere, Daedalus Encounter, with this page of screen shots. Click on Tia at the bottom of the page to find an option for accessing the company's hint file. There you can find solutions to aid in winning the game without even trying. Technical support and company information are also only a click away.

Daedalus Encounter
http://www.webpages.com.au/wizards-lair/IBM/daedalus.htm

This page—one of the many posted at the Wizard's Lair—offers a map of the spaceship found in the Mechadeus game Daedalus Encounter. Those who scroll down the page will also discover a few cheat codes and some hints for solving specific problems within the game. At the bottom of the page, a link leads back to other Wizard's Lair pages and is well worth the jump.

The Daedalus Encounter
http://spoiler.et.ee/ADVENTURE/Mechadeus/daedalus.encounter.1.txt

David Tanguay leads gamers through the science fiction known as the Daedalus Encounter game. Broken into nice, easily digestible chunks, this spoiler also offers a diagram or two. Check it out if you find you're spinning in a void of nothingness with no hope of ever recovering alone.

THE DARK EYE

The Dark Eye
http://pathfinder.com/
@@FKKXcwQADhYHeeHL/inscape/DKY/
DKYHome.html

Inscape promotes its game of nightmare worlds and unexpected fate on this official page. Find images from the game, QuickTime movies, and troubleshooting tips. When the game becomes too troublesome, hints to help get through the rough spots are also featured.

The Dark Eye
http://www.pcentertainment.com/games/
Feb96/dark296.html

David Israels critiques The Dark Eye, the game based on the writings of Edgar Allen Poe, and rates the game as deserving only a D in this February 1996 review. Find out why the critic pans the game and what problems led to his decision. Interwoven through the text, find an overview of the story line. Hints to speed toward the game's resolution are also featured for those who have as much trouble with The Dark Eye as the reviewer.

The Spoiler Centre: Dark Eye
http://spoiler.et.ee/ADVENTURE/Inscape/
Dark.eye.html

Those needing help to solve the mysteries of The Dark Eye can refer to the hints and cheats posted here.

DARKSEED II

DarkSeed II
http://www.pcentertainment.com/games/
Mar96/dark396.html

Peter Olafson marks DarkSeed II as deserving a B and states the game offers a "more full-bodied adventure" than its predecessor. Read this March 1996 review, which features a general overview of the game. Those

AUTHOR'S PICK

Lord Soth's Games on the Internet
http://happypuppy.com/games/lordsoth/

A piece of the Happy Puppy site, Lord Soth's area is so rich in resources, it deserves another mention. Links lead to over 1,243 games— freeware, shareware, or demos—organized by platform, multiplayer option, and category. Of course, Lord Soth has his favorites, and that's a separate sort. Other links lead to cheat codes, FAQs, walkthroughs, strategy guides, move lists, and editors. Plus there's even more stuff on site for players to browse through and enjoy. A site for a gamer's sore eyes, Lord Soth likes to load his visitors down. Let the games begin!

looking for game tips can link to those as well as company information.

CyberDreams: DarkSeed II
http://www.cyberdreams.com/current/
darkintro.html

CyberDreams uses this official page to promote its sequel to the winner of SPA's 1993 award for the Best Fantasy Role Playing/Adventure Program. DarkSeed II offers players an engrossing storyline that resumes the nightmare of Mike Dawson's encounter with the Ancients. The game features chilling graphics and the latest computer technology, which allows players to converse with over 30 characters.

GameSpot: DarkSeed II at a Glance
http://www.gamespot.com/adventure/
darkseed/

Enjoy downloadable audio and video files, plus two versions (one complete, one abbreviated) of the walkthrough for the adventure DarkSeed II. Read reviews, browse the game overview, and check out technical information. Links lead to official pages and sites of related topical interest.

DAY OF THE TENTACLE

Day of the Tentacle Walkthrough
http://www.gamesdomain.co.uk/walkthru/dott.html

Need help getting through the Day of the Tentacle? Visit this walkthrough for solutions to all those tricky sticking points in the game. The opening index is hyperlinked, so users can navigate the document quickly. Solutions are grouped by character; find help for when playing As Bernard, As Hoagie, As Laverne, and As all three together.

Day of the Tentacle Non-Playable Demo
http://happypuppy.com/games/lordsoth/nonplay/day_of.htm

Visit this directory to link to FTP sites where non-playable demos of Day of the Tentacle can be downloaded. Get a look at the situations, a sense of the humor, and a listen to the sounds found in the full version of the game.

DEATH GATE

Death Gate
http://www.gamesdomain.com/walkthru/dgatew.html

Can't seem to guide Lord Xar in his quest to free his ravaged people? No problem. Visit this page for the walkthrough of Legend Entertainment's fantasy adventure based on the Death Gate book series by Margaret Weis and Tracey Hickman. The walkthrough is broken into very usable nuggets, and screen shots add visual interest.

Death Gate Cycle Series Tribute
http://www2.holli.com/~jschatte/

Dee Schlatter hosts this fan salute to the worlds and people of Sundered Realms. Take the Sundered Realms Fantasy Tour, access a sight-and-sound feature

on the Death Gate Universe, and meet Margaret Weis, one of the authors of the Death Gate Cycle series. Links lead to other fantasy and science fiction sites of topical interest.

Death's Gate
http://www.cypronet.com/~dg/

Check out the multiplayer role-playing game based on the Death Gate Cycle. A circleMUD, Death's Gate is introduced to new players on this page offering news, player information, and a live link to the Telnet site where the MUD is played. Those who wish can join the mailing list or take Dee Schlatter's tour of the Sundered Realms, the fantasy worlds created by Margaret Weis and Tracy Hickman in their best-selling fantasy series.

THE DIG

The Dig
http://www.lucasarts.com/pages/Product.509.html

At this official promotion posted in the LucasArts Company Store, find out what the company has to say about its science fiction epic adventure The Dig. Those impressed enough to want to order will find the information they need on site. Those who'd rather look around some more can link to the other product offerings in the LucasArts line.

The Dig
http://www.pcentertainment.com/games/Feb96/dig296.html

Shane Mooney rates The Dig a solid B in this February 1996 review. Find out what's so strong about this graphic science fiction adventure, get an overview of the game, and marvel at the high-powered talent that came together to make the project happen. Game tips are available for those who can't get through a game without cheating, and another link leads to general information about the game's maker, LucasArts.

The Dig

http://www.worldvillage.com/wv/
gamezone/html/reviews/thedig.htm

Rich Cunningham rates The Dig in this 1996 review, posted to the Gamer's Zone at the WorldVillage site. Screen shots are interspersed throughout the text of the favorable review, and a link leads to the LucasArts Entertainment Company home page. The Gamer's Zone Scorecard provides a quick overview of system requirements to play, and the overall enjoyment score gives the game 4 Worlds.

The Dig Complete Walkthrough

http://www.algonet.se/~averpil/common/
solve/dig.html

Dig this! Here's the complete walkthrough for the LucasArts outer space adventure The Dig. Find all the tactical tricks and puzzle solutions needed to waltz through the game with flair. But be careful. This walkthrough is not broken into sections, so chances are pretty good you may find answers you weren't even looking to uncover.

DINOTOPIA

Dinotopia

http://www.turner.com/interactive/dino/
index.html

Discover the adventure game where players set out to explore a world in which dinosaurs live in harmony with men and roam the land freely. The game features 11 distinct cultures and over 130 characters for players to interact with, piecing together puzzles and solving mysteries. An overview of the game and its features can be found at this promotional site along with screen shots and sound files.

Dinotopia Spoilers

http://spoiler.et.ee/ADVENTURE/Turner/
dinotopia.1.txt

Ted Triggs treats Dinotopia players to a complete walkthrough of the game. Organized with numbered info-nuggets, the page is fairly easy to navigate despite its lack of hyperlinks.

DUST

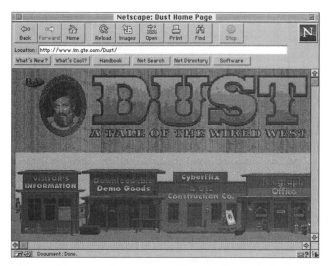

Dust Home Page - A Tale of the Wired West

http://www.im.gte.com/Dust/

GTE Entertainment hosts this official "howdy do partner" in honor of the Cyberflix game Dust, winner of *MacWorld*'s 1995 award for Best Multimedia Game. Read all about what the experts have to say about the game, download demos (currently select from four different pieces of game), or jump to the players' forum to join in or start topical discussions and swap cheats. Stop by the Visitor's Info center for system requirements, the official FAQ, an introduction to the game's townsfolk, and purchasing information.

AUTHOR'S PICK

Douwe's Game Cheating Page
http://wwwedu.cs.utwente.nl/~achterka/

Either because of a game's difficulty level or a player's unfamiliarity with the strategies necessary to win, cheats, hints, and other aids are often called into play by gamers at all levels. Often used to speed the learning process of exploring and exploiting a game's design, these cheats vary in their effect on the game's outcome. Some cheats merely offer hints for solving a puzzle, others give complete game solutions, and still others provide players advantages not normally allowed in standard play. A variety of sites are online that cater to serving players these cheats. Douwe's Game Cheating Page is just such a site. In addition to its large online collection of cheats, the page also offers cheating programs and points to other sites offering similar information. Some of these additional cheat sites include Complete Walkthroughs and Solves for Adventure Games at http://www.algonet.se/~averpil/norm/solve/ and The Spoiler Centre and http://spoiler.et.ee/.

Official Dust FAQ
http://www.happypuppy.com/games/lordsoth/cheats/faqs/dust.txt

Stop by this site hosted by Happy Puppy for the official GTE Vantage FAQ for the game Dust. The text-only document offers no game cheats or walkthrough solutions but does provide an informed look at the adventure game and its requirements. Find help setting up the software and solving general problems making it work on both PC and Mac machines. The document itself is not hyperlinked, so users must scroll through the entire text to find the answers they seek. A table of contents provides some assistance in this regard.

FADE TO BLACK

Fade To Black
http://www.ea.com/eastudios/f2b/eastudio1.html

Conrad B. Hart, the hero from Flashback: The Quest, is back, and you're he in this shoot-'em-up action adventure from Entertainment Arts. Read the official line spelling out the game's premise, enjoy screen shots, and demo a version of the game. Links lead to other EA pages offering information on other products.

Fade To Black Solve
http://spoiler.et.ee/ACTION/Delphine/fade.2.black.1.txt

Can players trust somebody named BONeHeAD for the correct solution to Entertainment Art's Fade to Black adventure? Find out by giving this "been there, done that" a whirl. The solution opens with a detailed explanation of the keystrokes required for a successful outcome in the game, then moves through solutions for various locations in the game. Users are required to read large chunks of text to find the answers they seek.

FREDDY PHARKAS, FRONTIER PHARMACIST

Freddy Pharkas, Frontier Pharmacist
http://www2.brecknet.com/games/fpfp.html

From the mind that came up with Leisure Suit Larry, here's another unforgettable character at odds with his environment. Freddy was a gunslinger in the wild west, but gave it up to pursue pharmacology. Enjoy the resulting good humor created by this curious career change. Find a general overview of the game, enjoy screen shots, and download a movie sample. A shareware version of the game is also available for immediate downloading.

Freddy Pharkas, Frontier Pharmacist
http://www.webpages.com.au/wizards-lair/
IBM/fpfp.htm

Wizard's Lair doesn't offer much in the way of hints this time, but there are two tips to keep Freddy moving along. Find ideas for purifying the town's water supply and for combatting the flatulent horses.

FULL THROTTLE

Complete Walkthrough for Full Throttle
http://www.algonet.se/~averpil/common/
solve/throttle.html

Those who can't seem to get their cycle to crank may want to check out this text-only walkthrough for tips on Full Throttle motorcycle maintenance. From start to finish, the game is laid bare for those in need and those in despair. Find the document's text broken into sections, but there are no hyperlinks to aid quick fact retrieval. Users must page through the whole document in search of the nugget of knowledge that will get them on the road again.

GameSpot: Full Throttle at a Glance
http://www.gamespot.com/adventure/
fullthro/

The LucasArts adventure game Full Throttle falls under the GameSpot spotlight on this page. Read a game overview, a system requirement synopsis, and reviews. Plus, enjoy a full walkthrough of the motorcycle adventure, download a boot disc maker, and link to official, independent, and topic-related sites. Online technical support includes the full readme file, tips for troubleshooting, and a player's discussion.

GABRIEL KNIGHT I & II

Gabriel Knight: Directory
http://members.aol.com/UnclePita/
gabriel.htm

Help is here for those stuck under the spell of Sins of the Father who can't seem to solve the mystery that will set them free. Organized by day and problem, this walkthrough features hyperlinks to aid quick and efficient navigation.

Gabriel Knight Hints
http://www.gem.co.za/GameBytes/issue19/
misc/gabriel.html

Gabriel Knight fans burdened and befuddled by the Sins of the Father will find a complete game walkthrough posted here. Organized by day and problem, the text-only document offers no hyperlinks to aid navigation. Players must scroll through the text to find the solutions they seek.

Gabriel Knight Home Page
http://lasarto.cnde.iastate.edu/Personal/
Adam/gk/

Explore the world of the Gabriel Knight mysteries through this look at both games in the series: Sins of the Father and The Beast Within. Enjoy game overviews, walkthroughs, information on the games' actors, and information on the games' author, Jane Jensen. Also find patches and links to sites exploring topics relevant to the games. Screen shots add graphic interest to the overall presentation.

Gabriel Knight II: The Beast Within—Hints and Tips
http://student-www.uchicago.edu/users/
jjkeyte/gk2hints.html

Jeff Keyte points players to gaming tips and hints he has collected from the Sierra On-Line forum at AOL about the game The Beast Within. The hints are organized by chapter and question; hyperlinks aid quick and easy navigation.

Gabriel Knight II: The Beast Within Walkthrough
http://www.megatoon.com/~t15/hint/gk2solve.htm

Posting hints provided by Sierra On-Line, this site walks players through The Beast Within. The information is organized by chapter and topic. The text-only document offers no hyperlinks to aid navigation; players must scroll through the entire document in search of the answers they seek. Because of this oversight in the walkthrough's presentation, it is possible for a player to uncover hints by accident.

Gabriel Knight 2 Unofficial Home Page
http://home.earthlink.net./~dandavid/

Michelle David (a.k.a. the Black Wolf) posts and hosts this fan tribute to the Gabriel Knight mystery The Beast Within. Find answers to Frequently Asked Questions, hints, tips, and walkthroughs. Meet the characters and meet the game's author, Jane Jensen. Enjoy the lyrics from the opera, a drinking game, and screen shots. Links also lead to many pages that explore a range of related topics, from computer stuff to werewolves.

GameSpot: The Beast Within: A Gabriel Knight Mystery at a Glance
http://www.gamespot.com/adventure/beastwit/

GameSpot throws its light on The Beast Within, offering a general game overview and favorable reviews. Enjoy screen shots, downloads, and a complete game walkthrough. Links lead to official and unofficial pages related to the game and its predecessor. Also featured is technical information that includes patches and drivers, and a player discussion on technical issues.

HELL: A CYBERPUNK THRILLER

Hell: A CyberPunk Thriller
http://www.gametek.com/webfinall/other_products/hell.html

GameTek promotes its star-studded interactive adventure where the conservative right wields might and nothing seems to be all right. Find an overview of the game, enjoy screen shots, read a review, and link to support services where patches are available to download. Pointers to other GameTek pages lead to demos, FAQs, and information for the company's other products.

Hell: A CyberPunk Thriller
http://virtualtimes.com/vidgames/3dohell.htm

When the government wants you dead, what are you going to do—roll over and play possum? No need if you have this handy walkthrough, offering all the answers for coming out of Hell: A CyberPunk Thriller victorious. The text-only document isn't much to look at (in fact, its design makes it hard to look at), but it delivers the goods.

I HAVE NO MOUTH AND I MUST SCREAM

I Have No Mouth
http://www.mgmua.com/interactive/nomouth/

Hosted by MGM/UA, here's the official declaration: I Have No Mouth And I Must Scream. Stop by for a general overview of the game based on the work of Harlan Ellison. Take a look behind the scenes for insight into the making of the game, credits, and biographies. Visit the multimedia room to download images, sounds, and video clips. And meet the game's characters through clips and a written narrative describing their trials as captives of AM.

I Have No Mouth Complete Walkthrough
http://www.algonet.se/~averpil/common/
solve/nomouth.html

For those who find themselves saying, "I have no clue and I must scream," here's a clue or two to alleviate some of the tension born of the game I Have No Mouth. Organized by character, this text-only walkthrough offers no hyperlinks to aid navigation, but the document isn't that long anyway. Still, players will find themselves reading large chunks of information to find the hint they seek. Careful not to read too far.

IN THE FIRST DEGREE

A Review of: In the First Degree
http://www.worldvillage.com/wv/
gamezone/html/reviews/degree.htm

Kathleen Keating posts this favorable report for the Brøderbund murder trial courtroom simulation, In the First Degree. Read this critique for an overview of the game's general premise and an idea of what makes the interactive drama rate so highly on the WorldVillage scale (5 Worlds). A review of system requirements to play the game rounds out the presentation.

Hints for In the First Degree
http://www.gamesdomain.co.uk/spoiler/
ADVENTURE/Broderbund/first.degree.1.txt

For those whose virtual legal careers are not moving along as swiftly as they'd planned, Al Terry offers these hints for scoring a conviction for murder In the First Degree and grand theft. Explaining there is more than one outcome to the game, Terry talks players through his winning strategy, offering tips and tactics for taking a bite out of crime.

INDIANA JONES

Indiana Jones and The Fate of Atlantis
http://sunsite.nus.sg/GameBytes/issue18/
greviews/ijones/ijones.html

Geoff Elbo rates the LucasArts adventure Indiana Jones and The Fate of Atlantis in this 1993 review for Game Bytes Magazine. Offering several screen shots, an overview of system requirements, and a look at the game's features, the review extols the virtues of "talkie" games and predicts that the standard set by this action adventure will become the norm rather than the exception.

Indiana Jones and The Fate of Atlantis Complete Walkthrough
http://www.algonet.se/~averpil/common/
solve/atlantis.html

Organized by game mode (team, wits, and fists) and by locales, this walkthrough helps Indy fans get to the bottom of The Fate of Atlantis. The text-only document has no hyperlinks, but its organization is easy to understand and to scroll through.

Help with Being Indiana Jones
http://www.softaid.net/msjohnso/
game.html

This page from Micah Johnson's full-scale fan page, dedicated to the Indiana Jones character and his many merchandising incarnations, offers Indy computer game help for both The Last Crusade and The Fate of Atlantis. Find game hints for each adventure and a collection of walkthroughs from different sources and in different languages (English, German, and Italian).

KINGDOM O' MAGIC

Kingdom O' Magic
http://www.sci.co.uk/kom/kommenu.html

Hosted by Sales Curve International, this site welcomes players to the Kingdom O' Magic, where snakemen are ... well, snakemen. Take a tour of this other world and choose a guide that meets the moment's want: creepy and subservient, nice and friendly, or just plain rude. Those who desire an overview of the kingdom can check the map, and anyone curious about the making of the game will find plenty to ponder. Stop by the Viewing Room to download clips of the Snakeman in action, and check out the hints and tips to find aid and assistance.

Kingdom O' Magic Strategy Guide
**http://www.nuke.com/cgr/strategy/
kingdom/kingdom.htm**

There's no mystery about what's offered here. Find a strategy guide for winning in the Kingdom O' Magic. Hints are organized by the various locations found in the game, although not every location is presented. Screen shots add visual interest to the presentation.

KINGDOM:
THE FAR REACHES

Kingdom: The Far Reaches
**http://www.interplay.com/website/sales/
kingdom1.html**

Interplay hosts this official look at its family adventure game Kingdom: The Far Reaches. Enjoy screen shots taken from the game, as well as a game overview and the official line on what sets this adventure apart from all the others. A link to the company's home page leads to information and demos of other Interplay games.

KING'S QUEST

Complete Walkthrough for King's Quest VII
**http://www.algonet.se/~averpil/common/
solve/kq7.html**

Organized by chapter and specific problems, this walkthrough helps the errant player succeed in working through the trials found along the way in King's Quest VII. At the end of each chapter's section find an inventory of items and where to find each. There are no hyperlinks to aid navigation, so players must scroll the body of the document in search of the clues desired.

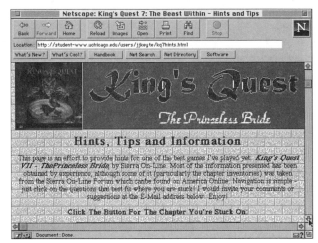

King's Quest VII Hints, Tips & Information
**http://student-www.uchicago.edu/users/
jjkeyte/kq7hints.html**

Jeff Keyte points players to gaming tips and hints he's collected from the Sierra On-Line forum at AOL for King's Quest VII: The Priceless Bride. The hints are organized by chapter and question; hyperlinks aid quick and easy navigation. Also find sections offering advice on troubleshooting, general tips, and hints for King Quest VI.

An Unsupported, Unconfirmed Walkthrough for King's Quest 6
http://student-www.uchicago.edu/users/
jjkeyte/kq6hints.html

Although posted by Jeff Kyte as a service to gamers, this text-intense walkthrough of Kings Quest VI has not been tested by Jeff for its accuracy. Still, it offers three different walkthroughs of the game. The first is a simple walkthrough. The second reveals how to score maximum points. And the third points the way to discovering an alternate ending for the game. Tested or not, it's worth a look; however, be warned that users are required to read large blocks of text to find the clues desired. Take care not to ruin the fun of the game by finding too many clues too fast.

LEISURE SUIT LARRY

Conversations with Larry
http://www.netg.se/~olausson/lslbook5.html

Visit this page to read excerpts from The Official Book of Leisure Suit Larry by Ralph Roberts and Al Lowe. One excerpt features an interview with the polyester playboy himself. In it, Larry Laffer reveals such things as great places to get great deals on leisure suits and what his favorite hobbies are. Also enjoy an extract from "How to Pick Up Chicks: A Hands On Tutorial" featuring "never fail" lines.

Leisure Suit Larry's Greatest Hits and Misses
http://www.sierra.com/games/lslcol/

Visit this official Sierra promotion to discover what's happening with the Leisure Suit Larry series. Find all six games bundled into one package, along with a whole bunch of extras including a playable demo of Al Lowe's comedy western, Freddy Pharkus. Descriptions of each of the Larry games are presented. Those interested can download a demo. Links to other Sierra pages lead to other free and hot stuff currently available from the company.

Leisure Suit Larry Spoilers
http://spoiler.et.ee/ADVENTURE/Sierra.html

Drop by this index for links to cheats and hints for the entire Leisure Suit Larry adventure series. One or two of the solutions come from the game's distributor, Sierra On-Line; the others have been submitted by Leisure Suit Larry fans who've managed to find their way through the games. How tough can a game about a guy in a cheap suit be?

MISSION CRITICAL

Mission Critical
http://www.legendent.com/gameinfo/
mission.html

LEGEND Entertainment hosts this official page toasting its science fiction adventure Mission Critical. Starring Michael Dorn of Star Trek: The Next Generation fame, the game offers full motion video in a 3D animated world of interstellar conflict and impossible choices. Download a demo, read reviews, enjoy screen shots, or stop by the trophy room to check out the game's awards. Those interested in what others have to say about the game can also link to reviews.

Mission Critical Review from Gamer's Zone
http://www.worldvillage.com/wv/
gamezone/html/reviews/mission.htm

Edmond Meinfelder rates Mission Critical in this review posted to the Gamer's Zone at the WorldVillage site. Screen shots are interspersed throughout the text of the favorable review. The Gamer's Zone Scorecard provides a quick overview of system requirements needed to play, and the overall enjoyment score rates the game 4 Worlds.

Mission Critical Walkthrough
http://www.legendent.com/hints/
mchint.html

LEGEND Entertainment posts this official walkthrough of the action adventure chosen Byte Magazine's Game of the Year in 1995. The presentation is organized and hyperlinked for easy use and quick reference. Be aware, however, that any play which deviates from the steps described in the walkthrough will affect subsequent sections.

MYST

Myst
http://www.cyan.com/

Here's the official Myst page hosted by the company that designed the game, Cyan. Find loads of Myst paraphernalia for sale, the Cyan FAQ that answers questions about a possible sequel to Myst, and an assortment of "recommended" links leading to Myst-related sites on the Web. Among the featured links find pointers to technical support, reviews, hint pages, and other items of interest to Myst fans.

Myst Help, Hints and Information
http://www.itsnet.com/home/lminer/myst/
index.html

Chris Miner boasts his Myst page is the best on the Web. Among the marvels featured, find a walkthrough, downloadable patches for each age, a pointer to the Japanese Myst fan club home page, pictures from The Making of Myst, and Myst sequel information. Also find answers to the questions, "What's the point of Myst?" and, "How do you win?"

The Myst Hint Guide
http://www.shrubbery.com/ingram/myst/
index.html

Doug Ingram advises players that this guide is not a walkthrough. Care has been given to reveal the clues

gradually, so there's little risk of getting too much information too fast and spoiling the game. Players link to sections on the various worlds to find the aid required. Another feature of this guide is a hyperlinked FAQ that answers questions about the game and this page. Pointers to a few game-related sites round out the helpful offerings presented.

Myst Infopage
http://www.probe.net/~lokety/myst_
index.html

Loke Teng Yan hosts this outpost for what he describes as the "only"—though unofficial—Myst FAQ. Read it online or download the file. Other site features link visitors to the home pages of Cyan and Brøderbund, the designer and distributor of the Myst game. Anyone with comments is encouraged to leave a message or rate the site.

Myst Walkthrough Plus
http://www.voicenet.com/~mmax/myst.html

Give up? This walkthrough promises to totally solve the challenges found in Myst. The site host, Mike Maxim (a.k.a. MystWalk), suggests players only look when they find themselves completely mystified. In addition to the walkthrough, find technical assistance and screen shots. Those interested can also join Mike for an IRC session Sunday nights.

For another Myst walkthrough, see:

Complete Walkthrough for Myst
http://www.algonet.se/~averpil/common/solve/
myst.html

NORMALITY

Normality
http://www.interplay.com/website/sales/
normal.html

Interplay Productions promotes the adventure game where normality just doesn't cut it anymore. Read an overview of the game and meet the locals. Download flicks offering hints and events. Get a load of what Kent, the game's protagonist, has to say. And check out some screen shots from the game. Other site features include press releases, customer support, and a link to the Interplay home page.

Normality
http://www.gremlin.com/games/normality/

Gremlin Interactive asks the question: What's so great about being normal? Enjoy this official look at the game where Norm is not just a name but a state of being—and something must be done about it. Read a game overview, check out what the reviewers had to say, download a screen saver, and find out how to cheat to win.

PHANTASMAGORIA I & II

Phantasmagoria
http://www.sierra.com/games/phant/

What's the buzz about Phantasmagoria? Find out at this official Sierra Entertainment home page. Read a game overview, view screen shots, enjoy the sheet music for the game's theme song (and a translation of the lyrics), plus download a demo file. Those who like what they see can order the game online; others who prefer to look around can find out about other games or check out the hot and free stuff currently available from the company.

Phantasmagoria
http://www.pcentertainment.com/games/ Oct95/phan1095.html

Peter Olafson gives Phantasmagoria an A- in this October 1995 review. Read a summary of the story line interwoven with facts about the game features that earn this seven-CD-ROM game such high marks. For those who need help to play, hints are available, and a

link points to general information about Sierra Entertainment, the company selling the game.

Phantasmagoria
http://members.aol.com/UnclePita/ scarydos.htm

Here's the ultimate in cheats! Download a copy of a saved game and view the ending of Phantasmagoria. Those who prefer the manual method for picking up hints and cheats can browse the walkthrough which is also provided. Divided into chapters, the walkthrough takes players step-by-step through the adventure.

Phantasmagoria 2: A Puzzle of Flesh
http://www.sierra.com/entertainment/ phantas2/

Visitors to this official Sierra Entertainment site are invited to read the Phantasmagoria 2 game overview and sneak a peek at the video preview. Also find tidbits from behind the scenes, a bit about the author, and free downloadable wallpaper. Those who like what they see can order the game online; others who prefer to look around can find out about other games or check out the hot and free stuff currently available from the company.

POLICE QUEST

Police Quest Collection: The 4 Most Wanted
http://www.sierra.com/games/pq4/

Catch the buzz on the Sierra's Police Quest series, where players are thrown onto the front line of action and must walk that thin blue line. This collection features the first four games in the series bundled in one package. Find an overview of the games, a review of the games' features, and comments from media reviews. Links to other Sierra pages point to the free and hot stuff the company currently has available.

Police Quest Spoilers
http://spoiler.et.ee/ADVENTURE/Sierra.html

Drop by this index for links to cheats and hints for the entire Police Quest adventure series. These solutions have been submitted by game fans who've managed to walk the walk, talk the talk, and put the bad guys behind bars where they belong.

PRISONER OF ICE

Prisoner of Ice
http://www.imotion.com/product/ice/ice01.htm

Here's the official page from I-Motion for its adventure game that takes players from the ice fields of Antarctica to the tropical climes of Buenos Aires ... always one step ahead of being captured and running through the wake of terror. Read an overview of the game's plot line, view screen shots, download a video trailer, and review system requirements. Links lead to other I-motion pages offering game hints, technical help, and ordering information.

Prisoner of Ice Complete Walkthrough
http://spoiler.et.ee/ADVENTURE/Infogrames/Prisoner.of.ice.html

Ian Ng Wai Yip offers this complete solution for the adventure game Prisoner of Ice. Beginning with a general tip for players to talk to all the game's characters, Ian then proceeds through the game's various locations, moving step by step to the game's two endings. A text-only document, this spoiler requires users to read fairly large sections of copy (six in all). There are no hyperlinks to aid navigation.

Prisoner of Ice Strategy Guide
http://www.pcgamer.com/s_ice.html

The PC Gamer Staff posts this handful of solutions for some of the tougher timed puzzles that pop up in I-Motion's adventure thriller game based on H.P.

Lovecraft's novel Mountains of Madness. Solutions featured include HMS Victoria parts 1 & 2, the stone, escape from the jail, and the mine door.

RIPPER

Ripper
http://www.nuke.com/cgr/reviews/9604/ripper/ripper.htm

Read this favorable review of Take 2 Interactive's adventure game, which employs the Jack the Ripper scenario but changes the location to New York City in the year 2060. Interwoven in the text find an overview of the game's story line, details about the making of the game, and indications of why Ripper ranks so favorably. Screen shots add graphic interest to the presentation.

SAM & MAX HIT THE ROAD

Complete Walkthrough for Sam & Max Hit the Road
http://www.algonet.se/~averpil/common/solve/sam_n_max.html

Can't seem to keep Sam and Max on the road to adventure? Stop by this walkthrough for assistance in solving the mysteries that rattle and otherwise interrupt uninterrupted play. Organized by location, this text-only walkthrough offers no hyperlinks to aid navigation. Players must scroll through the text to find the clues they seek.

Sam & Max Hit the Road
http://www-personal.umich.edu/~dhaller/samnmax/cdrom.html

Bill Williams (a.k.a. Haller) hosts this game page as part of his Official Sam and Max Homepage. Download a demo of the game where a dog and rabbit take a spin into gaming history. Also featured are an archive of screen shots to download and a hint page that players reach after correctly answering a series of Sam and Max questions. Good luck.

SHADOAN

Shadoan
http://www.interplay.com/website/sales/shado.html

Interplay hosts this official look at its family adventure game Shadoan. Enjoy screen shots taken from the game, as well as a game overview and the official line on what sets this adventure apart from all the others. A link to the company's home page leads to information and demos of other Interplay games.

Shadoan Walkthrough
http://pages.prodigy.com/mrstuff/shadoan.htm

Posted by a player who found himself stuck in the game, here's a Shadoan cheats and hints page to help fellow players through the stickiest parts of the game. Those who need additional help can access a complete walkthrough, which is available as well. Players may want to consider going directly to the complete walkthrough file simply because its presentation is so much easier on the eyes. The cheats and hint page features purple type on a variegated gray background; it's very difficult to read.

SHADOW OF THE COMET

Shadow of the Comet
http://www.interplay.com/website/sales/shadow.html

Here's the I-Motion sales sheet for its Call of Cthulhu adventure Shadow of the Comet. Inspired by the writings of H.P. Lovecraft, the game offers a labyrinth of

mystery and supernatural intrigue as players attempt to unravel the secrets of the a small seaside village. Find a plot overview, system requirements, and screen shots. Links lead to other company pages offering technical support and ordering information.

Shadow of the Comet Solution
http://spoiler.et.ee/ADVENTURE/Infogrames/shadow.of.comet.1.txt

Will John Parker solve the mystery of Illsmouth and defeat the horror that plagues this seaside town? And will he do it in time to film the arrival of Haley's Comet? With this walkthrough, he'd have to be an idiot to fail!

SHANNARA

Shannara
http://www.legendent.com/gameinfo/shannara.html

Loaded with screen shots, this official Legend Entertainment promotion for Shannara also offers a downloadable demo. Based on the popular fantasy novel by author Terry Brooks, the game offers a multimedia adventure quest where ancient magic and monsters must be defeated and destinies fulfilled. Read the companies promotional material about the game, or check out what reviewers had to say. Those so inclined can order online.

Shannara Walkthrough
http://www.legendent.com/hints/shanhint.html

Here's the official Shannara walkthrough, offering scene-by-scene, step-by-step assistance for defeating the evil warlock and setting everything right in the Four Lands again. Hosted by Legend Entertainment, the page links to the other pages at the company's site.

SHIVERS

Shivers
http://www.sierra.com/games/shivers/

What's the buzz about Shivers? Find out at this official Sierra Entertainment home page. Read a game overview, view screen shots, and check out what players have to say about this mysterious adventure. Those who like what they see can order the game online; others who prefer to look around can find out about other games or check out the hot and free stuff currently available from the company.

Shivers Walkthrough
http://www.bcl.net/~artman/shivers.htm

Got Shivers and can't seem to shake free from some particularly troublesome part of the game? Here's a helping hand for those in need. Written by Sharon Fernandez, this document features separate sections that offer general strategies, a walkthrough of the various locations in the game, hints for solving puzzles, Ixupi hiding places, pot and lid pair locations, flashback item locations, and trivia question. There aren't any hyperlinks to aid navigation, so players must scroll through the text in search of the assistance desired.

For another Shivers walkthrough, see:

Shivers Complete Walkthrough
http://www.algonet.se/~averpil/common/solve/shivers.html

SPACE QUEST

Complete Walkthrough for Space Quest 6
http://www.algonet.se/~averpil/common/solve/space6.html

Trapped in the pavement? Shoot, you've only just started the game, but here are the clues to set yourself free and continue through to a successful conclusion in the sixth episode of the Space Quest series. This text-only document has no hyperlinks, so users must scroll through the page to find the clues they seek.

Space Quest VI: The Spinal Frontier
http://www.sierra.com/entertainment/sq6/

Sierra Entertainment toasts its sixth installment in the Roger Wilco adventure series, Space Quest. Read an overview of the game to find out what Roger is up to this time, find out what the critics have to say about this adventure sequel, and check out screen shots from the game. Those who like what they see can order the game online; others who prefer to look around can find out about other games or check out the hot and free stuff currently available from the company.

The Ultimate Space Quest Site
http://www.wiw.org/~jess/roger.html

Posted by Jess Morrissette, this site delivers pretty much what its title promises. Find system files, walkthroughs, and reviews for each of the six games in the Space Quest adventure series. Background about the game and its central character, Roger Wilco, include the complete Space Quest story and an FAQ. Also find humor files, articles, and downloads, including a Space Quest I demo and different game patches. Links to other game-related pages lead to both official and unofficial sites.

STAR TREK DEEP SPACE NINE: HARBINGER

Star Trek Deep Space Nine: Harbinger
http://www.viacomnewmedia.com/deep9/index.html

Curious about the making of the game Star Trek Deep Space Nine: Harbinger? Stop by this official home page for a look behind the scenes. Also enjoy an overview of the story line, download screen shots and patches, and find help solving the puzzlers found in the ST: DS9 universe.

The image shows a Netscape browser window titled "Netscape: Star Trek: Deep Space Nine: Harbinger" displaying the Star Trek Deep Space Nine: Harbinger page at http://yoyo.cc.monash.edu.au/~cable/ds9.htm with text:

"You are visitor number 003969 to my homepage.

Deep Space 9: Harbinger is the creation of Viacom Newmedia, and is based on the television series Star Trek: Deep Space 9 (Paramount). This page is here to help you with information, resources, and so on relating to the game DS9:Harbinger. I am hoping to update this page with more and more info as it comes to hand, and will keep you informed through the aus.sf.star-trek newsgroup. If you have any direct problems that are not covered here, email me, and I'll do my best to help out."

Star Trek Deep Space Nine: Harbinger

http://yoyo.cc.monash.edu.au/~cable/ds9.htm

Greg Askew hosts this fan page devoted to the game based on the "Star Trek: Deep Space Nine" television series. Those looking for discussions about the game and other Trek-related topics might try the three newsgroups suggested. Links lead to the official Harbinger page at Viacom, the Viacom DS9 hints page, and a Harbinger puzzle solutions page. Other site features include a walkthrough for the Star Trek: A Final Unity game, as well as an FAQ.

Star Trek Deep Space Nine: Harbinger Spoilers

http://spoiler.et.ee/ADVENTURE/Viacom/Harbinger.html

Lost in space? Fret not. Here's a selection of game cheats sure to send you on your way again. Spoilers are compiled here, but submitted by game fans. Got any to spare?

STAR TREK: THE NEXT GENERATION "A FINAL UNITY"

CGR Strategy Guide: Star Trek: "A Final Unity"

http://www.nuke.com/cgr/strategy/sttng/sttng.htm

Tasos Kaiafas posts this walkthrough for Star Trek: The Next Generation game fans attempting to achieve Final Unity. The text is organized much like a report, in paragraphs, so those looking for clues will need to read large chunks of information to find the specifics they seek. Interspersed throughout the text are a few screen shots that add limited graphic interest.

Star Trek: The Next Generation "A Final Unity"

http://ftp.microprose.com/stunity.html

Here's Spectrum Holobyte's official "come and get it" for its gaming adventure based on the "Star Trek: The Next Generation" television series. Read the adventure that resulted in the adventure game as the company secures the rights, assembles the players, and animates the action. A game summary and sample screen shots are also featured to further promote this combination graphic adventure and space-flight simulation.

Star Trek: The Next Generation "A Final Unity"

http://www.pcgamesmag.com/games/Aug95/trek895.html

In his August 1995 review, Steve Klett rates Star Trek: The Next Generation "A Final Unity" a solid B, describing the game as "pure Star Trek" from start to finish. Read the review and find the game's plot interview woven in the text along with key features that help the game rate so well. For those who crave assistance with their adventures, playing tips are on site to aid game navigation. Also find a link to information about the company that released the game, Spectrum Holobyte.

Star Trek: The Next Generation "A Final Unity" FAQ
http://ftp.microprose.com/stfaq.html

Spectrum Holobyte-MicroProse On-Line Services posts answers to Frequently Asked Questions and technical tips to aid gamers get the most from their purchase of Star Trek: The Next Generation "A Final Unity." From crashing computers to soundless action, most basic and general problems receive attention. Links lead to other company pages.

Star Trek: The Next Generation "A Final Unity" Walkthrough
http://www.happypuppy.com/games/faqcht/stfusol.txt

Edited by Ron Chartrand, this walkthrough ushers gamers part by part (seven parts in all) through the Star Trek adventure that leads to "A Final Unity." The text-only document offers no hyperlinks to ease navigation, so users will find themselves reading large amounts of copy to find the clues they need.

TORIN'S PASSAGE

Torin's Passage
http://www.sierra.com/games/tp/

Sierra Entertainment promotes its family adventure Torin's Passage on this official page. Sprung from the mind that brought Leisure Suit Larry to the computer screen, the game promises entertainment for young and old alike. Site features include a summary of the game's story line, screen shots, and ordering information. Links to other Sierra pages lead to other product pages, as well as the free stuff currently available from the company.

Torin's Passage Complete Walkthrough
http://www.algonet.se/~averpil/common/solve/passage.html

Leading players step-by-step through Torin's Passage, this walkthrough also indicates the scores players can anticipate. Organized by chapter, the text-only document offers no hyperlinks to aid navigation. Players must read large bits of copy to discover the clues they're searching to find.

Torin's Passage Review
http://www.iinet.net.au/~quandary/issue5/torin.html

Rosemary Young points out what's right and wrong with Torin's Passage in this 1996 review of the game. Worth a read, the article endorses the game and gives voice to many of the general reactions players will have when playing this adventure suited for old and young alike.

VIRTUAL STUPIDITY

Beavis and Butt-head in Virtual Stupidity Walkthrough
http://happypuppy.com/games/lordsoth/cheats/hints/beavis.txt

Michelle Theriault and Paul E. Roberts offer Beavis and Butt-head fans the "direct solutions" for successfully moving from location to location in the game Virtual Stupidity. Although the text-only document offers no hyperlinks to aid navigation, the solutions are presented by location so users can easily scroll through the page.

Beavis and Butt-head in Virtual Stupidity Walkthrough
http://expert.cc.purdue.edu/%7Etimhalb/BeavButt/bbwalk.html

Tim Halbach has written and presents this walkthrough that is so simple to follow, even the virtually stupid can get through the game. The question-and-answer format is not divided in any way, however, so users need to scan through the whole document to find the tidbit they're seeking.

GameSpot: Virtual Stupidity at a Glance
http://www.gamespot.com/adventure/beavisan/

GameSpot throws its light on the Viacom release based on the animated antics of MTV's dim-witted duo. Read the official company line as well as what outsiders have to say about the game. Download four different demos and a QuickTime movie. Access technical support and tips that include a copy of the game's readme file. Find hints and cheats, plus follow links to other game-related sites.

MTV's Beavis and Butt-head in Virtual Stupidity
http://mtv.com/animation/beavbutt/VS/minigame.html

MTV hosts this promotional page to hype the game based on its air guitar-playing, loogie-hocking, cartoon teenage stars, Beavis and Butt-head. Read all about the adventure game from Butt-head's point of view and download two mini-game demos. Links lead to other MTV pages.

ZORK

Complete Walkthrough for Zork Nemesis
http://www.algonet.se/~averpil/common/solve/znemem.html

It's billed as the complete walkthrough but offers no clues for the third segment of the game. Sections one and two are well covered, however. Players can choose between mild or explicit clues. The text-only document contains no hyperlinks, so players must scroll through to find the clues they seek.

PC Multimedia & Entertainment Magazine Review: Zork Nemesis
http://www.mortimer.com/users/pcme/fantasy/nemesis/nemesis.htm

Read this favorable review of Zork Nemesis for an interesting look back at the Zork series' beginning as a text-based game. Follow the game's evolution through time and into its latest incarnation as a fully rendered multimedia adventure from Activision. Read an overview of the game, enjoy screen shots, and review the game's system requirements. Also download a copy of the original Zork text adventure free of charge.

Zork I
http://www.activision.com/zorknem/zorki.html

Download a copy of the original Zork text game adventure. Hosted by Activision, this offering is part of the company's promotion for its Zork Nemesis release.

Zork Nemesis
http://www.activision.com/zorknem/zorkhome.html

Hosted by Activision, this official page promotes the release of Zork Nemesis. Read the company line on what makes this offering so dazzling, review the game's system requirements, and enjoy free downloads including a Zork Nemesis Screen Theme package. Also find screen shots, illustrations of puzzles, and an online manual for the game.

Zork Nemesis Hints & Helpers
http://members.aol.com/Conspracy/zork3/zork.htm

Those who require aid in navigating the Zork Nemesis adventure need look no further than this trusty guide. Find a brief introduction to the game and a choice for each section of play: mild hints offering gentle guidance or forceful nudges giving explicit instruction.

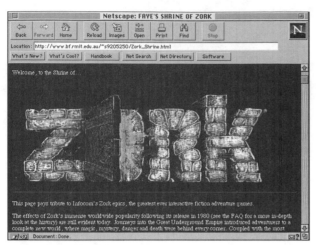

The Shrine of Zork
http://www.bf.rmit.edu.au/~s9205250/Zork_Shrine.html

Describing Zork as the "greatest ever" game of its genre, Faye P. hosts this shrine to the interactive fiction series that has evolved from its purer form into a grand multimedia adventure game from Activision. Find all manner of Zork literature: FAQs, news, game solutions, and maps. Links lead to official and unofficial pages related to the games. And there's even a link to John Holder's hypertext version of the Encyclopedia Frobozzica.

COLLECTIBLE CARD GAMES

BLOOD WARS

Blood Wars by Lord Kahn
http://www.andrews.edu/~sheltont/

The fantasy collectible trading card game pitting the "Battle Hand" of one "Warlord" against that of others receives post-release attention by its designer in an FAQ archived at this site. Also find The Official Blood Wars Trading Game Checklist ready for printout and use. The game was released by TSR, Inc. in 1995 and is set in the role-playing world known as Planescape.

Blood Wars: FTP Archive
ftp://tower.itis.com/pub/other.card.games/blood.wars/

Find the resources mentioned above (the checklist and FAQ) along with one large and several small articles devoted to strategic play. The articles were written by two gamers, both interested in the growth of the game, and are worth a read by any Warlord readying his forces for an encounter.

Blood Wars at Sprig's CCG Warehouse
http://www.itis.com/other-games/blood_wars/.www.html

Players rate the game and the results are tallied here. Also find player comments and a directory that lists Blood Wars fans by name and includes e-mail addresses. Card lists are available by deck.

DOOMTROOPER

Doomtrooper
http://www.algonet.se/~patrik_w/
doomtr_e.htm

A dedicated player's resource hosted by a Doomtrooper fan in Sweden, this site holds a wealth of information about the trading card game. Find FAQs concerning the original and subsequent expansion decks, Doomtrooper tournament rules and rules about Mortificator. Spoiler lists of all the cards in the various decks are organized for easy use, and the page's host even lists which cards he sells and which cards he wants. In English and Swedish.

Doomtrooper FTP Site
http://ftp.itis.com/ftp/pub/other.card.games/
doomtrooper/

Hosted by Bryan Winter, this limited FTP archive holds a Doomtrooper FAQ and a Doomtrooper Vehicles FAQ. Also find a card inventory checklist suitable for printout and use.

Doomtrooper: The Best CCG in the World
http://members.aol.com/lorgmole/imperial/
doomtrper.html

Here's an excellent introduction to the game Doomtrooper for any player interested in learning about the wildly successful collectible card game. Find a general overview of the game, take a look at a sampling of the cards, and read a game-fan's take on the Imperial corporation. There's a showcase for homemade playing cards, a posting of "house rules," and a listing of every card available. A player's survey and links to other fans' home pages point the way to leaning more about the game.

Doomtrooper: The Official Home Page
http://www.target.se/doom.html

Hosted by Target Games AB, this information archive holds a variety of fact and fantasy fiction concerning Doomtrooper, the collectible trading card game released in 1994 and based on the techno-fantasy universe of the Mutant Chronicles. The site features details concerning the game's first three expansion decks: Inquisition, WarZone, and Mortificator. The WarZone FAQ is online for quick reference, and a look at the Doomtrooper Player's Companion rounds out the offerings.

GALACTIC EMPIRES

Galactic Empires FTP Site
http://ftp.itis.com/ftp/pub/other.card.games/
galactic.empires/

A generous selection of Galactic Empires information is available for download via this FTP archive. Find a variety of card lists, questions and answers, a campaign scenario, and a game review. The information presented is compiled from different sources.

Galactic Empires: The Official Page
http://www.companiongames.com/

Companion Games hosts this limited but useful site promoting its science fiction collectible card game, Galactic Empires. Find comprehensive card errata, official tournament rules, and pictures from the Summer '96 competition. Also find a pointer to Ted Peer's far superior page on the game.

Galactic Empires: The Science Fiction Trading Card Game
http://www.netins.net/showcase/tpeer/galactic.htm

Presented by Ted Peers, this motherlode site offers players most anything they'll need to know in order to enjoy playing and collecting Galactic Empires cards. Find an overview of the game, a Quick Players Guide, the Universe Edition Rulebook, tournament rules, and card errata. Serious players will appreciate the sanctioned tournament events listing, while all manner of player can benefit from the online player registry. A selection of pointers to card lists helps make this site all but complete.

GUARDIANS

Guardians Home Page
http://www.aimnet.com/~taven/guardian.html

J. Andrew Hart (a.k.a. Taven) praises what he describes as the "premier Collecting Card Game" with this considered and considerable collection of aids and insights into the fantasy known as Guardians. Follow links to an example of play, a review of the game, an FAQ, an archive, tournament rules, and a glossary of terms. Spoiler lists and pointers to other players' home pages add to the excitement.

Guardians Official FAQ
http://www.itis.com/other-games/news/04051996.html

Originally posted to the newsgroup rec.games.tradingcards.misc, this FAQ is dated 4/5/96 and was written by Dave Gentzler, Joe Babinsack, Jr., and Luke Peterschmidt of FPG, the company responsible for the game Guardians. As the tag at the bottom of the Q&A states, if the answers don't come from FPG, they're not official.

ILLUMINATI: NEW WORLD ORDER (INWO)

Illuminati: New World Order
http://albert.astro.williams.edu/~93jay/inwo.html

Here's a fan page that's great for beginners looking to find entree into the conspiratorial weirdness that swirls around the trading card game Illuminati: New World Order. Gaming fan Jonathan Young hosts this "cut to the chase," offering an organized look at the basic rules, the card groups, the actions open to players, attack postures, and strategies. A glossary and cheat sheet offer a quick source of reference to help keep things straight.

Illuminati: New World Order Official Card List
http://www.isu.edu/~broomatt/inwo/il_html2.htm

No more and no less that the title suggests. Players can check their decks against this "official" card list for the INWO game. The list was posted in April of 1995.

Illuminati: New World Order Official Home Page
http://www.io.com/sjgames/inwo/

Players in search of the real deal concerning the trading card game based on Illuminati, the conspiracy fantasy from Steve Jackson Games, need look no further than the links assembled here. Get the latest news concerning the collectible card game, plus find link to INWO support material including the rules, official announcements and policies, strategies and tactics tips, and card lists. Links to newsgroups, mailing lists, and an FTP site point to online activities centered on the game.

Illuminati: New World Order Omni-League Rules
http://www.io.com/sjgames/inwo/official/omni.html

Another official INWO site, this page suggests ways to create an INWO Omni-League. Omni-Leagues are created so no player can "buy" a winning deck; decks must be built up a game at a time. Stop by for a general look at how to get started, what rules to use, how to manage cards, and how to handle other administrative details.

For more information on Omni-Leagues, see also:

What's an Omni-League
http://www.cs.arizona.edu/people/burnsb/games/omni/whats.html

HEAVY GEAR FIGHTER

Heavy Gear Fighter Web Page
http://mason.gmu.edu/~mcox3/hgf.html

Considered by the page author as "THE ultimate" in Mecha fighting card games, Heavy Gear Fighter receives heavy-duty treatment on this player's resource site. Find pointers to the official rules, the official Q&A rules clarification, the FAQ, a card list, strategy tips, and other gaming minutia. Links to Dream Pod 9, the company which created the game, and to the site author's Heavy Gear role-playing game page are also featured.

JAMES BOND

James Bond 007 CCG Official Web Page
http://poky.srv.net/~duncan/007.html

Posted by Target Games, this promotional site announces the 1995 release of the James Bond 007 Collectible Card Game. Based exclusively on the film "Goldeneye" (starring Pierce Brosnan) at its release, the card deck will later be expanded to offer Bond nostalgia. Visit this site to read the technical specifications for the game's starter decks and booster packs.

James Bond 007 CCG Unofficial Web Page
http://poky.srv.net/~duncan/007.html

Patrick Thomas Morgan hosts this double-naught site, sorting through the facts and fantasy surrounding the collectible card game patterned after the Goldeneye adventures of Bond, James Bond. Step into M's office for a rundown of the rules, card lists, spoilers, and FAQs. Then drop by Q Branch for a strategy session. Links lead to loads of Bond trivia pages based on the movies and books that detail the character's adventures.

LEGEND OF THE FIVE RINGS

Legend of the Five Rings
http://www.zzz.iipo.gtegsc.com/jwa/l5r/

An excellent introduction to the Legend of the Five Rings CCG, this page even explains what a CCG is. Find an overview of the game, the official FAQ, spoiler lists, annotated rulings, and sample decks. Links to the home page of fellow game fans offer additional resources and related background for further study.

Legend of the Five Rings Official Home Page
http://www.isomedia.com/homes/aeg/l5r.html

Five Rings Publishing Group hosts this player's resource built upon its signature collectible card game, Legend of the Five Rings, an Oriental fantasy in which players vie to ascend the throne of the dying emperor. Find the official rules, FAQ, and card lists. Other Internet resources available include links to the mailing list, a public forum, and related newsgroups. Players interested in competitive play can stop into the tournament center for topical information.

MAGIC: THE GATHERING

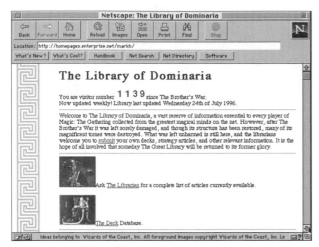

The Library of Dominaria
http://homepages.enterprise.net/markh/

Despite being ravaged after The Brothers War, this official unofficial library houses a vast store of knowledge concerning the CCG Magic: The Gathering. Find collected wisdom from many a great mind across the Internet organized for easy accessibility. Simply tap The Librarian for a complete and current list of the articles available. Or enter the east wing of the library and ask The Sage if you might look at the deck database. Contributions (of knowledge) to the library are always welcome.

The Mage's Library Home Page
http://members.aol.com/MTGLord/WWW/index.html

Here's a PC-only freeware product designed to aid Magic: The Gathering players better manage their decks. Stop by to find out how The Mage's Library program works and download a copy.

Magic: The Database
http://www.public.iastate.edu/~playground/magic/index.html

A well-organized resource for Magic: The Gathering CCG fans, this site's premier feature is its complete information on every card in the decks, strategic combinations, and assistance on building killer decks. FAQs, game rules, and game news are also featured. It's a must-see site for those serious about the game.

Magic: The Gathering
http://marvin.macc.wisc.edu/deckmaster/wotc.html

Darrell Budic claims his page to be "the Net's Best" among Magic: The Gathering home pages. He may be right; he does offer a diverse collection of game resources, which includes a general game overview for newcomers and a glossary of must-know terms. Official rules information, rule variants, card data, and a customizable card list generator are also among the page's highlights.

Magic: The Gathering FTP Archives
http://ftp.itis.com/ftp/pub/deckmaster/

Hosted by Darrell Budic, Network Archivist for Wizards of the Coast, this site archives Magic: The Gathering material collected from topical mailing lists and newsgroups and contributed by fellow game fans. Browse FAQs, press releases, information lists, rules, card lists, and product information. Another good source for official answers, serious players will want to read what's online here.

Magic: The Gathering Official Home Page
http://www.wizards.com/Magic/Welcome.html

Wizards of the Coast hosts this collection of files, facts, and fantastic features centered on its mega-hit CCG Magic: The Gathering. The uninitiated will appreciate the article discussing the game's "multiverse" setting, Dominia, as well as the general rulings summary and the quick reference guide to sequence play. Tournament rules, an in-depth analysis of event timing, and current game news will be of interest to veteran players. Official FAQs answer questions for all.

Magic: The Gathering
Online Trading League
http://www.ecis.com/~leshrac/index.html

For those players looking to expand (or get rid of) their Magic card decks, here's a dedicated online service which can aid in the endeavor. Register to buy, sell, or trade Magic: The Gathering cards with other players.

Magic: The Gathering
the Ultimate Deck List
http://www.trenton.edu/~belardo/magic/decks.htm

Though the disclaimer suggests the list that has been compiled and posted to this page is not yet complete, the goal is to make it so. Find "some of the best" Magic: The Gathering decks organized by type. Hyperlinks lead to each deck's card configuration.

Magic: The Gathering
the UnOfficial Magic Home Page
http://cwis.usc.edu/users/rbaily/magic.html

Site host Robert Baily serves a fine selection of Magic: The Gathering features fit for both beginners and players well-versed in the game. Find FAQs for the game in general and its various decks, links to newsgroups where players can chat and build their decks, and answers to questions concerning rules. Game variants, tournament rules, a collection of card lists and links to other players' pages are also featured.

For more information on Magic: The Gathering, see also:

Magic: The Gathering Tournaments
http://ourworld.compuserve.com/homepages/nathan/mttourny.htm

Web Across Dominia
http://www1.usa1.com/~magic/

AUTHOR'S PICK

Sprig's Collectible Card Game
Warehouse
http://www.itis.com/other-games/

This is one of those sites that reflects what the Internet can be when it's at its best. It's a free resource—well designed and maintained—that provides folks interested in collectible card games a single site where they can come and get information. Currently indexing 66 released games and 16 announced games, the warehouse can be searched alphabetically or by game category. Game listings feature results to reader surveys, card lists, current news, and links to fan and official pages offering information of interest about the game. A player registry for each game is also included, so players can search out others with similar interests. Other warehouse features include links to CCG-related software and magazines. Stop by; it's worth a visit.

MIDDLE-EARTH:
THE WIZARDS

Middle-earth: The Wizards
http://bvsd.k12.co.us/~tstone/metw/

Trevor Stone has posted this fantastic site devoted primarily to the cards found in the Middle-earth: The Wizards CCG. Topping the list of resources available here, a card list generator aids players in managing their decks. Card lists of every possible organization method are also online, as is an inventory of the contents of five fixed packs. Expansion rules for Middle-earth: The Dragons, the site host's Ring Rolls probability page, and links to tons of trade sites round out the offerings presented.

Middle-earth: The Wizards, Enter Lothlórien

http://www.randomc.com/~craig/metw.html

Pete Craig posts this gaming site devoted to the CCG Middle-earth: The Wizards. Browse the usual card lists and links to player pages, or join the site host and his group playing Me:TW by e-mail. A directory of players involved and instructions for joining the fun are featured.

Middle-earth: The Wizards Guide

http://www.non.com/metw/

Compiled and presented by Alex Mohr, a devoted fan of the Middle-earth: The Wizards CCG, this excellent site holds answers that many who play the game will certainly seek. Along with the expected rules and FAQ, also find card lists and technical information about the print runs and pack orders. Players new to Tolkien's fantasy world will appreciate the game overview, the history of Middle-earth, and related maps. The section on playing strategy will be of benefit to all, especially the mirror of Trevor Stone's Ring Rolls probability page.

Middle-earth: The Wizards Official Home Page

http://www.ironcrown.com/metwm.html

Hosted by Iron Crown Enterprises, this player's resource offers official rules, FAQs, and card lists for Middle-earth: The Wizards, a CCG that is based on the writings of J.R.R. Tolkien. Link to information on the Council of Lorien, the official U.S. sanctioning body for Middle-earth, and review a comparison of the limited and unlimited card sets. Pointers to over a dozen players' home pages round out the available offerings.

MONTY PYTHON AND THE HOLY GRAIL

Monty Python and the Holy Grail CCG Home Page

http://members.aol.com/relkin/mphgmain.htm

Join King Arthur, brave Sir Robin, and the other Knights of the Round Table on their quest for the Holy Grail in this CCG based on the classic Monty Python movie send-up of the Arthurian grail legend. Find general information about the game, rules, and a card list that (even without illustrations) is sure to inspire chuckles if not doubled-over laughter. Oh! And pay no attention to the Knights Who Say "Ni!" They're just after more shrubberies.

MORTAL KOMBAT KARDS

Mortal Kombat

http://www.accessone.com/~rmthayer/mkkards.html

Based upon the video game of the same name, this Kards version of Mortal Kombat pits two or more players against one another, and the one who takes two of the three rounds wins. Each player holds a single deck and each deck is based upon a single Kombatant. Visit this page hosted by Reed Thayer for an overview of the game, a look at the complete Kard list and official FAQ, plus a link to the Mortal Kombat Kards Player Connection. Illustrations of sample Kards are also online for review.

Mortal Kombat Kards

http://www.mcp.com/brady/cards/mkcards/

Hosted by Brady Games, this official Mortal Kombat Kard game site offers players the Kard List, the Kard Game Rules, and the MK Kard game FAQ. Based on the best-selling video game, the full 300-card set allows for unlimited multi-player martial arts combat action. Read the company's press release for a list of Kard subsets and details on how the sets are packed.

Mortal Kombat Kards at Spriggs CCG Warehouse

http://www.itis.com/other-games/martial/ mortal_kombat/.www.html

Players rate the game and the results are tallied here. Also find player comments and a directory that lists Mortal Kombat Kards fans by name and includes e-mail addresses. Card lists are available by deck.

Mortal Kombat Kards Player Connection

http://www.accessone.com/~rmthayer/ contact.html

This player's resource aids Mortal Kombat Kards players find one another. Link to any state to find who's registered and ready for play. (At present the directory is a bit thin, but then MK Kards is a fairly new game—released in January of 1996. Over time, this could prove an invaluable resource to MK Kards players around the country.)

MYTHOS

Mythos Alternative Card List

http://www.io.com/~pardoz/ alt.mythos.list.txt

Hosted by Brent Heustess, this site offers gamers a printable card list for use in cataloging their collection of playable Mythos cards. Cards are grouped by type and coded to show from which decks they come and the relative frequency with which they appear.

Mythos CCG Official Page

http://www.sirius.com/~chaosium/ mythos.html

Chaosium Inc. provides at this mega-resource site the kind of service every game publisher should provide its customers and game fans. Players can find out most anything they want to know about Mythos, the Chaosium collectible card game based on the writings of H.P. Lovecraft. The list of resources includes the game's rules (with solo and tournament variations), the card list, an FAQ, a summary of adventure cards, and a typical game scenario. Comments from a play tester are also featured, as is an overview of the game's system of play. This site is a must-see for anyone interested in the Mythos game.

Mythos Unofficial Adventure Archive

http://www.io.com/~pardoz/mythos.html

Mythos players from across the Net add their adventure ideas to this growing archive. Stop by for ideas or to add a new twist. While on site, you may want to check out the links for pointers to other Mythos sites. Among the featured jumps find both official and unofficial pages.

Mythos Unofficial Card Database

http://www.dtek.chalmers.se/~d2agby/ mythos.shtml

Mythos players looking for listings of the cards available for the Mythos CCG can check these "canned" lists posted and hosted by Jens Agby. Five lists are available for review: a long spoiler list, a short spoiler list, a checklist, a list of locations, and a list of allies. Sorting options for the checklist and spoiler lists help visitors find what they're looking for more readily.

NETRUNNER

DM's Netrunner Page
http://www.atnf.csiro.au/~dmar/netrunner/

David Mar offers fellow Netrunner CCG fans game trivia compiled from a variety of sources, a card deck checklist, gaming strategy ideas, and multi-player game variants. A link to the unofficial Netrunner Omni-League page leads to another variation on play. Pointers to official pages and other players' home pages complete the items online.

How To Play Netrunner
http://www.connect.ab.ca/~bigmanm/ subpages/netrunnr.htm

Players uninitiated in the ways of the Netrunner CCG will benefit from this brief, player-prepared tutorial. Find sections on corporation strategy, runner strategy, and combination cards. As examples of solid decks, the host places both his Corp and Runner decks on display. Any questions? Simply ask.

Netrunner Omni-League
http://www.cs.arizona.edu/people/burnsb/ games/omni/netrunner.html

An unofficial site, this page suggests ways to create a Netrunner Omni-League. Omni-Leagues are created so no player can "buy" a winning deck; decks must be

built up a game at a time. Stop by for a general look at how to get started, what rules to use, how to manage cards, and other administrative details.

Netrunner: Singapore's Home Page
http://home.pacific.net.sg/~bitbyte/

Posted by a Netrunner CCG enthusiast in Singapore, this page features card lists, product information, and articles of interest to all Netrunner players. Those living in or traveling to Singapore will appreciate the collection of local resources, including outlets for the game and a players list. Links to the home pages of players and an invitation to join Netrunner play via IRC round out this site's offerings.

The Official Netrunner Web Site
http://www.wizards.com/Netrunner/ Welcome.html

Another Wizards of the Coast gaming site, this page posts the official line on Netrunner, a science fiction CCG which is set in the bleak techno-corrupt future world of R. Talsorian's Cyberpunk. Visit to read the online rulebook, review the FAQ list, or look into tournament rules. An overview of the game will help new players get their bearings. Also find announcements for new expansion decks and other Wizards of the Coast products.

ON THE EDGE

On the Edge at Spriggs CCG Warehouse
http://www.itis.com/other-games/ote/ .www.html

Players rate the game and the results are tallied here. Also find player comments and a directory that lists On the Edge fans by name and includes e-mail addresses. A customizable card list generator and game news round out the items offered.

On The Edge: Drawn's Workshop
http://public.carleton.edu/~djohnson/onte/dw.html

Evolved from the role-playing game Over the Edge, On the Edge is a CCG released by Atlas Games that is based on the power struggle that takes place on the fictional island called Al Amarja. Drew Johnson, proprietor of this workshop, and several pals draw upon their enthusiasm for the game and present an extensive collection of fictional cards for OnTE expansion decks. Also find a list of OnTE Conspiracy cells that dot the north and central U.S, as well as information on the Omni-League.

The On the Edge Official Page
http://www.io.com/~presage/onte/onte_index.html

Hosted by Atlas Games, this gamer's resource holds the key to unlocking the mysteries of the surreal conspiracies which arise from the On the Edge CCG. Find an FAQ and mini-FAQs, card lists for every deck, and variant rules. Information on the Atlas Game's players' league, The Conspiracy, is also featured along with pointers to players' and the Conspiracy cells' pages. Those looking for outlets to purchase decks will also find links to companies dealing in cards.

On the Edge: The Mystery Cards
http://www.io.com/~malcolm/mystery/mystery.htm

For some On the Edge players, certain cards seem more myth than fact simply because they are so rare. For the doubters, an avid player has scanned these cards and posted them for display. Behold the Resounding Bell! Also see these sample cards: Saleem Helicopter, Scythian Ring, Throckmorton Domination, Quantum Flux, Desperate Ritual, the Bavarian Illuminati, and C.A. Radford. The chase cards Chris Robinson, Janis, Grim Linden, and Signe Lathiere are also featured.

On The Edge: The Omni-League
http://www.io.com/~presage/onte/omni.html

This official page written by Jonathon Tweet explains what is and how to start an On The Edge Omni-League. Omni-Leagues are created so no player can "buy" a winning deck; decks must be built up a game at a time. Find easy-to-follow rules and step-by-step instructions for introducing this "playing field leveler" to an On The Edge gaming group near you.

For more information about On the Edge, also see:

On the Edge Cards by Trait
http://nickel.ucs.indiana.edu/~khiller/the-list.html

On the Net
http://www.hamline.edu/~jltidbal/onte/index.html

Zipper's Hideout
http://www.pacifier.com/~michael/Onte/

OVERPOWER

Marvel OverPower Page
http://www.swarthmore.edu/cc/staff/yue/OverPower/

Frank Yue has compiled an extensive player's bonanza for anyone interested in the OverPower CCG. Find an unofficial FAQ, rules, rules clarifications, sample decks, and strategy ideas. Computer programs for organizing card decks are also featured in both PC and Mac formats. The Card of the Week Series features essays about individual cards, and the online checklist offers collectors a complete card list for comparison purposes. Links to the OverPower mailing list and other topical Web pages make this a truly useful site.

OverPower Page
http://gramercy.ios.com/~nbperp/overpowr.html

Examine the heroes of the OverPower CCG one card at a time and vote for the Hero of the Week. Various card sorts allow visitors to compare the heroes for their energy, strength, and fighting ability. Also find dates and times for tournament play and other Over-Power activities. Pointers to other OverPower players' home pages are also featured, including one page with details about online OverPower play.

QUEST FOR THE GRAIL

The Quest for the Grail Official Page
http://www.ccsi.com/~graball/quest/

Hosted by Stone Ring Games, this exceptional player's resource welcomes one and all into the fictional Kingdom of Logres, where knights go on quests based on Arthurian legend. Visitors can read an overview of the game, compare the preview and limited editions, learn about upcoming events, and read reviews which discuss the game. Rules of play, FAQs, information on game variants, and illustrations of sample cards are also online. To set the proper tone, samples of Arthurian poetry and a virtual visit to Britain round out the ample offerings at this mythical card game site.

Quest for the Grail at Spriggs CCG Warehouse
http://www.itis.com/other-games/fantasy/Quest/.www.html

Players rate the game and the results are tallied here. Also find player comments and a directory that lists Quest for the Grail fans by name and includes e-mail addresses. Card lists are available by deck.

Quest for the Grail Concordance
http://www.stcloud.msus.edu/~schultz/gameroom/quest/quest.concordance.html

A must-read for any gamer serious about the Quest for the Grail CCG. Learn about the legends behind the settings, characters, and creatures found in the game. Information presented is divided into Domains (current and future) and Quests. Hyperlinks lead to addi-

tional background information, and a bibliography suggests resources for offline reading and study.

For more Quest for the Grail information, see also:

Quest for the Grail: Brocelialande
http://members.aol.com/thalkyudes/broceliande/index.html

RAGE

Official Rage Answers Home Page
http://www.et.byu.edu/~moorej/rage.html

The site itself is not official, but the site's host has attempted to compile the official White Wolf company line on rulings and clarifications regarding the fantasy CCG Rage. An extensive resource and well organized for easy use, this answer database dates and gives credit to the sources for its information. Well worth a look by novices and veteran players alike, this effort attempts to add more than just general knowledge to the Rage information base already online.

Omesh's Rage Page
http://coeds.eng.miami.edu/~ochowdhu/rage.html

Omesh Chowdhury presents this excellent starter page for anyone just getting involved with the Rage CCG. Among the basic resources find Rage rules for standard and tournament play, official FAQs, and card lists. Almost two dozen deck ideas offer further insights into the game and introduce different Rage players from across the Web. And to round things out, links to other players' pages offer a jump-off point for additional research into the game.

Rage Page
http://student-www.uchicago.edu/users/cls6/rage/rageindex.html

Cory L. Scott offers another strong page for Rage CCG enthusiasts. Expect to find the expected: rules, FAQs, and different card lists. But also find information on the Rage mailing list and link to a collection of sites where Rage decks are available for sale.

SHADOWFIST

Shadowfist
http://www.innocence.com/~durrell/
shadowfist/index.html

A committed Shadowfist player maintains this player's resource offering game news and links to official rulings, contests, and tournament announcements. Also enjoy a collection of fan fiction, new cards, and humor. A Shadowfist players directory and strategy notes make this site worth a look.

Shadowfist
http://www.nuc.berkeley.edu/fusion/lopez/
shadowfist/fist.html

Eric Lopez hosts this comprehensive Shadowfist CCG archive offering excellent resources for first-timers and old-timers alike. Begin with an overview of the Shadowfist world, progress through the rules of the game, brush up on play dynamics, and find answers to specific questions in the FAQ. A card list, an image gallery, and game reviews help bring things into tighter focus. For players curious about product availability, there's a section on products and prices.

Shadowfist Official Home Page
http://www.aracnet.com/~bruce/daedalus/

Daedalus Entertainment, Inc. hosts this official look at its Shadowfist CCG and Feng Shui, the RPG set in the world of Shadowfist. Combining sorcery and Kung Fu fighting, these martial arts action adventures challenge players to save the world from the evil forces conspiring for total domination. Find game details, stories, and information on sanctioned events and contests.

SIMCITY: THE CARD GAME

SimCity: The Card Game
http://www.acs.oakland.edu/~jjhoxsey/
simcity.html

Based on the popular Maxis computer game, Mayfair's SimCity CCG challenges players to build cities and, in so doing, build up bank accounts. Visit this abundant site for most anything needed to begin and progress in play. Find complete rules, card lists, FAQs, and pointers for deck building and acquiring cards. Links to sites of topical interest lead to a gamer's directory, as well as the Mayfair and Maxis companies' home pages.

SPELLFIRE:
MASTER THE MAGIC

Spellfire FAQ
http://www.cdc.net/~othrwrld/spellfaq.html
Visit this page to read the Spellfire CCG FAQ revised and posted December 14, 1995, to the alt.card-games.spellfire Usenet newsgroup. The document is authored by Jason E. Brown of Other Worlds Games.

The Spellfire Spider
http://pubpages.unh.edu/~matthewm/
spelfire.html

Anyone interested in getting to the nitty gritty as it relates to TSR's Dungeons and Dragons-based fantasy CCG Spellfire need only stop by Matthew Montminy's well-organized information bank. Rulings, reviews, and card lists (including chase cards) offer the basics. Alternate rules, trading information, rumors, and the Spell-Fire newsletter provide advanced player knowledge. Links to related newsgroups and Web sites, including the unofficial TSR Info Page, point to resources for further study.

Steve's Spellfire Page and Trading Post
http://home.earthlink.net/~arioch/steve.htm

Here's a page for Spellfire CCG players interested in making a deal. Find information on card sales ... or perhaps Steve's wish and duplicate lists will prompt a trade. Those just looking for card and game information will find plenty to ponder in the strategy, tidbits, and Q&A sections. And while on site, why not take the Spellfire survey?

STAR TREK: CUSTOMIZABLE CARD GAME

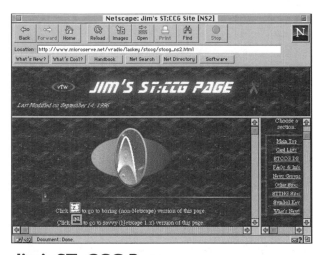

Jim's ST: CCG Page
http://www.microserve.net/vradio/lackey/
stccg/stccg_ns2.html

James L. Kinoshita has his phaser set on stun. He must because his Star Trek: TNG CCG site is stunning—both for the depth and volume of the information presented and for the organized, thought-out manner in which it's offered. Beam aboard for card lists, information on database computer programs, FAQs, news, and links to newsgroups. Pointers to fellow players' home pages and sites related to the Star Trek phenomenon are also featured.

Star Trek: The Next Generation CCG Official Home Page
http://www.decipher.com/stccg/

Permission is granted to come aboard the official home base of the Star Trek: The Next Generation customizable card game. Once onboard, find official game rules, FAQs, card lists and other "cool stuff." Be sure to sign in at the Player Registry and stop by the bulletin board to check for messages that may be of interest. Company news and game events round out the sights to see; just settle in and enjoy this well-rendered site hosted by game publisher Decipher, Inc.

Star Trek: The Next Generation Customizable Card Game
http://www.worldonline.nl/~ldp/STCCG/

Hosted by a Dutch fan, this Star Trek: The Next Generation CCG site provides card lists and FAQs. Of special interest, check out the ST: CCG Card of the Day series of articles for reviews of the various cards and suggestions for related strategies. Links to the official ST: TNG CCG page, as well as the home pages of fellow players, are also featured.

For more information on the Star Trek CCG, also see:

Interrupt!
http://www.webbuild.com/~telling/interrupt.html

ST: CCG Online
http://www.terranet.ab.ca/~bjudt/STCCG/
STCCG.html

STAR WARS: CUSTOMIZABLE CARD GAME

Star Wars: CCG Official Home Page
http://www.decipher.com/swccg/

Another gaming site hosted by Decipher, Inc., this player's retreat houses the official postings concerning the customizable card game based on the Star Wars movies. Find game rules, FAQs, card lists, and other "cool stuff." Be sure to sign in at the Player Registry and stop by the bulletin board to check out the discussion forums. Those interested in running a tournament can download the official kit.

Star Wars: Customizable Card Game
http://www.megatoon.com/~raika/swccg/swccg.htm

Simon Asselin hosts this excellent player's resource devoted to the Star Wars CCG. A great place for players new to the game to begin, the site offers the official rules, rules supplements, FAQs, and spoiler lists. Advice and strategic tips compiled from sources across the Internet, information on the SW:CCG mailing list, and tons of links to official and unofficial sites round out the generous offerings.

Star Wars: Customizable Card Game
http://www.psnw.com/~grime/main.html

Here's another good, all-purpose site for beginners and experienced players alike who are interested in the Star Wars Customizable Card Game. Hosted by Matt Braunstein, the site features a sizable library of rules, FAQs, spoiler lists, and tournament information, as well as contests, pricing, and distribution information. Those interested in strategy will find ideas for deck construction and help with playing techniques. Information on software of practical interest and loads of links to the Star Wars outposts in the far reaches of cyberspace round out this collection.

Star Wars: Customizable Card Game
http://www.isu.edu/~tangdere/swccg.html

Players looking for Star Wars CCG decks that "kick booty" need to check out this player's postings. Offering only a bit of the expected, this site goes a step beyond the status quo. Find strategy and statistical FAQs, information about the two-player introductory game, strategic advice, and an "index/glossidex." Card lists, of course, are also online.

VAMPIRE: THE ETERNAL STRUGGLE (JYHAD)

Jyhad On Line
http://shangrila.cs.ucdavis.edu:1234/gfink/jol/jol.html

Join the gamers playing Vampire: The Eternal Struggle online via e-mail. All is handled through a central server; players need only familiarize themselves with the house rules and game policies, then sign up for play. All the information needed to join in the action is posted here, along with a list of ongoing games.

Rulemonger's V:tES
http://www.HomeFree.Net/cgi-shl/dbml.exe?template=/homefree/view.dbm&pageid=236

Here's yet another fantastic site devoted to the gothic horror collectible card game Vampires: The Eternal Struggle. Drop in for news updates or to search the Usenet newsgroup postings in the archive. Other useful features include a searchable card list and an archive of rules for team play. The site's host even offers to answer any questions his guests might have.

Vampire: The Eternal Struggle (and Jyhad)
http://zen.btc.uwe.ac.uk/~np-olver/jyhad/jyhad.html

Nik Olver hosts this player's resource offering a compiled collection of fantastic facts for fellow Vampire: The Eternal Struggle players to enjoy. Following an overview of the game, recent game news tops the list of items offered. Also find rules, rule changes and unofficial rules, card information, and bits of interest taken from the game's newsgroup. A link to the newsgroup and the mailing list archive are also featured.

Vampire: The Eternal Struggle at Sprig's CCG Warehouse
http://www.itis.com/other-games/vtes/ .www.html

Players rate the game and the results are tallied here. Also find player comments and a directory that lists Vampire: The Eternal Struggle fans by name and includes e-mail addresses. Card lists are available by deck, or players can create lists using the Customizable Card List Generator. Recent game news and links to players' home pages round out the offerings available.

Vampire: The Eternal Struggle Official Home Page
http://www.wizards.com/VTES/ Welcome.html

Formerly known as Jyhad, Vampire: The Eternal Struggle is a gothic fantasy collectible card game published by Wizards of the Coast and based on the game Vampire: The Masquerade. Visit this page for an overview of the game's intrigue, a look at the official card list, and answers to players' most Frequently Asked Questions. The page is hosted by Wizards of the Coast and links to the company's home page.

WILDSTORMS

Wildstorms CCG Official Home Page
http://www.wildstorm.com/home/trading_ cards/wsccg.html

Players interested in the super heroes collectible card game based on the Wildstorms comic book series will find answers to most questions online here. Features include an introduction to the game, an explanation on how to play, the official FAQ, a card list, and tips for superior play and deck construction. Information on hosting tournaments and an interview with the game's creator are also included.

ROLE-PLAYING GAMES

COMPUTER-BASED RPGS

ANGBAND

The Unofficial Angband Page
http://www.paranoia.com/~jth/ angband.html

Jason Holtzapple lays it all out for those interested in learning about the rogue-like game Angband. Read a background on the game and how it has developed over the years. Download the game, the source code, and patches. Select from a variety of FAQs manuals, guides, and spoilers. Plus find links to related pages and pointers to pertinent Usenet newsgroups.

ANVIL OF DAWN

Anvil of Dawn
http://www.nwcomputing.com/anvil/ anvil.html

New World Computing hosts this official page to promote its fantasy role-playing adventure Anvil of Dawn. Read what the critics have to say and find out why the game won a Golden Triad Award. Find an overview of game features and system requirements, enjoy screen shots, and link to an FAQ offering answers to the most common technical and game questions. Links to other New World Computing pages lead to other game promotions, which include demos and FAQs.

Anvil of Dawn Walkthrough
http://www.gamesdomain.com/walkthru/
anvil.html

Veikko Danilas tells players what they "absolutely need to know" in order to succeed at Anvil of Dawn. Converted to HTML by Ken Fishkin, the document is hyperlinked to ease navigation, but the explanatory copy appears in large blocks. Players must read through dense sections of text to find the clues they seek.

THE BARD'S TALE I, II, & III

The Bard's Tale
http://andreae.unbc.edu/jgaudet_html/bard/

J. Gaudet hosts this repository offering maps for the first two Bard's Tale games. Find a full complement of Tales of The Unknown dungeon maps and a set of Destiny Knight city maps. Eventually, the plan is to add maps for the Thief of Fate game as well.

Extracts of the Bard's Tale
http://tdkt.org/~tcarpent/bard/
bardstale.html

A bit of a bard himself, Todd P. Carpenter hosts this archive of tales and tidbits about the Bard's Tale gaming series. Featured stories include Wedding Bells (a tale of vandalism) and The Duality of a Mage (a tale of

love and destruction). Also find poems and other game background material.

Nels' Bard's Tale Page
http://weber.u.washington.edu/~nelsb/

Nels Bergquist offers Bard's Tale enthusiasts a nice resource for finding items of interest. Link to manuals for each of the three Bard's Tale games, find walkthroughs for each, and also enjoy screen shots taken from the games. Those interested can download The Bard's Tale Construction Set, and pointers lead to both official and unofficial pages related to the games.

BLACKTHORNE

Blackthorne
http://www.interplay.com/games/
blckthrn.html

Interplay hosts this official page for Blizzard Entertainment's action role-playing adventure Blackthorne. Find an overview of the game where quick thinking and a quicker trigger finger are required to defeat the enemy and save the home world. Other site features include screen shots, an overview of system requirements, press releases, a sales sheet, and a reviewer's guide. Those who wish to download a demo will find a PC version is available.

Blackthorne Download Page
http://happypuppy.com/games/link/
blacktho.htm

Visit this Happy Puppy page to download a playable demo of Blackthorne that features the first three levels of the game. While at Happy Puppy, you may want to save yourself a trip and hop on over to the cheat file as well. There's a page of cheat codes for Blackthorne.

AUTHOR'S PICK

Macray's Keep

http://www.relation.com/macray/

Unlike other sites that offer indexes to role-playing game information resources, this site sponsors actual play. Masters can use the site to organize and launch message-based campaigns; players can use the site to join these campaigns. A list of games currently running is featured along with details for joining a game or starting a new one. Those who are just curious and want to look around can visit the guest area, while those actively campaigning may find a visit to the chat room both relaxing and beneficial. It's an easy-to-use site, a great service, and another step in the evolution of gaming on the Web.

Blackthorne Codes

http://www.websolutions.mb.ca/realm/
cheats/blacktch.html

Here's another site to find cheat codes for the game Blackthorne. Codes are listed by level.

DRUID: DAEMONS OF THE MIND

Druid: Daemons of the Mind

http://www.pcentertainment.com/games/
Mar96/druid396.html

Christopher Lindquist gives Druid: Daemons of the Mind a B- in this March 1996 game review. Bothered by what he describes as the game's "quirks," the author supports his rating and provides a general summary of the game's central quest. Those who require gaming tips to make their play fun will find a few cheats. A link to general company information is also featured.

Druid: Daemons of the Mind Walkthrough

http://spoiler.et.ee/RPG/Sir-Tech/druid.1.txt

Offering few breaks in the text, this dense document opens with five general rules for playing Druid: Daemons of the Mind, then launches into a walkthrough of the game. Prepare to read; nothing is offered to aid navigation through the text, so users must scan the whole thing in search of the clues they seek.

GameSpot: Druid: Daemons of the Mind at a Glance

http://www.gamespot.com/rpg/druiddae/

GameSpot presents this limited look at SirTech's fantasy role-playing adventure Druid: Daemons of the Mind. Read reviews and a game overview. Link to the official SirTech sales page and sites of related interest. Or access technical information including the game's readme file and a players' discussion on topical issues.

DUNGEON MASTER II

Dungeon Master II Cheats

http://www.fys.ruu.nl/~fdijkstr/cheats/
Dungeon_Master.html

Freek Dijkstra tells fellow gamers how to improve their stats in Dungeon Master 2 using the Macintosh Cheat II program. Those without Mac computers won't find a visit to this spot a total loss. The codes for spells are also listed.

**Dungeon Master II:
Legend of Skullkeep**

http://www.spice.co.uk/~richard/dm2/

Richard Nuttall indexes a variety of resources to aid in play of Dungeon Master II. Find answers to Frequently Asked Questions, a saved game, and two different versions of a walkthrough. A complete spell list, a set of maps, and useful notes on the game are also featured. Those who wish to pursue their inquiry into the game further are pointed to the Usenet newsgroup where discussion can most likely be found.

GameSpot: Dungeon Master II: the Legend of Skullkeep at a Glance
http://www.gamespot.com/rpg/dungeonm/

The sequel to Dungeon Master, one of best selling titles of all time, comes under scrutiny here. Read Interplay's official company material and compare it to what the reviewer has to say. Download a demo, a patch, and a spell chart. Check out the readme file and players' discussion for technical info. Or link to the FAQ and the guide to Skullkeep magic.

Original Dungeon Master Helpful Hints
http://www.gamesdomain.co.uk/spoiler/ RPG/FTL/dungeon.master.1.txt

Although this is not a complete walkthrough of the first Dungeon Master game, it does offer solutions for some of the hardest puzzles in the role-playing adventure. Find a chart of spell codes divided into offensive, defensive, and general magic. A level-by-level look at the game's biggest challenges is also featured.

ELDER SCROLLS

The Daggerfall Info Zone
http://www.crown.net/~r6g020/ daggerfall.html

Rich Gade (a.k.a. PPD or Kalimar) offers fellow Elder Scrolls fans an impressive resource for learning about the second chapter in the game's series, Daggerfall. Find out how to get a demo, view unauthorized Daggerfall images, access the game's mailing list archive, and read the unofficial FAQ. Also discover the secret behind Alt-Q and find solutions for the demo's problems. Gamers' comments on the demo are welcome and available for review.

Daggerfall: The Elder Scrolls Chapter 2—Unofficial Legends & Lore
http://tahoma.cwu.edu:2000/~greenwel/ daggerfall/daggermain.html

Enjoy these (slightly modified) stories from the realm of Tamriel taken from the Daggerfall demo. Organized and grouped by type, they offer an enjoyable read for fans of the Elder Scrolls series.

The Elder Scrolls: Arena Info Site
http://www.cris.com/~Kronald/arena.html

Here's a chart that lists the location and price for the "special items" found in the first chapter of the Elder Scrolls series, Arena. Those who need answers to any of the riddles will also find help in this arena. The riddles are written out with the answers hidden behind a pulldown insert.

The Elder Scrolls Chapter 2: Daggerfall FAQ v0.98
http://www.newforce.ca/~jackel/dagger/

Andrew Franklin and Dave Humphrey pool their talents to produce this unofficial FAQ for the Daggerfall chapter of the Elder Scrolls series. Sections include General Information, Features, Previews, Encounters, Artifacts, Power Ups, and Bugs. Also find links leading to Bethesda Software and other game-related pages.

Eric's Daggerfall Page
http://www.ecn.uoknor.edu/~esglenn/ dagger.html

Check the Previews area for tons of demos and downloadables for the Daggerfall release. The Beastiary offers illustrated descriptions of the "thingies" in the game. And the Strategy section offers hints for better enjoying the game. Also find a section on Arena, a link to Bethesda and a cursory look at the next chapter in the series, The Elder Scrolls 3.

Ryan's Elder Scrolls Page
http://tahoma.cwu.edu:2000/~greenwel/daggerfall/tes.htm

This elaborate presentation explores the first and second chapters of the computer role-playing series, the Elder Scrolls. Enjoy game overviews, demos, annotated artifact lists, strategy clues, and spoilers for both Arena and Daggerfall. Links lead to other Elder Scroll fan pages, as well as other computer role-playing game fan pages.

The Unofficial Elder Scrolls Pages
http://www.newforce.ca/~jackel/esp/esp.html

With a little help from his friends, Dave Humphrey posts this rich archive of Elder Scrolls game resources. Well organized and easy to navigate, the hyperlinked directory points to FAQs, patches, demos, game editors, screen shots, reviews, and other items related to Arena and Daggerfall, the first two chapters of the game. Another site feature encourages fans to make suggestions for a third chapter in the series. Links point the way to Bethesda Software and to a few huge gaming sites.

EYE OF THE BEHOLDER

Eye of the Beholder Trilogy
http://fizzgig.glasswings.com.au/reviews/beholder.html

Find a description of Eye of the Beholder and its two sequels, The Legend of Darkmoon and Assault on Myth Drannor. Based on Advanced Dungeons and Dragons, these games offer heroic role-playing adventures that can stand alone or serve to complement the other games in the trilogy.

Eye of the Beholder Pages
http://tristan.arts.kuleuven.ac.be/~ibliss/eobpage.html

This gamer's resource offers a collection of documents relevant to the Eye of the Beholder Trilogy. Find original documentation files for all three games in the series and original maps for the first game. Solutions and complete maps for the first and second games are also provided.

Hints and Spoilers for Eye of the Beholder
http://www.gamesdomain.co.uk/spoiler/RPG/SSI.html

Visit this index to find links leading to puzzle solutions, character edits, and or/hints for the games in the Strategic Simulations Inc. trilogy Eye of the Beholder. Spoilers for other SSI role-playing games are also featured.

LANDS OF LORE

Lands of Lore: The Throne of Chaos
http://www.gamesdomain.co.uk/spoiler/RPG/Westwood/lands.of.lore.html

Having trouble living large in the Lands of Lore? Pick yourself up with this extensive cheat file. Find over two dozen maps to caves, mines, forests, and castle keeps. Plus, a walkthrough takes you by the hand and escorts you through the perils of the game. Scotia may have her magic, but you've got something more powerful: the answers to the game!

Lands of Lore: The Throne of Chaos Home Page
http://www.westwood.com/lol1/lol1info.html

Westwood promotes its interactive animated role-playing adventure where players must save the king and defeat the evil crone who would have him die. Read the game overview illustrated with screen shots, download an introduction movie and non-playable demo, and listen to music selections from the game including the "Lands of Lore I" theme song. Links to other Westwood pages offer an 800-number for ordering and pointers to other product information.

Lands of Lore I Hints and Tips

http://www.westwood.com/infodir/hints/lol1hints.html

Find hints and tips for moving through some of the tougher, more complicated areas of the Lands of Lore. Find out how to get past Scotia's Barrier and ultimately defeat the old hag. Find out where the Valen's Cube is, and uncover the mystery of the White Tower in the third level. This hint page is provided by the game's designer, Westwood Studios. Those who need additional help can order the complete hint book from the company.

Lands of Lore I Tech Support

http://www.westwood.com/infodir/techsupport/techlol1.html

Find answers to the most common questions by players who can't seem to get their Lands of Lore game to run. Over a half dozen questions are asked and answered. For those who don't find the solution they seek, an e-mail link is provided for ready service.

Virgin Interactive Entertainment Lands of Lore: The Throne of Chaos Technical Page

http://www.vie.com/low/support/sup.vir60.html

Virgin Interactive hosts this Lands of Lore cache. Download a playable demo that promises challenges that will take more than a day to get through. Check out the hint file for game tips not available on the company's call-in hintline. Download two game patches and find quick answers to technical questions in the comprehensive FAQ. Want to see what else Virgin Interactive offers? Just follow the links to other company pages.

AUTHOR'S PICK

Mud Connector

http://www.mudconnect.com/

One of the favorite haunts of role-players is the Internet because of the diverse opportunities for online play. It is not unusual for the popular role-playing game systems to inspire several MUDs offering gamers online experiences based on the premise of the game. Here's an opportunity to explore those games and the MUDs that have sprung up to serve role-players online. This searchable collection of MUDs indexes over 300 titles (not all offer role-playing). Entries include a basic description of the game plus links to the game's Web home page (if applicable) and its Telnet gaming area. Other site features include MUD client resources, links to topical newsgroups, and pointers to FAQs. For those new to MUDs and role-playing, this site offers another entree into the hidden worlds that await online. For more MUD information and links, see the Telnet Guide, Chapter 13.

LOST VIKINGS

Lost Vikings

http://www.interplay.com/games/lostvik.html

How about a day of seafaring and pillaging with three Norse adventurers? Well, first you have to help them find their way home—they've been sucked into an alien spacecraft. More of an arcade action game, Lost Vikings also has elements of a role-playing adventure. Read a game overview, review the game's features, view screen shots, and download a PC demo of the game. Links lead to other Interplay pages and to the home page of the game's developer, Blizzard Entertainment.

MIGHT AND MAGIC I – V/
HEROES OF MIGHT AND MAGIC

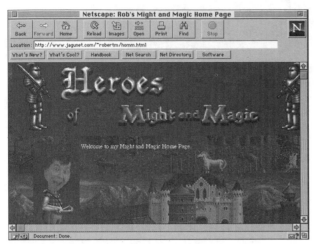

Might and Magic (and Heroes of)
http://www.jagunet.com/~robertm/
homm.html

In addition to information about the strategy game Heroes of Might and Magic, Rob Merritt treats fans to a mini-tutorial on the five-part role-playing series Might and Magic from which the "heroes" come. Find Rob's reviews and overviews of the games in the series, plus solutions for games 2 through 4.

Might and Magic/
Heroes of Might and Magic
http://www.nwcomputing.com/

New World Computing uses its site to promote its award-winning strategy game, Heroes of Might and Magic, as well as its long running, five-part role-playing series, Might and Magic, on which "Heroes" is based. Find downloadables for both the strategy game and the RPG series, FAQ files for both, and a promotion for the next installment in the "Heroes" series.

Heroes of Might and Magic FAQ V1.1
http://www.users.fast.net/~ktolar/geoweb/
homm/homm.htm

Stop by this page to find the answers to the most Frequently Asked Questions regarding the strategy game based on the role-playing series Might and Magic.

Heroes of Might and Magic
http://www.egr.uh.edu/~yxq60120/hero/
hero.htm

A great introduction to the game for new players, this strategy guide provides a look at basic concepts and general hero information. Also find links to other players' home pages and to another strategy guide.

MORIA

The Dungeons of Moria
http://139.56.200.11/moria.html

Robert Alan Koeneke and James E. Wilson post this manual for learning about and playing the single-user, fantasy role-playing adventure game Moria. The document is available to be read online or downloaded in a PostScript format. Easy to use, the HTML version of the manual features a hyperlinked table of contents that aids easy navigation. Topics cover most aspects of the game, from choosing a character and adventuring to spells and wizards.

The Moria Page
http://www.ecst.csuchico.edu/~beej/moria/

Explore one of the more popular rogue-like role-playing fantasy adventures, Moria. Among the site's features, find links to FTP archives where the game is available, various guides to the game and its components such as magic and dragon-slaying, a game-specific FAQ, and pointers to newsgroups of topical interest. An FAQ answering questions about rogue-like games is also featured.

NETHACK

The Nethack Home Page

http://www.win.tue.nl/games/roguelike/
nethack/

Boudewijn Wayers hosts this extensive resource devoted to what he considers one of the more "complicated" rouge-like games, Nethack. Among the site features find an introduction to the game, tips for beginners, a guide book, and spoilers. Also find links to the game program and source code, code for Hack (Nethack's predecessor), utilities, and game variations.

REALMZ

The Books of Realmz

http://www.seas.ucla.edu/~grayson/realmz/
Realmz_Books.html

Visit this archive to browse a collection of books that provide all the details for playing the Mac-only role-playing game Realmz. The library includes the Realmz Scenario Summary (RSS), the Realmz Acronym Dictionary (RAD), The Book of Items, The Realmz NPC Doc, The Book of Beasts, and the History of Realmz. The books are also available in DocMaker format for offline reading.

The Realmz FAQs and Files Page

http://www.outreach.com/realmz/

This gamer's resource offers pointers to Realmz FAQs, scenarios and scenario tip sheets, and character files. Visitors can also download the latest edition of the game updates and demo editors. Links to other Realmz download sites and the home pages of other Realmz enthusiasts round out the offerings posted here.

The Realmz Page

http://www.cae.wisc.edu/~foley/realmz.html

Pick up the latest version of Realmz and learn how to write your own scenarios at this page hosted by Tim Phillips. Also find FAQs, news, and links to other play-

ers' home pages. A pointer to the newsgroup where the game is discussed is also featured.

ROGUE

A Guide to the Dungeons of Doom

http://gw.cronyx.ru/software/FreeBSD/doc/
usd/33.rogue.txt

Michael C. Toy and Kenneth C.R.C. Arnold post their treatise on playing Rogue, the role-playing fantasy that lent its name to a whole genre of game that includes Angband, Moria, and Nethack. The document includes both general information and specific details to aid players in finding their way through the Dungeons of Doom. Mostly text, the guide does have some diagrams to illustrate various points. However, there are no hyperlinks nor any table of contents to aid navigation. Players must scroll through the text to get their bearings and find the information they seek.

The Rogue Home Page

http://www.win.tue.nl/games/roguelike/
rogue/index.html

Download the original game (in a variety of formats) from this site hosted by Rogue fan Boudewijn Waijers. Other site features include spoilers and a utility that plays the game by itself. Also find a link to the page authors' Roguelike Games Home Page.

STONEKEEP

Stonekeep

http://www.interplay.com/website/sales/
stonek.html

This official Interplay site presents the fantasy role-playing adventure Stonekeep, where players must regain their humanity while saving the world. Enjoy a non-interactive demo, sound samples, and screen shots. Read the company's promotion for the game, reviews from others, and an overview of the story line and system requirements. Links lead to the game's unofficial FAQ and other Interplay pages.

Stonekeep FAQ
http://www.spice.co.uk/~richard/stonekeep/index.html

Richard Nuttall maintains this index pointing to Stonekeep resources found across the Web. Find FAQs, a game walkthrough, hints, a saved game editor, and a patch. Also find a pointer to a Usenet newsgroup where other assistance can be found.

THUNDERSCAPE

GameSpot: Thunderscape at a Glance
http://www.gamespot.com/rpg/thunders/

Doing what GameSpot does best, this site pokes around the SSI release Thunderscape. Read the official company line plus a few well-chosen words from reviewers, find a patch to upgrade the game, access a walkthrough with hints and tips, or link to topic-related pages. Technical information is also featured and includes the game's readme file and a discussion forum for players.

Thunderscape
http://www.ssionline.com/cgi-bin/omixlink?1400746673+games/ssi/thunder/index.html

Here's the official word from Strategic Simulations, Inc. on its role-playing "steampunk fantasy" game. Set in the SSI-created world of Aden, the game combines machinery and magic, monsters and mayhem for an adventure full of battles to be won and puzzles to ponder and solve. Find an overview of system requirements and selected screen shots from the game. Links lead to the company's other pages.

The Spoiler Centre: Thunderscape
http://spoiler.et.ee/RPG/SSI/thunderscape.1.txt

James Meloy has prepared and continues to work on this combination FAQ, hint, and spoiler guide. Prepare to spend time with the document. It is extensive and unfortunately offers no table of contents or other aids to navigation.

ULTIMA

Auric's Ultima Online Home Page
http://users.visi.net/~auric/index.html

Here's an Ultima player's resource if ever there was one! Find opportunities for private reflection on the game and interaction with others. Site features include a chat room and chat zone, information on the guilds, the game's history, runes, a library, a music gallery, an IRC channel, and links to game-related pages. Find out exactly what Ultima means to the page's author.

Dragon Press: Ultima Fan Fiction
http://crash.ihug.co.nz/~charlton/andrew/fanfic.html

Andrew Charlton host this repository of fan fiction written by Ultima enthusiasts. Enjoy almost twenty tales based on the fantasy-rich characters and settings found in the role-playing game.

Ultima Dragons—Internet Chapter
http://www.udic.org/

A virtual club established in 1992, the Ultima Dragons are dedicated to assisting others in adding to the fullness of their Ultima experiences. Anyone with an interest in the game is welcome to join. This page offers assistance in that regard. Find an FAQ about the group and information about joining. A collection of links leads to Internet resources concerning the game including newsgroups and one of the Ultima Dragon's favorite hangouts, the Weyrmount MOO. A photo gallery, member roster, and group history round out the offerings.

Ultima World Wide Web Archive
http://www.ea.com/origin/english/ultima/

Origin Systems welcomes players to this resource for its popular fantasy role-playing series Ultima. Find out exactly what the game is and about, plus find overviews for various games in the series with walkthroughs, manuals, maps, technical help, and other aids. The complete Ultima Story-Line FAQ summarizes the tales in the series. Pointers lead to information on the latest Ultima resources, including a Gargoyle Language tutorial and a preview of Ultima Online.

The World of Ultima
http://www.emanon.net/~redjr/world_of_ultima/

Rich De Francesco, Jr., invites the uninitiated to explore the world of the Ultima role-playing series. Find resources for each of the games in the series, including hints, walkthroughs, utilities, maps, music, and patches. Find a collection of FAQs (five in all) plus links to sites of related topical interest. Laid out to allow adventurers the pleasures of discovering for themselves where the treasure are hidden, a short cut also leads to the cache.

For more information on Ultima, also see:

The Bard's Library
http://www.geocities.com/TimesSquare/1750/

Beregard's Unofficial Ultima Online Tour
http://www.aa.net/~jtraub/uol/

Prawn Dragon's Ultima Online Page
http://www.top.net/dstephen/uoscre1.htm

UNLIMITED ADVENTURES

The FRUA Home Page
http://www.contrib.andrew.cmu.edu/usr/jk9t/

Forgotten Realms Unlimited Adventures (FRUA), often just called Unlimited Adventures, is a DOS- and Mac-based game through which players can play Forgotten Realm (AD&D) modules. To find out more about the game, stop by this page hosted by John Kochmar to read the FAQ, check out the FRUA mailing and newsletter lists, or jump to the FTP sites. Links lead to other players' home pages and FRUA experimental art.

WARHAMMER: SHADOW OF THE HORNED RAT

GameSpot: Warhammer: Shadow of the Horned Rat at a Glance
http://www.gamespot.com/rpg/warhamsh/

What does the electronic version of Warhammer offer that the original version of the game does not? Find out at this GameSpot probe into Warhammer: Shadow of the Horned Rat. Find an animation of the game to download, hints and tips, plus links pointing to official, unofficial, and related sites.

Warhammer: Shadow of the Horned Rat
http://www.gamepen.com/ledge/games/sothr/sothr.html

This 1996 review, which appeared on the Gamer's Ledge, provides an excellent place to begin exploring Mindscape's electronic version of the popular table game Warhammer. Receiving a total 90 out of 100 points, the electronic version seems to remain true to most of the original game's rules and nuances but adds animation and sound into the mix. Find an overview of system requirements, screen shots, and a game summary interwoven with the critical comments made by the reviewer, Nathan Bamford.

Warhammer: Shadow of the Horned Rat
http://www.mindscape.com/msgames/WHRat/index.html

This official Mindscape page promotes its electronic adventure-strategy game based on Games Workshop's wildly popular tabletop fantasy battle game.

Read the company's spiel, check out screen shots, and if so moved, order a copy online. Links lead to other company pages.

Warhammer: Shadow of the Horned Rat
http://www.au.malaysia.net/people/tangcm/hornrat.htm

Those needing, wanting, or just curious about cheats and hacks for Warhammer can stop by this compiled resource for help in winning the game. Also find a list describing the locations of the magic items.

WASTELAND

Rubblefanger!
http://www.math.ttu.edu/~kesinger/wasteland/

Jake Kesinger posts this informative page on Interplay's computer role-playing game set in a post-apocalyptic southwestern United States. Originally released in the mid-80s, the game is under current re-release on the Interplay 10 Year Anthology CD. Those interested in downloading emulated versions can do so here, along with images and the game's paragraphs. Pointers lead to other game-related resources.

Wasteland FAQ
http://www.cris.com/~chbaer/wasteland.txt

Chris Baer and Stephen Sedmak have coordinated their efforts to produce this document offering answers to the most Frequently Asked Questions about the game Wasteland. Find tons of specific help including a key command summary, equipment and attribute summaries, and game hints. The page offers no hyperlinks to aid navigation; players must scroll through the whole document in search of the answers they seek. And the document is rather large.

WIZARDRY

Wizardry I and II Item List
http://www.archi.is.tohoku.ac.jp/~kommy/wizitem.html

Find no more and no less than what the title suggests: a chart of items from the Wizardry I and II games.

Wizardry Gold
http://sir-tech.com/games/wizgold/

A reworking of the acclaimed role-playing epic Wizardry: Crusaders of the Dark Savant, this Gold version improves upon the original, offering new animated sequences, better sound effects, and new music. The game also includes screensavers, wallpaper, and other desktop accessories. Visit this official game promotion for a game description and screen shots. Links to the Sirtech company store and other company pages are also featured.

Wizardry: The Wizardry Trilogies
http://sir-tech.com/games/wizardry/

Sirtech Software hosts this promotional page for its popular role-playing series Wizardry, which is now bundled in two trilogy packages. Read an overview of the games and their scenarios, and if so inclined, order online.

LIVE ACTION RPGS (LARPS)

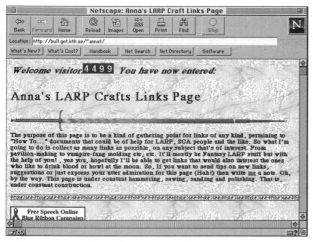

Anna's LARP Craft Links Page
http://bull.got.kth.se/~annat/

Anna Troy points the way to massive amounts of information compiled because of its potential interest to those who engage in Live Action Role Playing. Learn about making weapons and armor, general costuming, and leather working. Also find tips for make-up and mask making, plus other arts and crafts.

Central Action Role Playing Society
http://www.industry-dm.com/~lorchard/carps/

This home page for a Michigan-based fantasy LARP society helps keep members (and others) informed of upcoming events and news. Stop by to visit the online gallery, browse the member ranks, and even join. Be sure to check out the Discussion Forum; useful comments are always welcome. Planned site upgrades include the addition of an Online Character Creation System, plus games and puzzles.

Dagorhir, The Sport
http://www.charm.net/~dagorhir/

The Dagorhir Battle Game Association hosts this look at the "sport," which pits players in a free-style simu-

lation of battles that might have taken place during the Dark Ages. Link to the home pages of player groups around the country or the national office, review the Live-Action Battle Gaming Group List, or sign up to play. Loads of information on costuming, props, and rules help players get into character.

Darkon
http://www.cat.cc.md.us/~darkon/

A full-contact medieval combat group/system based primarily in the Baltimore-Washington, D.C., area, Darkon recreates fierce hand-to-hand combat scenarios using padded weapons like maces and clubs. Make a virtual visit to the world of Darkon, review the system's prevailing rules, find out about upcoming events, and see photos of past battles.

Fantasy Quest
http://www1.usa1.com/~stryfe/fquest/index.html

Get into character in Connecticut with fellow gamers involved in the medieval role-playing fantasy that is Fantasy Quest. Find a general introduction to role-playing games, a look at how the FQ gaming system is structured, and an invitation to the next events. An FQ FAQ, photo album, and storybook help fill in the details.

Generic Live Action Role-playing Enterprises
http://linetap.com/csit/glare.htm

With an emphasis on character development and interaction rather than slash and plunder quests, the GLARE rules support an "open" system easily tailored for different gaming styles. Find out more about GLARE and its medieval fantasy world, Ariel. General game information plus details about GLARE combat, magic, characters, and races are featured. Those interested can also find out how to join the action.

AUTHOR'S PICK

The Roguelike Games Home Page
http://www.win.tue.nl/games/roguelike/index.html

Billions and billions of years ago ... well not quite, but it was back in the computer dark ages, long before the advent of the Web and graphic computer games. The best game in town was a text-based adventure called Rogue. Players roamed a dungeon slaying nightmares, garnering treasures, and growing in power. It was fun, and the game became the first of a whole genre. The story of rogue-like games is an interesting tale and is presented with many illustrative links on this page hosted by Boudewijn Waijers. Among the featured items find a few FAQs, newsgroups, an FTP archive housing game codes, and utilities. Links to other fan pages round out the offerings presented. Even those not interested in text-based adventuring may want to stop by this page. It really brings home just how far gaming technology has come in so few years.

The International Fantasy Gaming Society
http://charlotte.npixi.net:80/ifgs/society/

A Live Action Role-Playing (LARP) organization in the United States, the International Fantasy Gaming Society promotes its chapters and role-playing in general through this official page. Find links to chapter home pages, the IFGS FAQ, a gallery of photos, and links to other LARP organizations around the world.

Legends Roleplaying
http://users.aol.com/legendsweb/legends.htm

A medieval fantasy role-playing system, Legends recreates the mist-shrouded days of an era gone by. Always open to new players, the site hosts an introduction to the fantasy for folks new to role-playing. Information

geared to the veteran player is also featured, along with a players forum and an event photo gallery. AOL users are invited to join in the weekly get-together at the Red Lantern Tavern chat room.

Live Role Playing Game FAQ
http://www.cs.wisc.edu/~desmet/live-action.html

From the Usenet newsgroup rec.games.frp.live-action, this document answers most everything anyone could want to know about live-action fantasy role-playing. Find out what it is, how it works, and why people do it—some of the reasons, anyway. Those with questions not answered in the FAQ can contact the volunteers listed for more information.

New England Roleplaying Organization
http://www.nero-int.com/

Here's the official international home page and Web site for NERO, a live-action medieval fantasy game that boasts being the largest role-playing system in the United States. Visit this page to get most all the details: who, what, when, and where. As for the why ... that's up to each individual player.

The Shade's LARP Games List
http://www.coil.com/~zargonis/shade.html

An excellent resource for anyone interested in Live-Action Role- Playing games, this list points to the home pages of LARP systems and organizations in North America and elsewhere in the world. Also find general news and information resources of interest to the whole LARP community.

Society for Creative Anachronism
http://www.sca.org/

Here's the home page for the international organization that helped take role-playing off the stage and turn it into a passionate avocation for folks of all ages. Learn all about the organization, as well as the period in history its members study and recreate. A list of SCA groups will help those interested locate active SCA members nearby.

Southern Organization for Live Action Reenactments
http://www.georgia-usa.com/solar/

Based in Atlanta, Ga., SOLAR offers a skill-based, mythological fantasy live-action role-playing game. Build skills while battling monsters and questing for treasure. Find an introduction to the game and its member-players, event announcements, and background on Sutherlands, the world in which the fantasy takes place. Also find a section on how to make weapons.

Trolling for Taillights
http://www.eaglequest.com/~spett/TFT/
TFT_Intro.html

Here's a role-playing game of another kind, requiring no costumes, no knowledge of legend and lore, and no weapons. It's illegal to pretend you're a policeman, but it's not illegal to "pretend" to be a radar gun. Find out what simple electronics are required to stimulate other drivers' radar detectors and how to turn highway high jinks into a game. Rules, safety precautions, and a scoring system are featured.

WORLD OF DARKNESS

B.J. Zanzibar's World of Darkness
http://ezinfo.ucs.indiana.edu/~adashiel/wod/
wod.html

Those seeking an introduction to or in-depth information about the World of Darkness need only drop by this archive. Find pages devoted to each of the games: Vampire: The Masquerade; Werewolf: The Apocalypse; Mage: The Ascension; Changeling: The Dreaming and Wraith: The Oblivion. A collection of WoD-related links is organized by type: information, metalist, gopher, FTP, and more. The FAQ is also online for those needing quick, general answers.

Web of Darkness
http://enuxsa.eas.asu.edu/~buckner/
wod.html

Ben Buckner posts this extensive index offering 177 World of Darkness links, including 10 FAQs. Also find pointers to six Rage-related Web sites as well as an FTP site. If it's about the World of Darkness, it's probably listed here if it's worth a look.

White Wolf's World of Darkness Timeline
http://www.cyberenet.net/~sten/vampire/
jburt/timeline.htm

Compiled from official White Wolf sources by Jonathan Burt (with a little help from his friends), this timeline mingles real life historical events with those of the fictitious World of Darkness. See when the clans first appeared and trace the major events in the World of Darkness through 1995. An excellent resource for building stories and settling trivial disputes.

CHANGELING: THE DREAMING

Changeling: The Dreaming Official Home Page
http://www.white-wolf.com/white-wolf/
Pages/Changeling%20Page.html

White Wolf hosts this brief look at its role-playing fantasy game about spirit possession. A product list is available for those needing supplies, and anyone with a question need only send their queries to the e-mail address provided.

The Dreaming
http://www.ionet.net/~sidhe/dream/
dream.html

An extensive resource for players who enjoy Changeling: The Dreaming, this site hosts links to the Changeling FAQ, official errata, essays, and clarifications on rules and the world. Also find faery tales and art, links to "Glamour" found across the 'Net, and pointers to people who play. A great starting place for anyone new to the game, the site is also laden for veteran players as well.

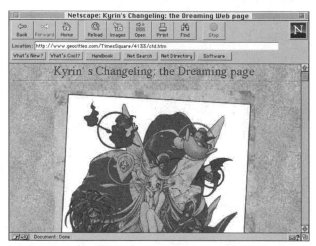

Kyrin's Changeling: The Dreaming Page
http://www.geocities.com/TimesSquare/
4133/ctd.htm

Read an excerpt from the official Changeling: The Dreaming Rulebook and discover what this role-playing game is all about. Also find Kyrin's personal contributions to the game and links to other players' home pages.

MAGE: THE ASCENSION

Mage: The Ascension
http://www.lancs.ac.uk/postgrad/thomasc1/
rpg/wod/mage/mage.htm

This organized index presented by C. Thomas features general rules for the Mage: The Ascension magical role-playing game. Links to other players' home pages and miscellaneous storyteller aids are also included.

Mage: The Ascension Official Home Page
http://www.white-wolf.com/white-wolf/
Pages/Mage%20Home%20Page.html

White Wolf hosts this brief look at its role-playing fantasy game about magical charms and charmers. A product list is available for those needing supplies, and

anyone curious can read the developer's notes for a look into the mind of the game's mastermind.

Mage Stuff
http://www.monash.edu.au/people/
damiene/wod/mage/index.html

This compiled archive offers a gold mine of resources pertaining to Mage: The Ascension. Find directories offering information on character creation, paradigms, realms, spheres, technomancers, traditions, and about a half dozen other aspects of the game. Articles of general interest to Mage players are also on file.

Peter's Mage Page
http://www.cs.umu.se/~dvlpen/rpg/mage/
mage.html

Peter Eriksson hosts this mega-Mage page with lots to read and enjoy. Browse through a big collection of articles on traditions, conventions, magic, and settings. Also find chronicles and fiction. Plenty of links to other players' Mage pages lead to even more topical sites to see.

VAMPIRE: THE APOCALYPSE

Vampire: The Apocalypse Official Home Page
http://www.white-wolf.com/white-wolf/
Pages/Vamp%20page.html

Explore the World of Darkness at this official home page for the White Wolf studio's Vampire role-playing game. Sink your teeth into product lists, game summaries, and fiction. A player's registry and information about joining the White Wolf team are also featured. And those with questions need only ask.

The Elysium - Vampire: The Masquerade Page
http://www.novia.net/~truehand/

Role-players into The Masquerade of the vampire world should stop by this player's resource to browse the nice collection of game-related items. Find quick answers to questions about the game in the FAQ. Read vampire fiction and character profiles. And link to pages offering additional information and other items of interest to players.

Red Rose Vampire Network Node
http://www.planetx.com/vampire/

Stop in here for the blood and guts of the Live-Action Role-Playing game Vampire: The Masquerade. Find an overview of the game plus links to the clan pages of various vampire types. Pointers to other sites of interest to the vampire community are also available.

Vampire: The Masquerade, Second Edition Errata
http://www.cs.wisc.edu/~desmet/mbn/errata.html

Players missing rules from White Wolf's The Masquerade, Second Edition need only stop by this page to solve the problem. The text-only page can be printed for off-line reference.

WEREWOLF: THE APOCALYPSE

Werewolf: The Apocalypse
http://www.atlcom.net/~jlacour/velvet/velvet.html

Welcome to the Velvet Shadow, a page created by a player for players of the World of Darkness roleplaying fantasy where werewolves prowl the night. Visit the archive to browse the selection of useful gaming files, check the game registry to locate players games open for play, or check out the "best" characters of all time. Information on the thirteen known Unbral Realms is available to explore and chronicles are online to read.

Werewolf: The Apocalypse Official Home Page
http://www.white-wolf.com/white-wolf/Pages/Werewolf%20Page.html

White Wolf hosts this look at its role-playing fantasy game Werewolf: The Apocalypse. Read a general description of the game, browse a product list, and check out the developer's notes. Links to other White Wolf pages point the way to other role-playing games played in the World of Darkness.

TRADITIONAL AND OTHER RPGS

AMBER

Amber Diceless Roleplaying Game
http://www.ens-lyon.fr/~jcdubacq/amber.html

Hosted by Jean-Christophe Dubacq, this page offers rules, alternate rules, an FAQ, and art associated with the diceless role-playing game (DRPG) released in 1991 by Phage Press and based on the Amber universe created by the sci-fi books of Roger Zelazny. Visit the library for a timeline of books, a quick who's who, and an elemental mythology. The page is available in English and French.

Princess Invidia's Amber Page
http://www.io.com/~wileyc/anne/webpage3.htm

Jen Kitchen hosts this useful fan page devoted to the Amber diceless role-playing game (DRPG). Link to the "highly recommended" Roger Zelazny Page, the Amber FAQ, and "metric tons" of Amber-related sites including campaigns and other players' home pages, FTP sites and Telnet sites for online play. The princess also points to her personal Amber playground and information on her current campaign.

AUTHOR'S PICK

The RPG Archives
http://www.lextech.com/rpg/

Michael P. Duff, Jr., boasts his is the oldest site on the Web devoted to role-playing games. Perhaps that's true, but the site is definitely one of the best. Its contents include gaming news, tools, links to MUDs, electronic texts, event announcements, and companies. And that's just a sampling. The offerings range from the general to the specific and provide a great collection of information and resources for newcomers and old-timers alike.

ARS MAGICA

Ars Magica
http://www.io.com/~presage/arm.html

Atlas Games hosts this official site for its Ars Magica role-playing game. Features include company and game news, an FAQ, a product list, and a link to the U.S. mirror of Project Redcap, a site reputed to contain links to all known Ars Magica sites on the Web. A link to Sanctum Hermeticum, an Ars Magica fanzine, is also featured.

Ars Magica FAQ
http://www.trin.cam.ac.uk/users/dc132/ ArM/FAQ/Welcome.html

Practically a whole village of folks came together to produce this document offering answers to the most frequently asked questions about the role-playing game Ars Magica. Among the topics featured find answers to general game questions, answers to specific rules questions, an overview of the game and its history, and information about Ars Magica resources on the Internet. A list of material for suggested reading is also included.

The Crossroads of Order
http://telmaron.com/ars-magica/Redcap/ redcap.html

This site is the U.S. mirror of the Redcap Project, a central clearinghouse for links to Ars Magica resources on the Internet. Among its principal pointers, find jumps to the Atlas Games' Ars Magica Page, the Ars Magica FAQ, and Sanctum Hermeticum, the online fanzine. Pointers to other topical sites, including covenant archives, are also featured.

Sanctum Hermeticum
http://www.gnawing.com/sanctum/ index1.html

Centered on the game Ars Magica and the realm of Mythic Europe, this online, ongoing project allows players to explore the concepts found in the role-playing series by Atlas Games. Visitors are welcome to read or add to the collection of fan fiction and to the growing description of the Village of Flamor. Information on the Order of Hermes and its structure is also featured, including the group's constitution.

BATTLETECH

BattleTech: The Future of Warfare
http://www.fasa.com/BattleTech/ BTMAINPAGE.html

Sponsored by FASA Corporation, this official home page introduces the board-based role-playing game where players "strap on" BattleTech armored war machines and fight for planets and empires. Stop by for the rules and regulations, a look at the answers to Frequently Asked Questions, errata, a product guide, and a monthly release schedule. Visitors can also find out how to join the official fan club, submit material to FASA, and get BattleTech licensed material. Those interested will also find a link to information about the collectible card game.

BattleTech Virtual Reality FAQ
http://http.bsd.uchicago.edu/~c-henkle/faq3-0.html

Fielding frequently asked questions, Charlotte "Freya" Henkle and Norman "Beaver-1" Choe post this unofficial page of answers about BattleTech (Virtual Reality), an arcade simulation based on the role-playing board game BattleTech. Find out exactly what BT (VR) is, where it is available, and how much it costs to play. Instruction on how to play, including a brief look at tactics and suggestions, is also included. Links to other BattleTech information sites round out the offerings.

The Bloody Clans
http://home.earthlink.net/~ice_tbc/index.html

Rich Meyers, Ice to multiplayer BattleTech enthusiasts, posts this semi-official page for one the game's oldest and most respected "mercenary" groups, The Bloody Clans (TBC). Turned bad after having their fill of winning for the cause of right, the 40-member group now leaves a dark trail of destruction in its wake. Link to TBC pages to read fiction and catch a glimpse of the group at its bloodiest.

Locke's BattleTech Page
http://www.nmia.com/~locke/btech.html

Browse this arsenal of mech designs which have come straight from the imagination of David Locke. Among the machines, find light, medium, heavy, and assault mechs with armament and engine details fully articulated. (The Mechworks Mek files should be available soon.) A history of the Cavalier-type mech paints a colorful background story for the deadly machines. Links to other BattleTech-related pages point the way to additional war zones of potential interest.

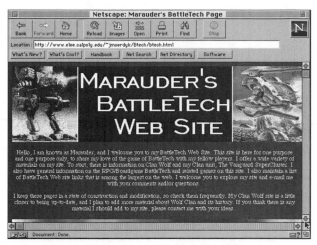

Maurauder's Battle Tech Page
http://www.elee.calpoly.edu/~jmoerdyk/Btech/btech.html

A good resource for newbies looking to get a feel for the role-playing world of BattleTech, Jeff Moerdyke's site posts a question-and-answer explanation of the game and its universe, and features a map of Inner Sphere. For those looking to find even more information, links to archive sites and other BattleTech pages point the way. Also find jumps to the BattleTech Player's List, BattleTech Multi-User Simulated Environment (MUSE) telnet sites, and BattleTech Virtual Reality sites.

Welcome to BattleTech
http://www.virtualworld.com/BattleTech/BattleTech.html

J. Howard hosts this resource offering a brief history behind the BattleTech Universe and a look at the World of BattleTech as presented by FASA. The Weapons Data File details the capacities of the various weapons, and the BattleMech Data File posts illustrations of the mech designs. Finally, a roster of those who've achieved the status of BattleTech Master and joined the Legendary Order of Burton is also available for those who'd like to pay tribute.

CALL OF CTHULHU

Call of Cthulhu
http://www.sirius.com/~chaosium/coc.html

Based on the writings of H.P. Lovecraft and others, Call of Cthulhu (kuh-THOO-loo) is a horror fantasy role-playing game set in the 1920s and peopled with monsters, powerful entities, netherworld terrors, and their worshippers. Join the fun and investigate things unknown and never spoken of before. This official game page will help those interested in the game find all they need to get started. Links lead to product and ordering information, plus other Call of Cthulhu resources on the Web. (The link page is worth the visit; this collection points in most every RPG direction possible.)

Call of Cthulhu RPG
http://146.19.2.3/~alquier/HPL/web_coc.html

Laurent Alquier posts this nice directory of sites related to Chaosium's Call of Cthulhu, the horror role-playing game based on the writings of H.P. Lovecraft. Link to the official (buy it here) page hosted by Chaosium Inc., three FTP archives hosting pictures, character aids and manuscripts, and over a dozen players' home pages offering articles and resources of topical interest. Among the featured pages, find two character generator PC software programs.

DOCTOR WHO

Doctor Who
http://www.tardis.ed.ac.uk/~type40/who-rpg.html

Fans of the British science fiction fantasy series Doctor Who with a desire to play a role-playing e-mail game based on the good doctor's fictional adventures will find plenty of interest on this page by Ian McDonald. Features include information about the Who-RPG mailing list with links to new and old archives, a rule book for the game, character information, adventure outlines, and timelines. Ideas about where to find a game and help for playing on different systems are also available.

CYBERPUNK

Cyberpunk 2020 Web Archive
http://falcon.cc.ukans.edu/~heresy/cyber/

Paul Tobia posts this extensive resource which offers loads of interest to anyone who enjoys R. Talsorian Games' futuristic RPG Cyberpunk 2020. Among the featured items find official rules, errata, home-brew rules, reference tables, fan essays, and a look at some new worlds players can add to their Cyberpunk worlds. Plus there are new "technologies," humor, and links to other game-related sites. The site is well organized and easy to use.

Mockery's Cyberpunk 2020 Page
http://www2.connectnet.com/~dluther/cpunk.htm

Players working strictly from the original Cyberpunk book will appreciate the offerings presented at this site. Find conversions for all sorts of new weapons, gear, and cyberware options. Also find sections on programs, corporations, vehicles, places, and rule modifications. A look at characters, campaigns, and other Cyberpunk fan pages round out the offerings.

Morninman's Cyberpunk 2020 Archive
http://users.aol.com/morninman/cybrindx.htm

Favoring a reprieve from the sweaty urban outrage of the Cyberpunk world, this archive explores the life under, on, and around the sea. Find an Oceanpunk players guide, as well as information on Oceanpunk equipment and gear. Other interesting items include a list of German words and phrases (makes sense if your character is German), and deck plans for the Weston Class Boost Freighter and the Sea Spider DMP. Links to other Cyperpunk 2020 sites, general and science fiction gaming sites, and related media are also included.

DUNGEONS & DRAGONS

Advanced Dungeons & Dragons
http://web.cs.ualberta.ca/~wade/HyperDnd/

A no-frills site that gets right down to business, this one's a gem of simplicity, order, and resources. Find a link to the Multi-Player Games Network FTP site offering the Internet's only "legal" resource for TSR gaming information. Two FAQs are on tap, as are a half dozen databases offering riddles, encounters, spells, and prayers. Three rules summaries help clarify various points of the game, and links point to other AD&D sites of interest, including other fans' pages and the Usenet newsgroup.

Advanced Dungeons & Dragons FTP Site
ftp://ftp.mpgn.com/Gaming/ADND/

Upload or download files at this archive for Advanced Dungeon and Dragon gaming resources. Among the files available find dragon articles, an FAQ, hexmaps, rules, stories, programs, and reviews. Information on monsters, spells, and worlds is also featured. Plus, there are character sheets and lots of other items of related interest.

Dungeons & Dragons
http://www.sfn.saskatoon.sk.ca/~aa499/dnd.htm

An avid gamer and active programmer, Christopher A. Brooks welcomes fellow players to the various AD&D utilities he has created. All are invited to stop into the Gallery of Magical Blades and grab a blade. Those looking for character sheets can check out the MS-DOS and Word for Windows sheets. And spellcasters may wish to download the Wizard/Priest Quick Reference Sheet. Also available here (but created by different folks) are six fonts which include Runes, Oghams, and Wiccan symbols. Among the other resources on site, find mailing list addresses, Usenet newsgroups, additional AD&D programs of interest, and links to other topical pages.

Dungeons & Dragons Section of Mini World
http://www.miniworld.com/adnd/

Here's a find! This site houses interactive online programs that generate characters, items, spellbooks, and gems. Look up monsters, check out Surges and Fumbles, and review Spelljammer Crew costs. Readers can use the online search to find information of interest from "Dragon & Polyhedron Magazine, " and links point the way to other selected AD&D sites offering additional gaming resources for players and masters.

Effie's Dungeons and Dragons Fantasy Role Playing Concordance
http://www.iinc.com/~envision/concorde/

Those in need of quick reference concerning the role-playing fantasy Dungeons and Dragons may want to try this compiled resource presented by Loy Ellen Gross. Find information on rules, armor, weapons, monsters, spells, magic items, artifacts, and modules. Reader submissions are welcome and appreciated.

The Great Net.Book Archive
http://onyx.arts.kuleuven.ac.be/~ezra/gnb.html

Archiver Ezra Van Everbroeck hosts this informative and helpful library of resources geared to the role-playing community. Browse The Guide to Herbs for RPGs to find tips on playing with plants. The Great Net Spellbook/Great Net Prayerbook presents thousands of spells and prayers. And the archive of Auxiliary RPG Programs offers a collection of automated generators that create items to enhance play. Those looking for more information can link to the dozens of related sites listed.

Dage
http://www.urich.edu/~ejd4g/dage/index.html

Eric Dobbs presents this detailed look at Dage, a fantasy world game setting he's developed for AD&D, but which can be used with other gaming systems. Find a

Dage FAQ plus game information including bits on magic, religions, monsters, and character kits. An overview of the civilization features a history of Dage and looks at the society and politics, the peoples, and the cities. Selected references including a dictionary round out the offerings.

EARTHDAWN

The Cage of Threads
http://www.usm.edu/~douglass/
edindex.html

This popular site features player-contributed Earthdawn resources compiled and presented by John Douglass. Among the links find the Earthdawn Mailing List FAQ, an FTP site, and players' home pages. Specific gaming resources include errata, characters' journals, and items of interest to game masters, including information on weapons, magical items, and disciplines.

Earthdawn Mailing List FAQ
http://www.dpi.qld.gov.au/~ryanc/
edfaq.html

Here's a good place for any player to begin (or continue) learning about the Earthdawn role-playing game. Find answers to the most Frequently Asked Questions, starting with an explanation of what Earthdawn is. Other answers point to an Earthdawn FTP archive and topical Web pages. Find out about rules, errata, the fanzine, available products, and the game's relation to Shadowrun, another FASA game. The site is maintained by Chris Ryan, with contributions from over a half dozen sources.

Earthdawn Journal
http://members.aol.com/swrdknght/
edjinfo.htm

Published four times a year by Sword of Knight Publications, Inc., the Earthdawn Journal is the official magazine for die-hard Earthdawn fans. Visit this page for subscription information and a look at the table of contents from each of the past seven volumes.

Earthdawn Official Home Page
http://www.fasa.com/Earthdawn/
EDMainPage.html

FASA Corporation hosts this official exploration of Earthdawn, the role-playing game set thousands of years ago when magic was a prevalent force and so were the Horrors. Check out the latest game news, review the product list, and look into what's scheduled for release. Also find the FAQs and errata offering the official line on the game. Those interested in submitting material to FASA will find guidelines, and links lead to other FASA pages offering information on their other games.

Strands Earthdawn Page
http://rhic4.physics.wayne.edu:8001/
Strands/Strands.html

Jeff Sheen and his fellow "dudes" offer this superior Earthdawn resource for the benefit of all who enjoy the game. Browse basic gaming materials such as rules clarifications and character sheets, but also find a library of spells, a collection of narratives and stories, and ideas for settings and adventures. Talk of characters, creatures, and magic items is also online; plus, the dudes answer readers' questions. Rounding out the extensive offerings are a collection of reader-submitted works and links to sites of topical interest.

EVERWAY

Everweb
http://www.english.upenn.edu/~rbarrett/
everweb.html

Rob Barret claims his to be the first page devoted to Everway, Rubicon's fantasy role-playing game by Jonathon Tweet, the designer responsible for Ars Magica and Over the Edge. Browse information exploring characters, magic and powers, spheres and realms, quests and campaigns. Links of interest point to the Everway mailing list and a collection of legends and family histories written by players and compiled by Alan Schwartz.

NIGHTBANE

Gargoyle's Roost
http://www.stlawu.edu/x8cg:http/index.html

James Cannon (a.k.a. Gargoyle) hosts this fan page devoted to the Palladium role-playing game Nightbane, where shape-shifters inspire horror, alienation, and paranoia. Read a brief introduction to the game, then browse the supplements James has created to the main game. Also find a few pieces of fiction and, of course, those "obligatory" pointers to sites of related topical interest.

Nightspawn
http://www-personal.engin.umich.edu/
~clsmith/nightspawn/nightspawn.html

Christopher Smith offers fellow Nightbane enthusiasts optional rules to spice up play, ideas for campaigns and adventures, and some new Nightlands denizens. Also find links to new Morphus forms tables, new talents, new magic, and new psionics. Many of the items offered were created by other players, and all are credited. Continuing contributions to the site's offerings are accepted and appreciated.

ThunderStrike-Nightbane
http://online.dct.com/~cyrkithra/
nightbane.html

An official Palladium site created by Kevin G. Rau (Cyr Kithra), this searchable archive holds articles on the Gargoyles of Nightbane, new OCCs for the game, character suggestions for game masters, and general articles of interest to players. Links to topical sites of related interest are also featured.

NURPG

The NuRPG
http://www.dragonfire.net/~Chandar/nurpg/
index.html

NuRPG relies on its players to literally write the interactive story that moves the game along. The setting is the world of Nu, and the battle is the age-old story which pits the forces of Light against the overwhelming forces of Darkness. Stop by this page for the official who, what, when, where, and why. Find a link to the FAQ, the story archives, a map of Nu, a list of characters, and recent submissions.

The NuRPG FAQ
http://www.dragonfire.net/~Chandar/nurpg/
faq.html

Find answers to the most Frequently Asked Questions regarding the Nu world's role-playing game. Start with a simple explanation of what NuRPG is, move to information about how it works, then explore the world of Nu—look over a list of its cities and their inhabitants, and review the "story" so far. Information on joining play and finding topical Internet resources is also included.

OVER THE EDGE

Games Descriptions: Over the Edge
http://www.brown.edu/Students/Fantasy/
gamedescriptions/overedge.html

At its most elemental, Over the Edge is a role-playing game about people doing the darndest things ... to each other, to themselves, to the neighbor's cat. It's a completely surreal environment where the unusual is usual. Still unclear about the game? Check out the vivid description posted to this page by player Caleb Welton. He minces no words in his telling, so people with soft centers in their heads should probably stay away.

AUTHOR'S PICK

woodelf's RPG Index
http://dax.cs.wisc.edu/~woodelf/RPG/
RPG.html

From 2070 to Ysgarth, virtually all the role-playing games currently in play are represented in this index of Web sites. Search the index by game title, genre, or game setting (country) to find a list of Web pages devoted to the game or games which are of interest to you. Other site features include listings for gamemaster sites, organizations, companies, and online stores. Whether new to role-playing or a veteran, this well-designed and well-maintained offering provides a valuable resource.

Over the Edge Home Page
http://www.io.com/~avi/ote.html

François "Fu" Uldry posts this piece of madness based on his experiences with the role-playing game Over the Edge. Enjoy fiction, weird stuff, character profiles, plots and places, and game goodies. Those wishing to find more pages devoted to Over the Edge or its collectible card game, On the Edge, will find pointers to the home pages of other players and sites of topical interest.

Over the Edge: The Psychosurreal Role-Playing Game
http://www.io.com/~presage/ote/ote.html

This official game page will help those interested in Over the Edge find all they need to get started. Browse the product list featuring over a dozen books to aid in role play. Each product is shown and fully described so players know exactly what to expect, both from the products and the game.

PARANOIA

Paranoia: The Computer is Your Friend!
http://www.teleport.com/~matasar/
paranoia.html

Those with the proper security clearance can access Ben Matasar's fan page devoted to West End Game's RPG tribute to writer George Orwell's novel 1984. Among the offerings find alternate rules, an adventure idea, loyalty tests, and names of traitors. Instructions for playing the game online are also featured.

Paranoia RPG: Instructions for Playing Online
http://www.teleport.com/~matasar/
paraonline.html

This page from Ben Matasar's fan site details the rules for playing Paranoia online. In Paranoia, the computer rules; players are its agents. The resulting bureaucratic madness spawns corruption, intrigue, terror, and death. Find a general game background, answers to basic questions, rules and mission rules, plus all the details that make the game fun.

PRIMUS

PRIMUS Home Page
http://www.cris.com/~smactyre/primus.html

Shelley Chrystal Mactyre hosts this unofficial site devoted to Hero Games' RPG based on the Primary Response and Interdiction Military Service, or PRIMUS. Among the designer's notes find an article about PRIMUS that provides a good start on figuring out what the game is about. Those seeking answers to specific questions about the game can "Ask the Golden Avenger." In addition to these resources, find actual U.S. government sites mixed with game materials to spur role-playing and keep things interesting.

ROBOTECH

Robotech
http://www4.ncsu.edu/eos/users/r/
rkswamy/www/robotech.html

Ravi K. Swamy treats players to a fairly complete background on Robotech. The FAQ alone offers a history of the phenomenon from its earliest forms as a television series through its various merchandising incarnation and onto the Internet. A section on the role-playing game and fan fiction points players to a few sites of special interest, but most links lead to general and related information about Robotech. The site is well worth a look to any true Robotech fan.

Robotech:
The Third Invid War Info Page
http://www.mcs.net/~deitrich/TIWinfo.html

Dave Deitrich, Chris Meadows, and friends present a sequel to the Robotech role-playing game as a supplement for additional fun and action. According to the authors, the Third Invid War (TIW) is an attempt to provide a viable conclusion for the "Return of the Invid" storyline. Read a general introduction to TIW, then follow pointers to information about new skills, OCCs, REF Cyclones, and REF Veritechs. Also find new Invid Mecha, NPCs, bases, spacecraft, and equipment. Links lead to other Robotech Web pages.

RIFTS

Avatar Industries Online Catalog
http://www2.hawaii.edu/~doyle/ai2.html

A good resource for finding general information on Palladium games, Edward Paul's site is primarily dedicated to the Rifts RPG, offering a catalog of techno-wizardry related to the game and "created" by players. Find firearms and accessories, gear and armor, cybernetics and bot upgrades, vehicles, and robotics. A character compendium, advanced gaming information, and

an excellent list of links to other notable Rifts-related sites are also included.

The Netbooks of Rifts
http://www.teleport.com/~morpheus/
rifts.html

Morpheus maintains this site offering The Great Net RIFTS OCC & RCC Handbook v1.5, a compilation of player-created OCCs and RCCs found on the Internet. This site also posts details on new critters and equipment and offers character sheets. News, miscellaneous Rifts materials, and links to Rifts sites round out the content-heavy offerings available here.

The Rifts MUD Home Page
http://rifts.tcimet.net/

Stop by this site to find out how to join fellow Rifts fans for online MUD action. Those unfamiliar with the game can link to information on the world of Rifts. A live link will transport those ready for action to the Telnet site where the MUD is played.

ThunderStrike—Rifts
http://online.dct.com/~cyrkithra/
riftscore.html

This searchable mega-site created by Kevin G. Rau (a.k.a. Cyr Kithra) offers Rifts RPG players a bit of it all and then some, beginning with the Rifts Game Master Companion. Find stats, details, and backgrounds for adventures and campaigns, personal equipment, computers, vehicles, and miscellaneous materials. Optional rules, new Occupational Character Classes, and articles detailing places in the Megaverse are also online. Plus sections on powers and spells add even more value to the site. This site is a must for Rifts fan.

RUNEQUEST

RuneQuest
**http://hops.wharton.upenn.edu/~loren/
Links/maloney/rq.html**

An excellent resource for any player browsing RPGs in search of a new home, this page offers an informative overview of RuneQuest and delineates its major difference from other fantasy role-playing games, i.e., Rune-Quest is based on myth and legend as opposed to fantasy fiction. Links point to the RuneQuest Archives (pages hosted by other players that offer a wealth of gaming information), the page author's and other player's campaign home pages, and conversion notes for players who'd like to switch over from AD&D.

Shadowrun
Grifter's Shadow

http://www.geocities.com/TimesSquare/2055/
index.htm

Among the prizes found on this player's site, find a collection of "every" article that could possibly be of interest to runners. Also enjoy player contributions, a character database, and images of all the Shadowrun miniatures.

Shadowrun Archive
**http://www.interware.it/users/paolo/sr2/
index.html**

Paolo "The Collector" Marcucci hosts the collection of Shadowrun files retrieved from all across the Internet. Find information in this searchable database organized under the headings: archetypes, corporations and societies, critters, errata, images, links, magic, miscellany, modules, places, programs, publications, reviews, rules, character sheets, and stories.

Shadowrun Home Page
**http://www.fasa.com/Shadowrun/
SRHOME.html**

FASA Corporation hosts this virtual showroom for its futuristic role-playing fantasy that mixes magic and machinery. Read a general introduction to Shadowrun and explore the products available for sale. Also find information on the Shadowrun fanzine and other licensed products. Those interested in contributing their talents to the game will find submission guidelines to follow.

Welcome to Shadowland
http://www.shadowland.org/

Here's a self-contained runners' world on the Internet. Register (free) to enter and explore the resources that await inside. First check out the online guide for answers to any questions about the place. Then enjoy. Find a character generator, a notice board, and an area for online gaming. Meet fellow runners either in character or out, send and read mail, or drop by the discussion forums.

STAR TREK

Federation Sim Group
**http://users.aol.com/fsghome/
page.index.html**

Sign up and beam aboard one of the ships in the Federation's fleet for a little online role-playing and Starfleet simulation. Find everything needed to get started at this orientation page. Learn more about the group and its fleet of Internet ships, find out how to sim via e-mail, check out the IRC channel, read the FSG Sim Manual, and stop by the FTP archive to download game materials. Links to fun Star Trek sites round out the offerings available.

For other Star Trek simulation games, also see:

The First Defense Fleet Space Corps
http://www.reno.net/fdf/

Holonet Simulations
http://www.geocities.com/TimesSquare/4252/

The Interstellar Alliance of Planets Command
http://www.sci.fi/~teddy/iap.html

Star Trek Interactive Universe Home Page
http://www.autobahn.mb.ca/~rob/STIUhome.html

Welcome to TrekComm
http://www.mgmainnet.com/staff/li/TrekComm.html

United Confederation of Interstellar Planets
http://www.geocities.com/SiliconValley/2104/ucip.htm

United Federation of Starships
http://www.getnet.com/~genesis/david/ufs/

United Interstellar Planets
http://www.indirect.com/www/bcpfrosh/uipirc.htm

STAR WARS

The Star Wars Home Page
http://www.stwing.upenn.edu:8001/starwars/rpg/

Players new to the Star Wars RPG will find loads of useful information at this growing resource hosted by Jason Ruspini. Link to over two dozen sources for modification charts, FAQs, character lists, rules, and guides of every sort. The technical information section offers rebel and stormtrooper training manuals, an explanation of hyperspace travel, and a look at lightsaber technology. Also find a library of adventures, lists of online games (MUDs and MUSHes), and several game reviews.

Star Wars RPG Home Page
http://www.kenobi.com/starwars/

The Web base of the Star Wars RPG Club, this site serves as an introduction to the group (one of the oldest of its kind) and to its approach to playing West End Games' Star Wars role-playing game. Links are provided to each of the site's four main branches of activity.

Star Wars: Central is the group's headquarters, offering general information. Star Wars: Empire and Star Wars: New Republic provide campaign information, and Star Wars: Independent offers information about the fringe elements in the Star Wars galaxy.

The Star Wars RPG Page
http://members.aol.com/fdawson/swrpg/index.html

Frank Dawson hosts this small but expanding gamer's resource. Find links to the Star Wars Home Page, The Star Wars Adventure Database, and the Star Wars RPG mailing list. An onsite chat room also allows players to mingle and exchange ideas.

TAIGA

TAIGA
http://www.helsinki.fi/~vvuorela/

Role-play the life and death excitement of a postmodern, edge of disaster, adult fantasy where governments don't care and players must take to the roads in a game of survival. Read all about the essence and origin of the TAIGA wilderness, check out the game designer's notes, and find out who makes the game available. Corrections and clarifications to the European rules are also featured.

TORG

TORG - Roleplaying the Possibility Wars
http://www.io.com/~nishio/torg/torg.html

Gen-ichi Nishio introduces players to a generic roleplaying system of alien invasion and altered realities. Read an overview of the game TORG, refer to the FAQ for quick answers, and check out the product list for possible purchases. The page is available in English and Japanese and links to the Official TORG page of Omni Gaming Products.

TRAVELLER

Imperium Games Home Page
http://www.imperiumgames.com/

Stop by this page for the official word on Traveller. Check out the latest game news, review the product list, read the most up-to-date postings from the Traveller News Service, peruse the errata, or link to players' sites that are dedicated to the game. Of special note, the Journal of the Travellers' Aid Society offers adventure hooks, scenarios, and background to aid Traveller role-playing.

Traveller
http://www.missouri.edu/~ccjoe/traveller/

Here's a searchable archive of Traveller information maintained by Joseph Heck. Access the Traveller mailing list FAQ, browse a compilation of bits and bytes taken from across the Internet, study rules modifications and related discussions, or comb the library for adventures and information of interest to those who inhabit the Traveler universe. Links point to both official and unofficial game-related pages.

Traveller Chronicle
http://eeyore.lv-hrc.nevada.edu/~indy/traveller.html

Sword of the Knight Publications promotes its magazine dedicated to Traveller and those who enjoy role-playing the science fiction adventure. Published three times a year, the magazine features articles and artwork relevant to keeping the game alive. Find cover shots and content summaries for the 10 issues that have been printed since the magazine's inception in 1993. Links to game-related and topical sites are also featured.

Traveller—Science Fiction Adventure in the Far Future
http://www.usa.net/~goldendj/Traveller/Traveller.html

Dave Golden and about a dozen other Traveller fans offer this collection of game goodies for others interested in the science fiction adventure based on the distant future.

Among the offerings find game news, rules and errata, and artwork. Adventure ideas, campaign backgrounds, and other useful ideas can be found in the resources section. And a collection of links points the way to other Traveller outposts in cyberspace.

WARHAMMER

Morten's Warhammer Page
http://www.ifi.uio.no/~mortenk/WHintro.html

Morten Krog presents a nice offering of resources related to the Warhammer fantasy role-playing game (which is not the same as Warhammer 40,000). Access the Warhammer Archives, check out the mailing list, browse the FAQ, or link to other pages dedicated to the fantasy role-playing game.

Warhammer Fantasy Battle— The University of Altdorf Home Page
http://www.statusiq.co.uk/%7Emike/warhammer.html

Go to school on the Warhammer Fantasy Battle game at this extensive site offering everything from warring strategies to painting tips. Get the latest update on the campaign currently being fought out over the Internet. Stop by the Library for reading material, inspiring art, and referrals to other sites of interest. Find maps in the Map Room and visit the lecture rooms for basic tutoring. Fun and very useful, the site offers something for beginners and veteran campaigners alike.

Warhammer 40,000

**http://www.games-workshop.com/
warhammer40k.html**

Though the company no longer supports the Warhammer FRPG (Hogshead Publishing does now), Games
Workshop does support Warhammer 40,000, the fantasy battle board game. Read the official company promotion on the game, find out how to get started
working with the game's miniatures, and check out the
art gallery for ideas and inspiration.

Warhammer 40,000

http://www.netwrx.net/users/brian/40k.htm

Brian Sinclair proudly presents Warhammer 40K animations prepared by his brother-in-law, plus a variety
of other fan submitted material including place names,
rules, and new characters. Humbly acknowledging his
site as only one of many, Brian also points out dozens
of other Warhammer 40,000 fan pages on the Web.
Better yet, he verifies the links he features to ensure
they're still active!

The Warhammer 40,000 Web Awards

**http://wybbs.wynalda.com/~zathras/
40kawards.html**

Who posts the best Warhammer 40,000 page on the
Web? Visit this page to view a gallery of past award re-
cipients and vote for tomorrow's winner.

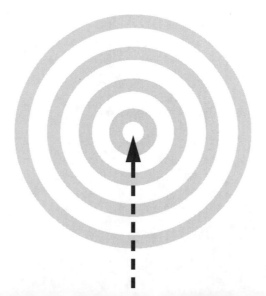

SIMULATION GAMES

A-10 Attack Demo Page
http://www.clark.net/pub/hutchens/a10.html

Download a demo copy of A-10 Attack—Parsoft's Mac flight-sim (2MB). While you're here, view a document teaching how to use the weapons, controls, and information systems of the aircraft (76K). Basically a no-frills page offering the free demo from the makers of Hellcats Over the Pacific.

A-OK! Spacecraft Simulations
http://www1.mhv.net/~InnovateT/

The year is 1962...the place is Cape Canaveral...the eyes of thousands turn skyward as a column of flame soars towards the heavens. "All systems are A-OK!" is heard from "Shorty" Powers, the voice of Mercury Control. Wish you could be there? How about one better...try out "A-OK! The Wings of Mercury"—a simulation of Project Mercury, America's first spacecraft. At this Web site, order the game, view screen shots, read reviews, or download the patch (if you already own it).

A Call to Arms! Home Page—Advanced Tactical Fighter
http://www.dynamite.com.au/~adglenn/atf.htm

This informative page from "down under" pays homage to Advanced Tactical Fighters (ATF), Jane's/Electronic Arts' sequel to U.S. Navy Fighters. Cheats, screen shots, missions, utilities, and related links are provided here. Check out the JPEG of an X-29 getting too close for comfort.

Advanced Gravis Computer Technology Ltd.
http://www.gravis.com/

Tons of graphics and an animated scrolling message bar greet you upon your arrival here to the official site of Gravis. If you have a slow modem connection, you can choose to view text only. Areas of interest are Customer Service, Technical Support, Product Line-Up and Info, Feedback, Software Upgrades, and a What's New area. Colorful, resourceful, and fun—from the world leader in PC joysticks and game pads.

Advanced Tactical Fighters
http://www.ea.com/janes/newatf/

This is the official page for EA/Jane's breakthrough single- or multiplayer combat simulation, Advanced Tactical Fighters (ATF). Download demos, movies, and the ATF patch or pore over screen shots, reviews, aircraft specs, system requirements, and product information. Sleek design (complete with a navigational GIF map) and useful data are offered here on this modern airborne fighter.

Aerodynamics and Flight Simulators (AFS)
http://www.web-span.com/afs/

AFS is an integrated set of tools used to create, edit, and check aerodynamics of aircraft models, and to train in flight navigation. AFS runs on a PC DOS in SVGA (1024x768) mode. It uses a graphical windowing system interface using both the mouse and keyboard. The purpose of this Web site is to supplement the support and tech services for their customers. View over a hundred screen shots, read up on the history and design of the program, report bugs, or download the shareware version and patches.

After Burn
http://www.geocities.com/CapeCanaveral/2955/index.htm

Eric Hansen's Web site is devoted to combat-based flight sims. Additions for games like Advanced Tactical Fighters, U.S. Navy Fighter, and Marine Fighters are featured. Separate sections include Windows 95 games, great fighting aircraft of WWII, and a two-volume "Air Combat in Pictures" area! Check out the "Scramble" shot from ATF. Awesome!

AH-64D Longbow
http://www.ea.com/janes/ah-64d_longbow/index.html

This is the official page to Origin and Jane's Combat Simulation's AH-64D Longbow—an authentic lethal helicopter simulation available on PC CD-ROM. Download the patch, get a complete product description/key features, read the FAQs and system requirements, or search through their links. For a *PC Multimedia and Entertainment* magazine online interview with Andy Hollis (the brainchild of the Longbow and Origin producer of the game), go to http://www.mortimer.com/users/pcme/strike/ah-64d/ahollis.htm

Air Havoc Controller
http://com.primenet.com/rainbow/

Read the game features and system requirements on Air Havoc Controller—the ultra-realistic Air Traffic Control game with 3D-rendered graphics. View screen shots or download up to three video clips to get a taste of the game. Don't fall asleep...there are lives at stake here!

Air Page Index
http://stega.smoky.org/%7Edlevin/airindex.html

For those of you capable of editing and building your own planes in BAO's Flight Shop or for Microsoft's Flight Simulator 5.1, visit the Air Page index to view the specs on literally hundreds of different planes from around the world. This building resource center contains a comprehensive alphabetized list of planes to model your own creations after. For the advanced flight sim gamer. Who knew the Israeli "Lavi" was designed in 1986 to replace the A-4 "Skyhawk" and F-4 "Phantom" II as a strike aircraft?

Air Warrior
http://www.shebop.com/

This Web page, sponsored by the EarthLink Network, introduces air combat fans to Kesmai's Air Warrior (AW) and explains how to get up and flying. A list of

online provider info, convention information, squadrons, forums, scenarios, and gaming links are accessible here. Neatly organized with cool screen shots grace these pages. A worthwhile visit for amateur or professional AW fanatics.

Air Warrior FAQ
http://ddi.digital.net/~rocket/faq/faq.html

Any gamer on the Internet must have heard the words "Air Warrior" at one time, but many of us don't know exactly what the sim game is, or how to get involved. Written by Darren "Rocketman" Beyer, this FAQ covers everything from setup to success. Download the FAQ if you don't have time to read the many pages online. A good beginner site for any budding pilot.

Air Warrior Web Site, The
http://cactus.org/AirWarrior/Main.html

Fan of the online or single-player Air Warrior? These pages, brought to you by Jim Knutson and CACTUS (Capital Area Central Texas UNIX Society) contain useful information on Kesmai's Air Warrior, including convention updates, a renovated FAQ file, screen shots, an AW Cam, a jump to the Air Warrior FTP site, links, hints, tricks, patches, and more.

Andy's Flight Simulator Page
http://www.geocities.com/CapeCanaveral/3922/

This page contains aircraft specifically for use with Microsoft Flight Simulator 5.0 or better, but you will need BAO's Flight Shop to fly these suckers. Choose between Propeller aircraft, Jet Aircraft, Helicopter Menu, Aircraft Panels, Sounds, Links to other Web pages,

Aircraft Of The Month (or vote for one), Scenery Files, and Special Aircraft Requests.

ATF/USNF San Diego Home Page
http://ourworld.compuserve.com/
homepages/cbaltrinic/

Chris's page was created for all Advanced Tactical Fighters (ATF) and U.S. Navy Fighters and Marine Fighters (USNF/MF) buffs. This site is also home to a special squadron of San Diego ATF Pilots. Download the patch, the utility to play the game without the CD, missions, and screen shots.

ATF Psycho Central
http://www.ao.net/~chuck/atf/atfsycho.htm

A sleek page focusing in on Jane's/EA's Advanced Tactical Fighter CD-ROM. Download missions and utilities (including the file to play the game without the CD), read cheats, enroll in online flight school (links to training stations), or peruse through the other related sites on the Net.

Auto Channel, The
http://www.theautochannel.com/sports/

Everything and anything to do with motorsports: Drag Racing, Trucks, Sprint Cars and Midgets, Touring, Stock Cars, Rally and Off Road, Open Wheel, Enduro, Motorcycles, Pennzoil Racing, and more. Brought to you by The Auto Channel™ (TACH), motorsports from around the world are given equal attention (Africa, Austral-Asia, Europe, and North/South America). Check first with their TACH index, which has its own handy search engine for their large site.

Back to Baghdad™: Military Simulations Inc.
http://www.military-sim.com/b2b.htm

See why Back To Baghdad—The Ultimate Desert Storm Simulation (B2B) is heralded as the most accurate PC representation of the F-16C Block 50 aircraft ever experienced. There is much to do here: scan

through product reviews; view screen shots; request for tech support; or read up on Desert Storm, Iraq, and Kuwait information.

The Bingo Zone
http://www.bingozone.com/

The Web's first real-time multiuser simulation Bingo game is FREE to play, but if you win they send you real $$ within five business days! The Bingo Zone can afford to pay out to winners due to their advertising and sponsoring (similar to how game shows operate). It plays like traditional Bingo by showing balls every 15 seconds; you use your mouse to click off your three cards. Leave the smoky bingo halls behind and try your luck every half hour against people all over the world at this awesome Web site.

Blue Knight's Web Page
http://stout.entertain.com/crawford/

You'd swear Steve "BK" Crawford works for ICI (Interactive Creations Inc.)—makers of WWII multiplayer combat flight sims WarBirds and Confirmed Kill. BK's home page takes you to his semi-authorized WarBirds Rumor Page (all the inside scoop and coolest downloads), his personal WarBirds and Confirmed Kill pages (screen shots and ICI news), and his WarBirds Air Races section (rules and tips for the races). WarBirds is a free online war flight sim but it'll cost you around $2.00 an hour (and $10.00 a month) to fly against others. For more info visit the ICI homepage (http://www.cris.com/~gunjam/).

Bunker, The
http://www.cris.com/~thunk/

Tom "KC" Basham has been chosen by Happy Puppy Games to head their "Remove Before Flight" forum—a flight simulation center including message/posting boards, chat rooms, file libraries, and a news and previews area. This page contains mainly screen shots (from Tom's personal collection) and links to other sim-minded pages.

CH Products Home Page
http://www.chproducts.com/CH/ chhome2.html

A beautiful site from the makers of many computer game peripherals. Hosted by GTE Entertainment, sections here include: CH background, Gaming Gear, Media Madness, What's New?, Downloadables (drivers, FAQs, installation disks, updates), and Got Something To Say? (comments, questions, suggestions). CH Products, established in 1977, offers a full line of PC, Macintosh, and 3DO systems joysticks, throttles, F-16 sticks, rudder pedals, flight yokes, gamecards, and trackballs.

Challenger Inn, The
http://www.crl.com/~stupid/chin.html

Eric Penn's site is based on Jaeger Software and Phillips Media's Fighter Duel (WWII dogfight simulator). This is a member-only (but free) challenge board for multiplayer play. The *ladder* is an ongoing competition which matches players of similar skill levels against one another. Register

AUTHOR'S PICK

Clubopolis
http://www.eskimo.com/~pcoston/co/

Patrick Coston should receive a key to the city for his Web site based on Maxis's popular game Sim City 2000. There are over 200 screens making up Clubopolis, containing original and other fan-related and official material for the breakthrough land-based sim. Designed to take advantage of Internet Explorer 3+ (for the cool music alone—by Mark Burton of Microsoft's Blue Ribbon Music Technology Department), Clubopolis has other handy options and sections: download and view the site offline, read cheats and strategy tips, try out custom-built cities (1000+), links, and much more. Also check out the related clubs such as Club Max (http://www.eskimo.com/ ~pcoston/co/cm_main.htm), run by Bridget Samuels, and Club Illusion, maintained by Jason Overland (http://www.eskimo.com/~pcoston/co/ci_main.htm). An excellent tribute site creatively arranged and chock-full of rich inventive content.

your Pilot name and read up on the history of the game and Challenge Ladder beginnings.

Classic Airliners
http://members.aol.com/TGFltsim/ index.html

Tom Gibson's award-winning page offers additions to BAO's Flight Shop software and Microsoft's Flight Simulator. Most of the custom-built planes are of the classic airliners such as the DC-3 (and other early monoplanes) up until the final glory days of the propliners (before the mid 70s). An exhaustive list of planes, scenery, sound files, and links are also given for your amusement.

Comanche, by NovaLogic
http://www.novalogic.com/comanche.html

This is the official page to NovaLogic's RAH-66 Comanche simulation. The world's most popular attack helicopter can be flown on a PC or Mac with fluid, photo-realistic graphics (using patented Voxel Space technology), and multi-layered digital sound. Read system requirements, and critic's previews, or enlarge the screen shots for a closer look.

Comox Valley Flight Sim Stopover
http://wings.ark.com/

The Comox Valley is located on the east side of Vancouver Island on the west coast of Canada. Round Robin king Al Pelletier (retired from the RCAF and the CAF after 25 years of service) has designed this award-winning page, containing many custom-built add-ons and scenery additions. New sim flights are added every three weeks. However, you must own either Microsoft's Flight Simulator 5+ or BAO's Flight Simulator Flight Shop to use these. News, Files, Links, an IRC, and Resources are also only a click away. Al isn't kidding when he says, "Land here for the latest and greatest PC flight simulation freeware."

Cyber Flight Deck
http://www.geocities.com/CapeCanaveral/1998/

A comprehensive page devoted to Microsoft's Flight Simulator (FS) 4, 5 and 5.1. Read up on Sim news and current happenings, view the "history of aviation" guide (1800 to present), or link to the two dozen or so FS-related resources. Most importantly, download from over 400 plane designs to use with FS and BAO's Flight Shop!

Cyber Sky Flight Sim Page
http://www2.linknet.net/tomcat/page3.html

Looking for a change of (s)pace? Troy Meyer's page salutes Microsoft's Flight Simulator 5 and BAO Flight Simulator Flight Shop. Download any of the free 24 planes in the Cyber Sky Aircraft Library or take the

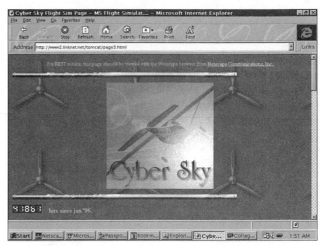

Cyber Sky FS tutorial by Chris Evans (the original maintainer of the Cyber Sky page). For those interested, join the e-mail newsletter to have all the latest happenings in the FS world come to you for a change.

Daniel's Flight Simulator Page
http://members.aol.com/dshay13/home/page1.htm

An English or French Web site with downloadable scenery and aircraft packs to use with Microsoft Flight Simulator 5+. A click on the "complete list" will take you to a huge FTP site with no descriptions, so you'll have to view what you're downloading first. Daniel is looking for Japanese and German speaking people who can volunteer their time translating his page into other languages.

Danny's Advanced Tactical Fighter Page
http://www.biddeford.com/~malkuth/

This site covers Jane's Combat Sim Advanced Tactical Fighter (ATF). Computer pilots (or those interested in becoming one) have quite a bit to sift through: mission files and outlines, screen shots, utilities, FAQs, and strategies on ATF and the expansion disk NATO Fighters. Related links, too.

Den norske Need For Speed Homepage'en
http://www.krs.hia.no/~mbhalvor/n4s/n4s.html

A Norwegian fan-related home page for Electronic Arts and Road and Track's racing sim The Need for Speed. Michael Halvorsen has designed a nicely arranged page using Java animation, large colorful buttons, and an interesting text layout with hot-key words. Download the demo, cheats, FAQs, tips and tricks, an editor, screen shots, and more.

Depot—The Platform
http://www.rtis.com/nat/user/18xx/default.htm

This Web site is devoted to the 18XX train game systems. The Depot is a non-profit reference for the titles of the 18XX board and computer game system and their variants. Descriptions of each of the 35 or so train sim games are outlined, but you can also read the FAQs for 18XX titles, game-specific information (city, company lists, maps, etc.), play-by-email game information, strategies, and tile and train information.

DoKtor GonZo Warbirds HatePage
http://www.cris.com/~Msmiller/WB/

A tribute to the online multiplayer WWII combat flight sim from ICI. Download scenarios, read the WarBirds FAQ, check what's happening at the Event

Information Center, get cool add-ons from a quick link to ICI's FTP site, and see why 1987's "4Q" is the longest surviving, most-hated, operational squadron for WarBirds and Air Warrior. DoK GonZo also has his "DiKta GonZo"—DoK's top 10 rules for living (and killing) in WarBirds and the WarBirds Quick Reference Card v1.01. Peruse related links or check out DoKtor GonZo's Air Warrior HatePage (http://www.cris.com/~Msmiller/AW/index.shtml).

Duke's Aircraft Hatchery
http://www.intr.net/theduke/

Essentially an accumulation of Flight Simulator (FS) 5 and FS Flight Shop aircraft by Robert Randazzo plus others collected from around the Net. Download from the selection of planes (and some scenery) and fly these babies on your own computer.

EF2000 1st EuroFighter Air Wing
http://www.ef2000.com/

The official page to EF2000 operations welcomes you to the first EuroFighter Air Wing (1 EAW). Get help with your game (training, FAQs, patches, info, and more) and you'll also find that the pilots of the 1 EAW are generally quick to offer advice and chat about one of the greatest sims around. If you don't own EF2000, take a tour through the base and see what you're missing. You'll find both product descriptions and purchase information. Sections include "Briefing Room," "Ground School," "Officer's Club," Maintenance Hangar," and the "Pilot's Forum."

Electronic Arts: The Need For Speed
http://www.ea.com/eastudios/nfs/nfs.html

The official page to Road and Track Presents The Need For Speed (NFS). This site is primarily screen shots and information about the game for each platform: Sony PlayStation, PC CD-ROM, Sega Saturn, 3D0, and Windows 95 versions. Regardless of the system, you get your choice to test drive eight purebred exotic cars in NFS, including the Lamborghini Diablo VT, Ferrari 512 TR, Acura NSX, Mazda RX-7, Dodge Viper RT/10, and the Toyota Supra Turbo.

AUTHOR'S PICK

E-Flight

http://e-flight.com/e-flight/

A modern-looking crisp Web site with scrolling animations and pilot command sounds in the background (Internet Explorer needed). You won't get jet lag here—get involved in the interactive discussion forums in the Pilot's Lounge (whether you are with CompuServe, AOL, MSN, or straight from the Net), test your wings with add-on packs for Microsoft Flight Simulator 5+, and soar through the various features on various commercial planes, military machines, and cool jets. E-Flight has a distinct magazine feel to it and is loaded with current news and neat utilities to download. Get your wings!

ELITE
http://www.flyelite.com/

ELITE stands for **EL**ectronic **I**FR **T**raining **E**nvironment and is the world's premiere, and most versatile, IFR flight and proficiency training program across all computer platforms. Developed by Initiative Computing in Switzerland, the ELITE Web page contains a free demo (Mac, DOS, Windows 95, or Power Mac), news, reviews of the products, and order options. Used in

training by real pilots, this highly accurate aerodynamic model also contains authentic cockpit instrumentation that makes flying at home a rewarding experience. Any budding cloud-buster should check out ELITE and read up on its innovative simulation technology.

Empire Builder
http://ntia.its.bldrdoc.gov/~bing/eb-rails.html

A game description and strategies are offered here for the train game Empire Builder—based on the layout of the continental U.S. and the lower third of Canada. To win, you must connect five of the six major cities: New York City, Chicago, Atlanta, Kansas City, Seattle, and Los Angeles. Read stories from Bill Ingram's own experiences in "Tales from the Rails."

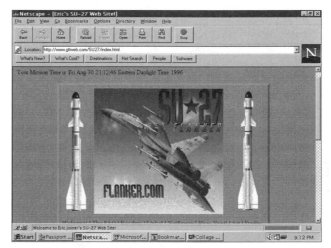

Eric's SU 27 Flanker Homepage
http://www.gttweb.com/SU27/index.html

Eric Joiner Jr.'s two other notorius flight sim pages (Virtual Fighter Command & Tornado Command and Staff College) have made a name for Eric as a discerning flight sim enthusiast. He saw something unique with SSI's/Mindscape's Russian SU-27 simulator, and this page is a thorough look at this Eastern bird. Read the FAQ, join the Net Forum, sift through related links, download homemade SU-27 Windows wallpaper, view cool art pix, and read heroic "stories from the battlefield."

F/18 Hornet
http://www.nwlink.com:88/~rhicks/erik/hornet/

A site by fan Erik Hicks, honoring the "coolest game for the Mac"—the F/18 Hornet (versions 2 or 3 and everything in-between). View screen shots, download the demo, or get info on playing it on the Net.

FANG's ATF Resource Page
http://home.earthlink.net/~jeg/

Fans of Jane's Advanced Tactical Fighter will find cool stuff at this site. Sections include the War Room (sample missions by contributing ATF pilots), FANG's Combat tactics (strategy tips), Q & A (posting board of FAQs…and answers), Modem Combat (info on setting up for multiplayer play), and links to other ATF and flight simulation pages.

FAQ! A-10 Attack!
http://www.seittipaja.fi/A10FAQ/

A thorough Frequently Asked Questions page for the Mac flight sim. Read up on the high-score competition or download/view the text, HTML, or graphics-plus frames FAQs to answer all your A-10 queries. If you have Netscape 2+ or Internet Explorer 3+, check out the frame-using version.

Fast Lane, The
http://www.nmc.edu/~browng/nfspeed.htm

The Fast Lane is an unofficial Need For Speed (NFS) page containing downloadable tracks, hacks, and other modifications and utilities. Join the e-mail mailing list to keep up-to-date on NFS track info and search through the list of related links. Test-drive the Lamborghini Diablo VT, Chevrolet Corvette ZR-1, Porsche 911 Carrera, Ferrari 512TR, and others.

Ferret's FST Home Page
http://mineral.uafsme.alaska.edu/ferret/fst/fst.html

Forest Pearson's Flight Sim Toolkit page contains FAQs, pictures, hints, shapes, tutorials, and links. Newsgroups and FTP-related sites are also provided for the FST activist. Created by Domark software, FST allows the gamer to customize, and exchange, his or her own flight simulator within the Windows environment. Each can create landscapes, 3D objects, and flight models, and attach them together with simulated weapons, cockpit graphics, and sound effects.

Fid and Son's Virtual Airport, The
http://www.inforamp.net/%7Edfidler/tindex.htm

An attractive page with luscious up-to-date flight sim filling. Visit the Aircraft Ramp and take a tour of the Museum Hangar, Commercial Hangar, the General Aviation Hangar, or Military Hangar (ever see an Aermacchi MB-339 up close?). Choose from over a dozen airplane panels, a worldwide scenery locator (namely Canada, U.S., UK and Ireland, Europe) and a Michael Jordan handful of other utilities. Also register yourself in the Dual Player Listing for some head-to-head action in your area.

Fighter Duel FAQ
http://www.charm.net/~kmarsh/fighter.html

This unofficial FAQ is maintained by Ken Marsh and provides answers to many topics surrounding Fighter Duel gameplay (single-player and head-to-head dogfight play). This site contains almost 15 pages of info, news, support, and related links on this flight combat simulation published by Phillips Media.

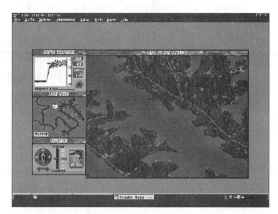

Fisherman's Review of Sierra's Trophy Bass
http://www.vvm.com/~fishman/trophy.htm

Hey—wouldn't you rather read a review of this fishing simulation from a *real* fisherman? Well, I dug one up for you so read the (subjective) product description, MANY screen shots, or preview Trophy Bass 2 hotlinked to http://www.cdmag.com/sports_vault/trophy_bass_2_preview/page1.html. Trophy Bass is available for the PC or Mac on CD-ROM.

Flight Sim Central
http://www.fscentral.com/

Not just an online store "strapping you into the cockpit of desktop aviation," but a group of gaming enthusiasts keeping you abreast of all the latest computer flight sim happenings. Order CD-ROMs, upgrades, hardware and joysticks, scenery, and strategy guides for door-to-door delivery service. Also check out Flight Sim Central's comprehensive link collection.

Flight Sim FAQ
http://www.lib.ox.ac.uk/internet/news/faq/archive/aviation.flight-simulators.html

An exhaustive 20+ page FAQ designed to prepare the amateur flight and space sim gamer with a comprehensive guide of terminology, products, and FTP/Web site

 AUTHOR'S PICK

Flight Sim 5.x and ATP Scenery Hall of Fame

http://www.vivanet.com/~gregor/index.html

The FS5 and ATP (Airline Transport Pilot) archive is an excellent up-to-date repository of scenery files and other utilities available on the Net. The Hall of Fame section recognizes the best scenery add-on designers such as Juan Cabeza, Alfred Grech, and William Austin—all their most respected contributions are easily available for download. Grab yourself over a dozen free flight sim screen savers, see "A Star is Born," view the newest scenery packs by month or alphabetical list (warning: there's quite a bit), or flip through cool links. A soaring Web page!

info. Read online or download the FAQ to read at leisure. Although often technical at times, this site is a good starting point for any blooming aviator. Useful links are included.

Flight Sim Library
http://cactus.org/~knutson/FlightSimLibrary.html

This is *cactus.org*'s flight sim library maintained by Jim "Red Beard" Knudson. Do a search through the vast catalogues of files available for Microsoft Flight Simulator, Falcon, Air Warrior, Aces of the Pacific, Strike Commander, and Tornado. This no-frills FTP site has some cool offerings but some files may be a bit dated.

FlightSim.com

http://www.flightsim.com/

FlightSim.com is a cutting-edge flight and aviation simulation Web site for the keen and ambitious gamer. Although it is free, registration is a must before entering and accessing the thousands of files obtainable: tips and tricks, forums, product reviews, photo galleries, and more. This is the type of site to bookmark—and visit when you've got, say, a few days to spare. Graphically frugal but packed with *mucho* information. Note your emergency exits and blast off!

Fight Sim Page

http://www2.dk-online.dk/users/michael_buus_nielsen/fltsim/flight.htm

Michael Buus Nielsen, a 15-year-old from Denmark, created this flight sim page offering downloadable scenery, planes, and panels. View screen shots of Michael's own plane creations or try them out for size with your own Microsoft Flight Simulator 5+.

Flight Sim Stuff

http://www.cyberhighway.net/~michie/flight.htm

Goose's Flight Sim site is really three pages in one: EA/Jane's Advanced Tactical Fighter, Microsoft Flight Simulator 5.1 CD, and U.S. Navy Fighters/Marine Fighters. Each showcases the games' missions and screen shots, but other downloads are available. After checking out this site and grabbing some files, check out the long list of Web links for further surfing.

Flight Sim Toolkit (FST)

http://www.etek.chalmers.se/~e3berlin/fst.html

FST is a program from Domark software (Total Mayhem and Big Red Racing) to develop flight simulators. If you don't have FST, you'll have no use for the shapes provided. But the completed sims are runnable by everybody. You can also join the FST mailing list, which is an interactive forum concerning the FST happenings. A lot of useful news lies in these pages for the inexperienced flight sim gamer or developer.

Flight Simulator Aircraft and Scenery

http://www.eskimo.com/~tyheyn/fltsim5/main.htm

A very popular and resourceful site to download additions for your Microsoft Flight Simulator 5.0 or 5.1. Lots of scenery to choose from (categorized by country), and many old and new planes and panels. Note: The Hawaii scenery pack is worth a look!

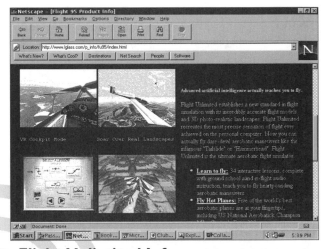

Flight Unlimited Info

http://www.lglass.com/p_info/findex.html

This is Looking Glass's official news source for their DOS, Windows 95, and Mac Flight Unlimited releases. Read the Tech support index to see what you need help on or download patches, demos, or updates (such as Direct X) immediately. Other product info and playing tips are given for all Looking Glass titles.

Flying High Internet Page, The
**http://www.mcs.com/~teleman/
flyhibbs.html**

Chicago, Illinois houses one of the premiere flight sim
pages on the Web. Complete with a scrolling animation newswire and a midi version of "Danger Zone"!
This links-happy site will guide you all around this great
blue globe of ours to all the coolest flight sim and avi-
ation-related Web sites, FTP pages, and newsgroups.
Check out the new lengthy Navigation section.

Flying Squirrel Home Page, The
**http://www.cris.com/~lgregory/fs/
fsmain.html**

Who are these guys? They are the 94th Composite
Group, FSFORUM Air Force—otherwise known as the
Flying Squirrels, or <FS> Air Warrior squadron.
Formed back in the Sierra Online Red Baron days of the
early 90s, this group of devilish pilots made their transition over to Air Warrior (AW) in late 1993 and are
one of the biggest AW squadrons to date. For information on the Squirrels visit this page for *mucho* info headed by Group Commander Lewis "Moose" Gregory.

Forum de Simulacoes Aereas (FSA)
**http://ourworld.compuserve.com/
homepages/fsa/homepage.htm**

Get your wings at this English and Portuguese Brazilian
Web site. Many sections in the FSA include a "Virtual
Pilot Journal" and a terrific "Photo Lab, " but you may
be preoccupied in downloading all the cool scenery
packs and other custom-made accessory tools. An FTP
and BBS area and a Portuguese mailing list are also provided. A scrolling bar travels across the bottom of your
page with up-to-date happenings and news on soon-to-
be-released add-on packs for Microsoft Flight Simulator 5. To Adriano Carvalho, the founder and coordinator of the FSA—a sim page well done!

AUTHOR'S PICK

Flying Thrill Seekers

**http://ourworld.compuserve.com/
homepages/flyby_flight_sim_school/**

The Flying Thrill Seekers (FTS) are self-declared flight
sim enthusiasts that create and provide scenery add-
ons for BAO Flight Shop and Microsoft Flight Simulator 5.x. The coolest part of this page is if your browser supports VRML, you can download these files from
the Virtual Art Gallery Of Aircraft (just add **/air-
gal.wrl** to the end of the URL above). Check out
Dennis Simanaitis's Wright Brothers Famous Flyer or
Chris Evan's Embraer EMB-312 Tucano (Flight Shop
and Flight Simulator required). Monthly giveaways of
aviation goodies are awarded in a draw-like fashion
and sim links are also displayed in a creative table
fashion.

Fox River Air Service Homepage
http://ddi.digital.net/~greyfox/greyfox.htm

This is a cool site to get lots of Flight Simulator 5.1
planes and scenery. There are various zipped libraries
to download and many screen shots of what you can
expect are laid out. Try out the Fox River freeware
and make some comments and suggestions.

FS Aero Home Page
http://www.flash.net/~rakeen/fsaero.htm

FS Aero Services makes aircraft, scenery, and panels for Microsoft Flight Simulator v5+. Tons of free goodies are available here including an Aircraft Combo Pack (2 C-421As, 1 C-421C, 2 Arrows, 1 Tomahawk.), a custom paint shop, and many other FS Aero aircraft and scenery libraries.

FS Search Engine
http://www.hlcs.com/fs_search/

Brought to you by the folks of the WAE club (see below), this falls into the "why didn't *I* think of that" category—a search engine designed to find *only* flight sim information on the Web. Choose to locate scenery, panel, situation, utilities, or sim product keywords. Each match displays your query's category, description, URL, and file size. An excellent idea (and it works, too!).

FS5 Scenery Tool:
Best Freeware Scenery
http://www.vianet.net.au/~kraybill/fltsim5/top20.htm

This Australian group has surveyed and collected the top 20 best free scenery add-ons for Microsoft's Flight Simulator 5.x. Here is the downloadable list of winners (88 entries were received from over 17 countries). Winners of the first, second, and third rank, respectively, were: Balearic Islands, by Juan Cabeza; Scotland, by Robert Wittick, Stuart White, and Alfred Grech; and New South Wales, by Tom Monnone (Ozpack). Besides the Top 20, twelve other finalists deserved honorable mention and their work is also obtainable via linked FTP and Web connection.

FS5 Simulator Scenery Page
http://www.pix.za/0/business/a.bruton/scenery.html

Land your browser on South Africa's Microsoft Flight Simulator 5.0 scenery home page. Many beautiful South African scenery add-ons are available for free, courtesy of André F. Bruton's patriotic flight sim site.

Other sections include books and magazines to help you create your own worlds for Flight Simulator 5 and an extensive list of other flight sim scenery add-on packs including Canada, Scotland, Japan, Australia, Hong Kong, Antarctica, Hungary, and Hawaii.

FS Fan BBS: Home of the Flight Sims
http://www.xs4all.nl/~fsfanbbs/

This site from the Netherlands lists flight sim BBSs, Web pages, FTP sites, and newsgroups around the globe. The massive BBS list can be downloaded or viewed online and contains country and city, BBS name and number, and maximum connection bps speed. Web pages, FTPs, and newsgroup links are separated and arranged alphabetically for easy navigation. You may also download free plane designs and instrumentation panels.

FSASM Home Page
http://www.halycon.com/zof/fsasm.html

FSASM is a powerful scenery program for use with Microsoft Flight Simulator 5.1. FSASM includes a large library of configurable objects you can use to design sim scenery and is suitable for novice or expert designers. Examples are shown of what you can create using FSASM—or if you're feeling ambitious, download FSASM and other add-on software.

FSNews
http://members.aol.com/fsnews/index.html

Flight Sim News keeps us Web pilots up-to-date with virtual aviation happenings. Headline article clips, screen shots, and discussion forums are accessed here and maintained by FSNews Editor and President, David Murr. Freeware scenery add-ons and other utility software packages are promised for the latter part of 1996. Informative page for the die-hard flight sim gamer.

FSWeb

http://www.surf-ici.com/fishman/fs51/
default.htm

There is an abundance of flight sim pages on the Web but CyberFish brings you a comprehensive on-line *how-to* and starting point for version 5+ of Microsoft Flight Simulator. Popular sections include a flight chart graphics page (50 or so U.S. scenery shots), flight shop, scenery and map additions, and an FTP and Web links area.

Full Throttle

http://www.cobb.com/fth/index.htm

Part of the Ziff-Davis family, The Cobb Group publishes this bi-monthly journal for flight sim enthusiasts. Heavily weighed toward Microsoft's Flight Simulator 5, this electronic information source brings all virtual pilots a jam-packed Web site full of free tips and tricks (like how to configure FS5 to work under Windows 95), screen shots, news, a message arena, and useful links. Subscribe to the Full Throttle print edition online or get a free issue to peruse through before committing.

GateWay Airlines

http://members.aol.com/dwite79/
gwamain.htm

A "virtual" airline company that stresses the *fun* side of flight simulation. Many games and flight sim programs can be a lot of work to get going, but the folks at GateWay encourage you to become a member of their leisurely airline. Download aircraft, scenery, and the manual to get started and maybe partake in their national or international flights.

GeoWright Group Home Page

http://www.agt.net/public/bigbill/home.htm

A place to get high quality Canadian scenery for Microsoft's Flight Simulator 5.1. Canada is one of the most beautiful, and diverse, countries in the world and here you can sample scenery from many provinces including Alberta and British Columbia. Panels, aircraft, and utilities are also provided along with a monthly feature and links.

Gone Fishin'

http://www.cdaccess.com/html/pc/
gonefish.htm

Gone Fishin' is a terrific fresh water simulation from a Canadian company called Amtex. This site is part of the online store CD-ROM Access and gives product description, published reviews, and a screen shot for most of their products. For only $29.00, pick up this awesome game (yes, only $29.00—there's *no catch*!).

Greg's Home Page—PC Based Driving Games

http://ourworld.compuserve.com:80/
homepages/gregh/

Racing Sims are Greg Hilton's forte, highlighting his faves Screamer, Destruction Derby 1 and 2, The Need for Speed, and more. Lots to read and download here—news, previews, cars, tracks, screen shots, demos, real-time animation/movie clips, best lap times, and hints n' tips.

GSC's Web Site

http://www.graphsim.com/

This is the official home page to the F/18 Hornet creators Graphic Simulations Corporation (GSC) out of Dallas, Texas. Read up on the past, present, and future products including F/A-18 Hornet 2.0, Tour of Duty: Korean Crisis, Hellcats Over the Pacific, Missions at Leyte Gulf, and the F/A-18 Hornet 3.0 for Mac and PC.

Hanger, The

http://www.serve.com/PuckHead/flt-sim/
airplanes/

As this Web site name says, it is a just virtual airplane hanger listing 25 or so planes to download for use with Microsoft Flight Simulator 5.x and BAO's Flight Shop. A no-frills site, but a promise from the Web designer to add over 300 new aircrafts in the near future. The Hanger is also part of the larger Jake and Pat's Flight Sim Web page (http://www.serve.com/jake-pat/).

Hatchlings
http://www.access.digex.net/~holland/

Hatchlings is designed to help you get the most out of ICI's WWII sim WarBirds—a multiplayer flight sim that can be played over the Internet. There are many things to do here, but I'd start off by grabbing all the necessary files first: the full game (for Windows 95, Mac, or DOS), plane and scenario files, joystick support, and other extras. Once that is done, read up on how to configure the game for online flight and then join the six Flight School classes. WarBirds is free but online head-to-head combat will run you around $2.00 an hour and a monthly fee of $10.00. Also surf the other many WarBirds links or visit the ICI home page (http://www.icigames.com/).

Hind and Apache
http://www.imagicgames.com/sims.html

This is Interactive Magic's site for Hind and Apache—two very popular combat helicopter sims. Access Hind and Apache demos, screen shots, system requirements, contests, FAQs, a slide show, reviews, development team profiles, updates, patches, give-aways, ordering information, and thorough product descriptions. The various pictures on these pages would make cool wallpaper as well.

Hornet Tactical Briefing
http://www.brunswickmicro.nb.ca/~dmg/ Hornet/hornet.html

This is the F/A Hornet Tactical Briefing illustrating tactics, films, and stories on how to be victorious in missions. The sections include: Mission Replay Database, Tactical Discussions (individual missions), Air to Air Combat, Mud Moving, Missiles and Missile Avoidance (read this part for help in F/A-18 Hornet flying), Fancy Flying, and Stories. Written and maintained by Michael Wehner and Richard Grant, this site is also mirrored in the U.K. (http://users.ox.ac.uk/~lady0266/hornet/ hornet.html).

Indiana University of Pennsylvania FTP Site
http://www.iup.edu/flight-sim/files/uploads/

An enormous list of over 60 pages, 1,000+ files of Microsoft's Flight Simulator add-ons, and accessory packs. Caution—you will have to know what you are looking for here (the index section is just as confusing as the straight list of files!). Touch down here if you are experienced in editing or creating your own planes and/or scenery for FS5, because there are lots of useful, custom-built files here. You may also upload your own designs to this large collection for others to enjoy.

Jake and Pat's Flight Sim Page
http://www.serve.com/jake-pat/

Cool features are at this page: view, vote, and download the plane of the week, contribute to the message board or join the chat area, subscribe to the newsletter, and more. Jake and Pat's colorful page leads you from section to section with funky icons, animation, and flight sim screen shots. Extensive links section as well.

Jerry's Aviation Page
http://www.tr2.com/jerry/aviation/ aviation.html

Jerry Kaidor's Flying Lesson Journals (along with Andrew Sarangan's) provide the meat of this site. Upon my visit, Jerry had 62 lessons posted! Learn how to pilot a craft or listen to official lessons in .AU format. Lesson postings can also be read in the newsgroup rec.aviation.student, and relevant links are also provided.

Jerry Moore's Sim Stuff Classic Corner
http://www.vcnet.com/jmoore/classic.htm

This Web site provides SimCity Classic cheats, building tips, sample cities (20 or so), editors, and other utilities. Find out how to "hex edit" your saved *.CTY file to get over $2 billion in funds, and more. Cool background you can save and use for Windows wallpaper.

Joe's SimCity 2000 Gallery
www.sartelle.org/Sim/

This award-winning Web page pays homage to Maxis's strategic game on designing, developing, and managing your very own mega-city. If you have the musical Crescendo plug-in for your browser you will hear the (appropriate) midi rendition of the song "Everybody Wants to Rule the World" by Tears For Fears! At Joe's Site visit the Urban Renewal Kit section to customize your Mac or PC game with new buildings. You may also trade your own levels and saved cities or download others by SimCity "experts" for your use with your registered SimCity 2000 game. A one-stop site for any SimCity fan.

Jon Booker's Need for Speed Page
http://www.ex.ac.uk/~jdbooker/nfs/

U.K. track-burner Jon gives his best Need For Speed (NFS) times (and replays if you don't believe him!), patches, editors, and NFS unofficial file specs. Using the Lamborgini Diablo, he has licked the Rusty Springs track (4 laps) in under 2 minutes and 38 seconds. Car racing sim links are also supplied.

Jorg's Flight-Sim Homepage
http://zeus.uni-duisburg.de/~stenger/FlightSim/

Although it hasn't been updated in a while (well, since my last visit, anyway), there is still some good information on Top Gun, US Navy Fighters, Tornado, and the Flight Sim toolkit. The student of mechanical engineering could have used some graphics or colors to brighten up his page, but some files are of use, including Dave Chaloux's Basic Flight Maneuver Lessons 1–5.

Jorg's U.S. Navy Fighters Home Page
http://zeus.uni-duisburg.de/~stenger/USNF/

Yes, it's the same Jorg as above. This site, however, is based on EA's U.S. Navy Fighters (USNF), and you can download the patch or FAQ, view the screen grabs, or read the Air Combat Story by Clark "Indiana" Janes. A plain site that needs updating, but some useful stuff here for the USNF game.

Mac Flight Simulators
http://www.xmission.com:80/~morrison/MFS/

Tom Morrison's frames-enhanced page is dedicated to Macintosh Flight Sims, which consists mainly of links (with descriptions) to related sites, game companies, or peripheral products. A neat gossip section lets you choose if you want the last 7 or 30 days' worth of rumors.

Martin Mathis' Need For Speed Page
http://www.primenet.com/~mmathis/need4spd.htm

Martin's site provides his best Need For Speed (NFS) times and fastest laps/speeds to download and view via "replay." Other sections include Head-To-Head, Time Trial, Single Race, Cheat Codes, and other NFS sites. Plain site but cool tables with stats.

Microsoft Flight Simulator
http://www.microsoft.com/games/FSIM/

This Web page is a monthly electronic publication courtesy of Microsoft and their Flight Simulator catalogue. Highlights include informative columns (read the past issues, too), Site-ings (cool Web links with descriptions), and their Tip and Tricks feature. Product Info and news is also available from the main menu.

Nice design and very useful to help you get off the ground with this revolutionary flight sim package.

Microsoft Space Simulator
http://microsoft.com/games/SSIM/

Microsoft's sleek 'zine, based on their Space Simulator product, is published monthly. Features, tip n' tricks, news, information, and links are all provided. Dive into the back issues and read the excellent "Apollo Dreaming" article written by Grant Fjermedal. As with the similar Microsoft Flight Sim electronic publication, this is a handy supplement to a respected space simulation.

MicroWINGS
http://www.microwings.com/

The International Association For Aerospace Simulations, MicroWINGs, is one of the most popular flight sim sites on the Web. There is a lot to do here: download files, read up on industry news, view numerous screen shots, chat live with other flight sim enthusiasts via their IRC channel (#microwings), or purchase sim goodies from the MicroWINGS store. Membership has its privileges, including paper magazines, give-aways, special Web and BBS access, a free software package to use with Microsoft's Flight Simulator 5, and more ($50.00 U.S.).

Mike Marando's Flight-Sim Uploads Page
http://www.naples.net/~nfn00200/iup.html

Once you feel you've mastered Microsoft's Flight Simulator 5, glide on over to Mike's page containing hundreds of extra add-ons to guarantee even more late nights and red, dry eyes. Basically a huge alphabetical list of freeware files to download, each with a brief description and file size. Fill your hard drive with scenery and plane add-ons, FAQs, screen-shots, and other miscellaneous files uploaded by FS5 fans from around the world. If you're reading this in Europe you might want to try Mike's new page in Germany (it will have more files and should be faster for you— http://www.rat.de/mikem/index.htm).

Morty's Sim City 2000 Web Page
http://www.creative-services.com/personal/simcity.html

A Mac-related Sim City 2000 site. Hints, tips, cities, utilities, and links fill this page, leaning toward resources to help you along with your game. Sections on "Making the Most of Commercial Zoning," "Combating Pollution and Crime," and "Tips on Making Your City Beautiful" are most noteworthy. A worthwhile page for the Sim City Mac enthusiast.

MS Flight Simulator 5.x Aircraft by Paul Hartl
http://netnow.micron.net/~pdhartl/

Preview, or download, quality craft from Paul's personal collection to use in conjunction with Microsoft's Flight Simulator 5.0, 5.0a, or 5.1. See screens of the USAF "Thunderbird" series, the "Top Gun" series, the McDonnell Douglas series, the Northrop all-Stealth series, and more. Remember you will need BAO's Flight Shop as well for these to work.

Multiplayer Games & Simulations
http://www.teleport.com/~caustic/

A resourceful site breaking down the different genres of gaming on the Web with product reviews, game company and magazine/e-zine links, and multiplayer news and info. Many sections such as commercial Internet gaming networks, BBS game servers, and multiplayer games separated into game category (simulations, 3D action, etc.).

My F/18 Hornet Page

http://www.widomaker.com/~jester/
hornet.html

Resourceful site for fans or wanna-be fans of the smash F/18 Hornet sim by Graphic Simulations Corporation. View screen grabs, read up on strategy tips and tricks, or download the demo and other files (including "The Debaucher"—a nifty utility that changes the planes in F/A-18 Hornet 2.0).

NASS '96

http://www.webcom.com/~twortman/
nasscar/

The North American Simulation Series (or NASS) '96 Racing Series is supported by the PC game NASCAR Racing from Papyrus. Each week has a different course, so download the free car set, run the race, save your results, e-mail them in, and compare your scores along with your other human competitors. Read the NASS '96 FAQ and Rules for further info.

Need For Speed, The

http://www.bossnt.com/~iwyatt/nfs/

Ian Wyatt's unofficial Need For Speed page contains a number of areas: downloadable files, cheat codes, track and car specs, screen shots, fastest times, etc. If you're here just to find out more about the game before you Buy it, check out the system requirements first. A well-organized links area follows the main page(s).

Need For Speed Page, The

http://www.atw.fullfeed.com/~bix/nfs.htm

Another unofficial site dedicated to Electronic Art's The Need For Speed (NFS). There's lots to see and download here including the playable demo, a What's New page, NFS and NFS SE cheats, a Best Lap Times page, a car specs page, and screen shots,; or sample the various NFS reviews by this Web site's creators, Glen Bicking and John Krutke.

Nels Anderson's Home Page

http://www.flightsim.com/arcanum/
index.html

Nels's site consists of general aviation, flight simulation, and weather information via links to other sources around the Net. Most are categorized into news, files, and anything else to do with flight simulators, like Microsoft's FS5. This would be a good starting point to see what *exactly* about flight sims you are looking for before wasting your time with random surfing.

Ozhost Air Warrior Web Site

http://www.ozemail.com.au/~dond/
awhome.htm

Ozhost is the Australian home of Kesmai's Air Warrior—a real-time, multiplayer air combat simulation. You may access Ozhost via a direct Ozemail connection in any of Australia's capital cities (numbers provided) or by Telneting to ozhost.ozemail.com.au and typing **connect** at the login prompt. This page also houses the Air Warrior FAQ for those interested.

P. Mok's Tips and Hints for USNF, ATF, and MF

http://www-acc.scu.edu/~pmok/
tips.htm#Bugout

A 15+ page HTML guide to beating the games U.S. Navy Fighters, Advanced Tactical Fighter, and Marine Fighters. Learn how to: create your own campaigns, follow your wingman home, edit mission files to fly any plane, target planes beyond TWS range, or fly at night or through fog. Also note P. Mok's secret keys of USNF and ATF and the handy Appendix section at the bottom of the page.

Papyrus: Hawaii Beta Test

http://www.sierra.com/papyrus/

Cool add-on for Papyrus' NASCAR Racing. Download the extra level here for FREE and all you'll need is a heavy foot and a copy of NASCAR Racing. (If you don't have a copy, you can pick it up at the online Sierra Store or by calling 1-800-757-7707.) Once you have downloaded the enhancement, follow the registration instructions and when you're ready, dial the server. You can race for free, but you will be responsible for your own long distance charges. The newest version of Hawaii was released July 2, 1996 and is now available on Sierra's FTP server (ftp://ftp.sierra.com).

PCM&E Interview—ATF's Paul Grace
http://www.mortimer.com/users/pcme/ intrview/pgint/pgint.htm

PC Multimedia and Entertainment magazine snagged a one-on-one interview with Paul Grace, executive producer of Jane's/EA's Advanced Tactical Fighter (ATF). Rod White probes into specific game details such as music, flight models, and secrets. Does Paul tell all? Visit and see...

PCM&E Review of AH-64D Longbow
http://www.mortimer.com/users/pcme/ strike/ah-64d/ah-64d.htm

Before you spend some hard-earned coin on this CD-ROM from Jane's/Electronic Arts, read Rod White's description of the game and the system requirements, or preview the many screen shots (check out the Mi-28 in action or the opening video sequence pix!). Don't be misled, there is a lot to this review (over 12 HTML pages), but at least you feel confident having a veteran gamer look at this combat helicopter sim thoroughly.

PC Pilots Club of Ireland
http://www.iol.ie/~langb/sim/

In 1993, the PC Pilots Club Of Ireland was set up to bring together all those interested in non-combat flight simulations. Although the club is based in Ireland, members can join from anywhere in the world. This Web site supplements the club's quarterly newsletter, which brings new flight simulator software news, new products and upgrades, and utilities. Download some files to use with your Microsoft Flight Simulator ver 5.1 (mainly panels, aircraft, and scenery).

Peter's USNF/USMF Page
http://www.swiftech.com.sg/~petertan/ usnf.html

Peter Tan breaks down the game summaries and distinctions between EA's U.S. Navy Fighters and Marine Fighters air combat sims. Lotsa screen shots and missions to download. Related links around the Web are also given.

PezPunk's Need For Speed Best Times Page
http://members.aol.com/pezpunk/index.html

This page is dedicated to Electronic Arts's Need For Speed racing simulation. View the fastest known times ever run for each car and each track. If you've beaten a time indicated, save your time as a replay and attach it to your e-mail (no sneaking around with snazzy track editors!). You just may win the Golden Pez Dispenser award!

Propeller Page, The
http://www.dragonfire.net/~Basement/ flight/flight.htm

This site is dedicated to personal and propeller-driven planes for MS Flight Sim 5.x; however, you will need BAO Flight Shop to play these. Choose between single engine planes (like the Embrair EMB-312 Tucano or Mooney TLS), twin engines (Cessna 421a or C310 Songbird, Piper Twin Comanche), or helicopter designs

(AH-64 Apache, Cobra, and more). Download 15+ models to try out.

Quasi-Authoritative SimTower Home Page, The
http://www.vivanet.com/~stewartd/simtower.html

A Mac and PC collection of SimTower downloadables and readables. The hot simulation game by Maxis lets you design, create, and maintain modern skyscrapers and fill them with more stories and Simtenants. If you're a novice at the game or just contemplating buying it, then read the system requirements, FAQs, and User's Manual deficiencies. Intermediate or expert sim gamers may want to try out the files available (including towers), peruse the SimTower oddities, and hot link to other SimTower-related resources.

rec.aviation.simulators

A Usenet newsgroup devoted to flight sim fans worldwide. Post or answer messages or download files (scenery, planes, panels, utilities, screen shots, sounds, extra missions, FAQs, movies, patches, etc.). Other newsgroups of interest are **comp.sys.ibm.pc.games.flight-sim (PC flight sims)** and **comp.sys.mac.games.flight-sim (Macintosh flight sims).**

Remove Before Flight
http://happypuppy.com/flight/index.html

Welcome to Happy Puppy's Flight Sim Forum headed by Tom "KC" Basham, Forum Administrator. Many sections including chat groups, news and editorials, links, and a HUGE library of planes and scenery. You may also upload any of your own creations. A great page and an excellent place for novice pilots.

Rick's Borrowed Pages
http://www.accessone.com:80/~riccrowe/

"I do like planes" is Rick's opening line to his site! As the Web page name suggests, this is essentially a laid-back links site broken up into military sites, flight-sim

companies, home pages of flight, and Windows 95 sites. There is also a flight sim "Picture of the Month" showcased here.

Rocketman's Air Warrior Web Page
http://www.inter-look.com/rocket/

Read the Air Warrior (AW) FAQ, view scenario screen shots, get strategy tips, or download the AW demo, maps, and terrain. Kesmai's hot game is a real-time multiplayer flight combat game. Darren's site also his own AW FAQ, worthwhile links, and news of the AW Convention.

Sam's Flight Simulator Page
http://www.naples.net/~nfn09227/flsim.html

15-year-old Sam Weigel's site offers Flight Shop and non-Flight Shop aircraft to download and use (including his own models). Besides aircraft, all kinds of neat stuff for Microsoft Flight Simulator can be found here: scenery, features, info, pictures and reviews, and tons of links. Great job, Sam!

Sandbox, The
http://ourworld.compuserve.com/homepages/rogers/sandbox.htm

The Sandbox is devoted to simulations of all kinds in all media: flight simulators and auto simulators; computer, board, and play-by-mail strategy wargames; training and research simulations. This page is designed like an extensive essay with many hot-linked words—various features and departments analyze the world of simulations as we know it. An interesting piece to note was on real-life emulation systems designed to simulate weather conditions, avionic and electrical systems, turbulence, engine performance, and aerodynamics.

SCURK Hall of Fame, The
http://home.earthlink.net/~sgomez/scurk.html

Each month Steven Gomez chooses a few of the best SimCity 2000 Urban Renewal Kit tiles (SCURK) on the Web and displays them for visitors; or, you can copy them and use them in your own tile sets. A few "quality" links to other SCURK areas on the Net are also provided.

Sergio Silva's MS Flight Sim Page
**http://www.geocities.com/CapeCanaveral/
4484/index.html**

If you want to add some flavor to your Flight Simulator 5 scenery, get a few custom-built Portugal add-ons complete with an Installation Tutorial. Choose between six or so scenery packs at this Portuguese and English Web site. Links to other flight sim pages are also offered.

Shadow Riders:
The VFA-13 Home Page
http://www.aimnet.com/~nicoli/

The VFA-13 Shadow Riders are a group of Mac flight simulator fanatics stationed in the Flight Simulation area (Section 13) in CompuServe's Macintosh Entertainment Forum (MAUG®). Their goal is to give Macintosh pilots a home to share stories, find and offer advice in a forum-like environment, and relish in the "camaraderie" that exists between these pages. The Shadow Riders also review the most popular Mac flight sims (such as the F/A-18 Hornet and A-10 Attack), house a glossary and resources list, offer tips, patches, FAQs and tricks, and more. If you're a CompuServe member, just type GO MACFUN.

Sick Puppy's Air Combat Series Page
http://www.cs.uct.ac.za/~dnunez/usnf.html

A South African page devoted to Electronic Art's U.S. Navy Fighters (USNF), Advanced Tactical Fighters (ATF), and Marine Fighters (MF). Dave Nunez offers missions, hacks, other flyers, a toolkit (you can customize almost every aspect of USNF and MF), links, and more. A description for beginners is available that explains how to play downloaded missions.

SimCap, Inc.—Home Page
**http://www.hooked.net/users/eob3/
simcap.htm**

This is the home of *Intercept*—a bimonthly hard-core flight sim magazine available through subscription. In every edition you'll find detailed software reviews (where the reviewer has flown at least 50 hours with that product), tech specs on the particular aircraft and weapons (if applicable), and strategy tips. At this Web site get a taste of the *Intercept* journal, sign up or order back issues, and read up on industry news from leading software and hardware manufacturers.

Sim City 2000 Info Page
http://arbornet.org/~lokety/sc2k_index.html

Singapore's Loke Teng Yans designed this site to honor Maxis's successful line of Sim games. Links, a guest book, and a Sim City sounds page are available here. You may submit your e-mail address to automatically receive updates for this page. Access to the Maxis home page is also given at http://www.maxis.com/.

Sim City 2000 Pit Stop Center,
The New
**http://www.inforamp.net/~sakhrani/
simpage.html**

If a midi version of "Mission Impossible" doesn't make you want to stay at a Web page, then I don't know what would. Many sections will prolong your visit including: What's New, mIRC (chat away to trade cities and cheats), The Help Pages, The Cheats, The Contest (a real one!), The Cities (a huge list of downloadables), The Huge List (Sim City 2000 related sites), and Ask Me! (have a query? Ask the Scott!). A nicely organized and attractive award-winning site.

Sim City 2000 Resource Page, The

http://www.bcubed.com/sc2000/

An award-winning, sleek page designed to supplement Maxis Software's hit game Sim City 2000. A colorful graphical map to click takes you to the various sections of the site: info, strategy, downloadable cities, what's new, game cheats, hot links, and an area on SCURK graphics (urban renewing files). Other points of interest: Chicago tile sets were a hot commodity on my visit (Mac, DOS, and Windows), a free e-mailing list to keep up to date with Sim City happenings, and a "Just For Fun" headline took me to cool wallpaper, a desktop Theme pack, and a sounds page. A terrific, modern Web page worthy of countless visits.

Sim City 2000 Resource Page By Jeff
http://www.geocities.com/SiliconValley/ 3694/simstuf4.html

"Press this button for the latest announcements..." is the first thing you see here and once you do...a scrolling message will appear at the bottom of the page welcoming you and telling you what you can find here. The Sim Circle section contains strategies, an FAQ, Jeff's own city creations, and links.

Sim Racing Online

http://www.simracing.com/

This all-in-one resourceful site pools together key talent in racing sim *savoir faire*: John Wallace, editor-in-chief of Sim Racing News; Neil Jedrzejewski ("The Pits" Web site creator; Michael Carver (AutoSim Webmaster); David "Gizmo" Gymer (Formula 1 Grand Prix king); and Tony Johns, the coordinator for the IWCCCARS Project (formerly at http:// www.xmission.com/~iwcc/project.htm). These men ARE the authorities in online racing simulation information and are committed to creating an easy-to-use and useful page. The bottom line: 15 separate respected Web sites are now under one roof with one URL to bookmark: http://www.simracing.com/.

SimCity Cheats
http://www.gis.net/~jcoiner/simcity.html

Many of us still play the original SimCity faithfully, and this site caters *only* to cool cheats and strategies to try with the classic Maxis game. Find out how to make cash or save money on transportation. Other stuff is available including pre-made towns and cities, tricks, and links.

Sim Forum
http://www.geocities.com/SiliconValley/ Park/7618/

Complete with a Real Audio introduction, Mike Wild provides downloads galore for your Maxis Sim titles: Classic Sim City, Sim Tower, Sim City 2000, and the Urban Renewal Kit. Grab custom-built cities and towers, read cheats and strategies, or upload your own creations.

http://www.vcnet.com/jmoore/simstuff.htm

Winner of the Maxis contest with his creation, "Spiralopolis," designer Jerry Moore provides an exceptional page devoted to all of Maxis's Sim collection: SimCity 2000, Sim City Classic, SimAnt, SimTower, SimIsle, and SimFarm. Plenty of cheats, strategies, cities, and other goodies can be found here including another one of Jerry's cities, "Rubigger" (featured in a Sim City 2000 book). For a change, the frames on this site actually are designed to display the content effectively, unlike most Web sites, it seems. Lots to read and download here, so poke around and see what you find…you'll be pleasantly surprised.

SimTower Web Page
http://www.geocities.com/SiliconValley/2929/index.html

A good-looking frames-enhanced page providing info on SimTower—the building management game from Maxis. Find here Tower strategies, tips and cheats, elevator Strategies, many Towers to download, and more. Read David Lee's SimTower FAQ (v1.2) or view the screen shots and suggestions for your hotels, offic-

es, condos, etc. Click on the works or the actual Tower icons. Nicely done.

Skull Squadron Home Page
http://members.aol.com/maveric024/homepage/skulls.html

Meet the big bad boys from the 24th Fighter/Bomber squadron, a.k.a. The Skull Squadron. They are a dedicated Air Warrior squadron out of America Online, have the largest number of pilots of the AOL squadrons, and are the second-highest ranking AOL fighter squadron. If you think you're good enough at Air Warrior, e-mail one of the team and find out how to join the Skulls.

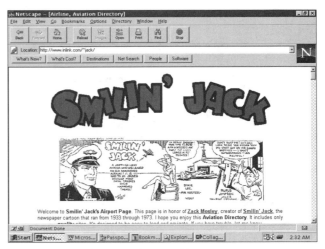

Smilin' Jack's Airport Page
http://www.inlink.com/~jack/

Since 1994, this award-winning site has listed hundreds of only the best aviation and flight sim pages in and around the Web. Sail through these lists or search their database for specifics. Named after Zack Mosley's newspaper cartoon that ran from 1933 through 1973, Smilin' Jack's quality links are easy to navigate through and will provide hours of engaging reading.

Smooth Operators Squadron Menu, The
http://www.smooth-ops.com/frames/

A very hip Web site designed by the Colorado combat flight sim group, Smooth Operators Squadron, not only to bring Web visitors up to date with the evolution of flight sim modem and network support, but also to offer technical help and education for flight sim fanatics around the globe. These Colonels push you to get Ocean's sim EF2000 and the free multiplayer Internet network Kali before taking advantage of their site. Or you may choose to hot link to the EF2000 Web site, Kali, or other various EF2000 links.

Space Simulator: Strategies and Secrets
http://users.aol.com/NickDargah/spacesimulator.html

For use with your Microsoft Space Simulator. This site features a free online viewing of the "Space Simulator Strategies and Secrets Book," Space Simulator situation files, and other utilities. Useful space and flight sim links are also provided.

Stallion's SimTower Page
http://www.geocities.com/TimesSquare/3488/tower.htm

Stallion's page has codes, cheats, demos, patches, screen shots, and many files to download. Each of the 12 or so towers has the file name, description, creator name, and Stallion's rating. Upload your own creations if you're you think you've got a neat design.

Steve Lol's The Need For Speed Page
http://www.imaginet.fr/~stevelol/jeux/nfs.htm

This French Web site honors Road and Track's/Electronic Art's The Need For Speed (NFS). System specs, general information, Steve' s personal record times, world times (download replay games), news, and links are presented in frames format.

Steven's SimCity 2000 Homepage
http://www.sundial.net/~integra9/sc2000.html

A simple and handsome page offering SimCity 2000 cities you can download, cheat codes, and hot-links to other Maxis Software links around the globe. Steven's "Download Ramp" contains roughly 25 custom-built zipped cities such as Manchester, New York City, and a few homemade creations.

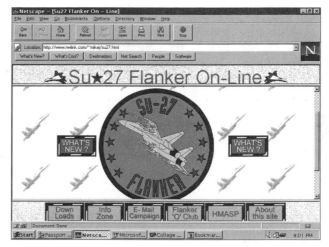

Su27 Flanker On-Line
http://www.nwlink.com/~mikej/su27.html

Maintained by Marek "Headcase" Paul, this Web page is dedicated to supporting users of SSI and Mindscape's Su27 Flanker flight simulator. Test-fly new missions or download the latest patches from the manufacturers. Su27 Flanker On-Line is also home of the Flanker Mailing List. Feel you've mastered the game already? Then why not take part in HMASP (Higher Military Aviation School for Pilots), put your throttle where your mouth is, and compete against others on the Internet? Or drop by the IRC chat to embellish on your successful missions to other pilots. Beginners can read the FAQ (all 40 sections!), read Flanker news, or view screen shots.

Tactical Air Combat Maneuvering

http://www.cs.vu.nl/%7Etnleeuw/hornet/ACM.html

A 13+ page guide to tactical air combat maneuvering in GSC's F/A-18 Hornet. From beginning to end, no stone is left unturned here: get to know ACM (air combat maneuvering) in Arena play, view figures on lead collision and lead pursuit intercepts and influencing Bandit's direction of turn, and view formulae on turn rate and radius. Heavy stuff for the die-hard Hornet flight sim fanatic.

ThrustMaster HomePage

http://www.thrustmaster.com/tm-home.htm

The official site for ThrustMaster PC products. Gaming peripherals such as wheels, pads, flight sticks, rudders—specialty devices are also available such as Pro Play Golf (electronic golf mat/tee) and a Flight Sim Cockpit. A Tech Support section, History of ThrustMaster, and Links are also worthwhile reading.

Tim's Flight Simulation Page

http://home.earthlink.net/~kimsguy/

Climb aboard this site Tim Daugherty has created to give back some of the hospitality that he has received from the online flight sim community throughout the past year or so. His objective is to provide a base for flight simmers to meet and exchange aircraft and scenery files. Each would have their own name, photo, e-mail, and/or Web address displayed along with their work. If you have something to contribute, send it on up to kimsguy@earthlink.net.

Todd's SKURK Depot

http://www.flinet.com/~irwin/scurk.htm

A cool (yet unrelated) Doctor Who AVI movie appears when you get to this page, neat idea! Anyway, this site offers SCURK object sets to view and use, notes on submitting your own creations, and a handful of Sim City and SCURK-related links. SCURK stands for Sim City 2000 Urban Renewal Kits—a utility to use in conjunction with Maxis's Sim City 2000 for building and editing cities.

Top Gun: Mission of the Month

http://www.holobyte.com/topgun/month.html

Top Gun: Fire At Will Mission of the Month is a free downloadable mission from the Spectrum Holobyte official Web site. If you own the PC version of Top Gun (sorry PlayStation owners!) you can keep up to date with an ongoing story and fly the pre-set interlocking scenarios. As in the Paramount movie of the same name, you are in a cockpit of a F-14 fighter jet, graduating from the Top Gun flight academy. To read more information and features of the game (and view screen shots), visit the main Top Gun page (http://www.holobyte.com/topgun/).

Tornado Command and Staff College

http://www.mindspring.com/~ejoiner/tcsc.html

A free winhelp file written to teach command level game play in Tornado—the flight sim sensation from Digital Integration a few years back that seems just as popular today as in late 1993, when it was released. CompuServe's Basil Copeland, Eric Joiner, and Heinz Bernd Eggenstein wrote this text embedded with pictures and tables (2.6MB zipped!) outlining all aspects of Tornado strategy and FAQs. Other cool add-ons (missions and scenarios), news, pictures, and links are also available.

Train Gamer's Association, Inc.

http://www.mnsinc.com/utopia/TGA/TGA.html

This organization is right on track (sorry, couldn't help it)—they publish a quarterly newsletter, *The Train Gamers Gazette,* and among other things, give reviews and descriptions for relevant board and/or computer train simulation games. Drop by the long list of links and start surfing the Net for train-related gaming info.

Trophy Bass Review

http://www.cdmag.com/sports_vault/
trophy_bass/page1.html

Well, if you didn't care for our fisherman's friend review of Sierra's simulation (above)—here's one from
the folks at Computer Games Strategy Plus Online.
This nine-page HTML guide will take you through all
the pertinent features of the game, including screen
shots and fishing tips. Info on Trophy Bass 2 can be
found at http://www.sierra.com/entertainment/tbass2/.

Twisted Page

http://www.cris.com/~Twist/

Another Air Warrior page designed to get more people into Kesmai's hot online multiplayer flight combat
sim. Web creator Rich "Twist" Lawrence liked the
game so much he decided to work for Kesmai! Download the demo, view screen shots and the planes page,
or check out the art of Frank Williamson (one of the
artists at Kesmai, and a member of the Air Warrior
team). To get info on how to sign up and play online,
visit http://www.cris.com/~Flitesim/.

Unofficial A-10 Home Page

http://www.cs.vu.nl/~tnleeuw/A10/A10.html

Tips, tricks, mission hints, FAQs, the demo, links, and
other stuff all connected to Parsoft's flight simulator
for the Macintosh. A plain site but a neat section on
CCIP bombing strategies, or view the A-10 slideshow
from Tom Morrison's archives.

Unofficial Hornet Home Page

http://www.cs.vu.nl/~tnleeuw/hornet/

This site is dedicated to F/A 18 Hornet, the flight sim
by Graphic Simulations Corp. (GSC). Download demos, extra missions, FAQs, tips, and the Hornet Air
Combat Manual (written by Matt "Popeye" Doyel—
real U.S. Navy Pilot). No graphics (except for a few
small pictures) so load time should be fast.

AUTHOR'S PICK

Unofficial Need For Speed Page, The

http://members.aol.com/speed1racr/html/
nfs_main.htm

Brought to you by Speed Racer (Doug Burg), this site
caters to the Need For Speed (NFS) fanatics—the
racing sim created in Burnaby, British Columbia at the
Electronic Arts Canada development house. The
award-winning site provides cheat codes, controller
advice, contests, the demo, FAQs, news, track tools,
tips n' tricks, modem game info, new tracks, links, and
other files. A very resourceful site to supplement
Road and Track and EA's excellent racing sim.

USENET Guide to Falcon 3, The

http://cactus.org/~knutson/UGF3.html

Written by veteran Jim Knutson, this is a huge resource center (based on hundreds of USENET postings) to provide tons of organized information on
Spectrum-Holobyte's classic Falcon 3. This FAQ-and-
a-half has everything from setup and system requirements to tips, tricks, tactics, and strategies, to maneuvering, weapon and plane info, to quirks, bugs, patches
and other information sources.

Uval and Harel's SimTower Page

http://www.dorsai.org/~blumenfe/
simtower.html

This duo's unofficial SimTower page contains tips, building restrictions, links and the cheat utility SimHex written by Jerry Moore (requires vbrun300.dll). Graphics of
actual stories created by the authors are throughout
this page (check out the 4x4 in the garage). Useful maintenance strategies and construction suggestions.

U.S. Navy Fighters

http://www.ea.com/usnfpcd.html

Electronic Art's official page on U.S. Navy Fighters. The modern dogfighting sim comes from the makers of Chuck Yeager's Air Combat with high speed graphics and special effects. This site offers an in-depth product description, key features, game and system specs, and various screen shots.

U.S. Navy Fighters (Marine Fighters) Home Page

http://wwwedu.cs.utwente.nl/~kamps/usnf.html

This unofficial page from Bart Kamps in The Netherlands highlights aspects of EA's USNF and MF combat flight games. Sections include Information, Custom Missions, Ukraine 1997 Campaign Resources, The Medal Page, Resources, and more. There is also an area on Jane's/EA's Advanced Tactical Fighters.

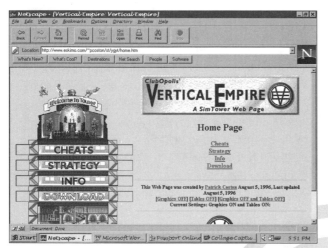

Vertical Empire, The

http://www.eskimo.com/~pcoston/st/

This site is brought to you by Patrick Coston and the Clubopolis folks (see above) catering to the SimTower fans. You have a choice if you want graphics or tables, or both (which is nice to turn off if you have a slow modem connection). Once inside, there are downloads, info, cheats, and strategies for Maxis's hit game. Check

out some of the custom-built Towers or grab some utilities and upgrades.

Virtual Fighter Command

http://www.mindspring.com/~ejoiner/vfc/vfc.html

Eric "Cougar" Joiner's award-winning site is the headquarters of Virtual Fighter Command (VFC—the home of the First Internet Cyber Strike Wing, equipped with Panavia Gr.4 and F.3 Tornado Fighters). The Purpose of VFC is to promote e-mail campaign play using Digital Integration's 1993 hit *Tornado*. At the popular VFC page, download scenarios and add-on missions, partake in the discussion forum, view the photo gallery, or, if you're good enough, join the Tornado Command and Staff College for free. Eric reminds you, "Fighter Drivers Make Movies…Strike Pilots Make History…"

Virtual Flights

http://intercity.shiny.it/moneta/main.html

Angelo Moneta's English and Italian flight-sim corner contains cool animations and frames. Sim utilities and add-on packs are offered along with a support page, links directory, and an update log to keep up with current changes. Don't forget to check out the "free files you can't afford to miss" section. Nice design and worthy content.

Virtual Pool

http://www.interplay.com/website/sales/vrpool.html

Chalk your billiards cue at Interplay's official Web site for their CD-ROM, Virtual Pool. These pages discuss the product description, game overview, reviews and awards, and the patch update for the video in the game (download it if you need it). View thumbnail or full screen shots, or download the playable demo to see if you're on the ball. If 8 Ball, 9 Ball, Straight Pool, or Rotation Snooker isn't your game—then visit Interplay's sister page for their game Virtual Snooker (http://www.interplay.com/games/snooker.html). For a long list of other pool or billiards Web sites (on books, companies, magazines, or organizations), go to http://www.yahoo.com/Recreation/Games/Billiards/.

WAE Web Page, The
http://www.hlcs.com/wae/

WAE stands for Weekly Airplanes by E-mail, a free service that has grown to over 7,000+ members since its debut in December 1995. High-quality planes are sent via e-mail every week to members that can be used with Microsoft Flight Simulator 5.x. The WAE Web page has an IRC chat arena, a hanger archive of past planes, news, product previews, other FS add-ons (e.g. clouds, panels), and a photo gallery.

Wally's World of Driving Simulators
http://www.oz.net/~wottenad/wheel.htm

Choose whether you want frames or not at this Netscape-enhanced site. Once inside this large award-winning site, Walt Ottenad will teach you how to construct a steering wheel and pedals for use with PC driving simulators. View pictures to get an idea of what they should look like, read the FAQs provided, or hotlink to other racing sites around the globe.

Werewolf vs. Comanche by NovaLogic
http://www.novalogic.com/wvsc.html

NovaLogic's best-selling sim is all-out assault battle between the Russian Kamov KA-50 Werewolf attack helicopter and its American counterpart, the RAH-66 Comanche. The gamer can choose either helicopter to play head-to-head, cooperatively via modem or network, or as a single-player challenge. This page contains news, product and mission, system requirements, and ordering info.

WildBunch Home Page
http://ourworld.compuserve.com/ homepages/cduffy/WILDBNCH.htm

The WildBunch is a group of over 50 active worldwide members who "thoroughly enjoy" Electronic Art's U.S. Navy Fighters (USNF). The group grew out of the

AUTHOR'S PICK

World of MS Flight Simulator 5.x Scenery

http://www.st.rim.or.jp/~kkitamur/fs5.html

You are in for a multimedia treat if you are using Netscape 2.x or higher, Microsoft Internet Explorer 3.x, and MacroMedia's Shockwave plug-in. On Koji Kitamura's Web site hear the roar of a plane engine, view a first-person perspective slide show of an aircraft carrier landing in Hawaii, or click on a globe of Earth to see and download scenery for your Microsoft Flight Simulator. Editors and other useful utilities are also available for free. An imaginative Web page from Japan that sets a great example of how to merge creative content with current Web technology.

Flight Sim Forum on CompuServe, which now holds contests, publishes an electronic newsletter, and creates missions for use with USNF, MF, and ATF. View the Planes, Resources, and Briefing Room page.

World Wide Web Guide to FS5 Scenery Design
http://www.vianet.net.au/~kraybill/fltsim5/ index.htm

Gene Kraybill's resourceful page teaches how to create your own worlds for Microsoft's Flight Simulator 5+. Various sections make up this page: The World Wide Award for Freeware Scenery (top 20 freeware scenery files), Understanding the Terminology (recurring terms of the flight sim trade), Getting Started (a step-by-step guide to creating scenery), and, for the advanced designer, an area on using special aids, tools, and utilities. Other informative areas are The Knowledge Bank (accumulated contributions from scenery creators) and Web Wonders (Web sites and connections of interest to scenery artists).

World Wide Web Virtual Library: Aviation, The

http://macwww.db.erau.edu/www_virtual_lib/aviation.html

Part of the humongous WWW Library series, the Aviation resource is accessed over 21,000 times a month. This Web page serves as a launching pad to the many diversified aviation pages around the Net. Click on the "Flight Simulation" sub-section to take you to the games-related pages. Read the description beside the Web page to see if the specifics of that site interest you. The WWW Virtual Library hot-link list is a good bookmarker to refer to for any budding flight sim fan.

WWI Flight Sims

http://www.dreamscape.com/noyzrulz/

This is a flight sim site dedicated to The Great War fighters, specifically anything to do with the Sierra games Red Baron and Red Baron II. The original game was released on Christmas Eve, 1990, and is considered by many flight sim enthusiasts to be the best WWI flight sim ever. Press releases, FAQs, pictures, and links are provided. Great Red Baron II screen shots (check out bridge2.jpg) and plane sounds (hey—it went from left to right…cool!).

XaBaRaS's NFS Page

http://www.nlights.net/xabaras/nfs.htm

Electronic Arts and Road and Track's Need For Speed (NFS) racing sim gets easier with help from this site. Download or read cheats, hacks, track editors, utilities, and rated links. Own the NFS SE (Special Edition)? Grab the patch here, too.

7

STRATEGY AND WAR GAME SITES

#CivNet Home Page

http://www.radix.net/~mikes/civnet.html

#CivNet is a meeting place for worldwide players of Sid Meier/Microprose's CivNet to chat or to arrange online multiplayer games. Patches and updates can be found here, add your name to the CivNet Enthusiasts Mailing List, and a competition center is in the works.

A Page of Panzers

http://www.ionline.net/~rcwh/panzer/

Craig Howard goes out on the Net and grabs Panzer General goodies for his visitors. Although the playable demo of Mindscape/SSI's smash hit war game is not available here, there are other files worth your while including strategy guides, FAQs, reviews, news, a cheat utility, or Panzer General icons of OS/2 users.

Afterlife

http://www.megatoon.com/~t15/issue16/alife.htm

Coming Soon magazine's review of Lucas Art's Afterlife is an extensive look at the highly anticipated strategic Heaven and Hell "God game." View screen shots, a thorough product description, game features, and system requirements. SimCity 2000 fans would dig this game (similar engine), plus it has a lot of comical aspects to it. Visit the Official Afterlife page at Lucas Arts at http://www.lucasarts.com/pages/Adventurer.439.html.

Age of Rifles

http://www.JointChiefsPub.com/dow/rifles.htm

Grab the large 6.8MB demo of Age of Rifles here (zipped), or if you already own the game, submit your own scenarios for others to download and play. Upload your U.S. Civil War, British Colonial Wars, or others, to http://www.JointChiefsPub.com/dow/submission.htm. This page is part of the larger Department of War site.

AUTHOR'S PICK

Ace Games On-Ramp

http://www.lonet.ca/res/aculver/ace01.htm

Andrew Culver's gaming emporium is an excellent Web site catering to strategy, action, and RPG fans alike. Ace's Onramp is a frame-based page that uses it effectively with the games listed on the left side and your main screen in the middle. Crescendo Duke Nukem 3D music keeps you company as you scroll through the game listing: Ascendancy, Doom, Quake, Warcraft II, Ultima VIII, Strife, Stonekeep, Red Alert, and Descent II. Each clicked choice brings up cheats, codes, strategy tips, FAQs, links, and various downloads. Cool animations and colorful graphics are seen throughout each game department. Bonus: This page has a modem listing section separated by area code so you can find a gaming partner in your region. As if this wasn't enough, there is also a posting message board, a live chat, guestbook, and a voting booth. Great job!

Addicted to Civilization II

http://www.pe.net/~king/civ2/civ.htm

An easy to navigate site for a pretty tough game! This Web page by Nicholas Clark glorifies MicroProse and Sid Meier's Civilization sequel, Civilization II (Civ2). He offers well-organized guides, strategy tips, and many other miscellaneous files for your perusal. These include Civ2 news, a huge archive collection of downloadable maps and scenarios, FAQs and Q & A, chats, and more. Fun stuff is also available such as icons, Civ Olympics, and Civ Playoffs. A very resourceful and fun one-stop place for Civ 2 goodies.

Alexei's Home Page

http://home.pacific.net.sg/~dsv/heroes.html

A Web site equally devoted to Heroes of Might and Magic gamers and the aim to convert Warcraft II and Command and Conquer followers! A game description, cheat codes, maps, an editor, and links are all provided for New World Computing's award-winning computer strategy game.

Allied and Panzer General Archive

http://student-www.uchicago.edu/users/ cp11/index.html

Download additions for Mindscape/SSI's award-winning computer war games Allied General and Panzer General. Each map editor, scenario/campaign, or equipment file, has a complete description and instructions on how to use it…prior to download.

Allied General Editor

http://www.lrz-muenchen.de/~t7121ag/ WWW/age.html

This site designed by Germany's Dirk Herrmann, salutes SSI's Allied General—a turn-based strategy game. Here you can find the saved game editor that he has written, release updates, an info desk, scenario files, equipment list, and links.

Arrrggh!—The Web Page

http://www.netmart.com/lostshaker/

Lost Shaker Productions presents "Arrrggh! The Pirate Game"—a graphical strategy game for Windows. Read the description of the game, system requirements, view screen shots, download the demo (2.3MB), or order the full game.

Battleground: Shiloh Hints & Tips

http://www.cdmag.com/war_vault/ battleground_shiloh_hints/page1.html

Computer Games Strategy Plus! Online provides helpful strategy suggestions, tactics, and tricks for Talon-Soft's Battleground: Shiloh. Screen shots supplement this extensive and resourceful guide (over seven HTML pages). Take advice from one of the leaders in the war game community.

Blizzard's Diablo

http://www.vistech.net/users/kingn/
diablo.html

One of the first sites on the Net dedicated to Diablo—the latest game from the creators of Warcraft II. Blizzard's dark gothic fantasy strategy game can be played either single-player or against others via modem, serial, network, and Internet play (through Blizzard's own battle.net system and Kali). This site provides a Diablo FAQ, screen shots, music, and a chat room.

Blud Redd's Warhammer 40,000 Page

http://www.geocities.com/Athens/3628/

A collection and compilation of new troops and rules, some Blud-Redd's (a Blood Angel Captain), some belonging to others (Inquisitor Isaac Tobin's The Sanguine Guard, J. Michael Tisdel's Space Marine Snipers, Eric Young's Space Marine Lieutenant), and more. Lotsa links to keep you busy for a while.

Captain Stern's Game Page

http://norcom.mb.ca/infernal/games.html

A four-in-one Web page highlighting the best of Command and Conquer, Quake, Duke Nukem 3D, and Mechwarrior 2 files. Captain Stern (who names himself after the character from the animated movie *Heavy Metal*) offers gamers a refuge here. All four gaming areas are equally stunning and keep you absorbed in the demos, FAQs, theme packs for Windows, levels, hints, e-mail mailing lists, patches, and cheats for the top games of the year. This Canadian fan-based multipurpose site is visually stimulating without lacking any substance. A good representation of how fan-based Web sites could look with zealous effort.

Case's Ladder

http://games.net-link.net/ladder/

Case's ladder is a ranking system for Internet multiplayer gamers that is based on consistency over a period of time—not on one particular match. Either stand alone, or in a team, you can play games such as Command and Conquer, Warcraft II, Quake, Duke Nukem 3D, Descent, and more, but visit this site to catch up on the particulars.

Reviews of the Battleground Series by The Nuke Site

Battleground: Gettysburg
Scott: http://www.nuke.com/cgr/reviews/9603/getty/sgrev.htm

Ted: http://www.nuke.com/cgr/reviews/9603/getty/tedrev.htm

Frank: http://www.nuke.com/cgr/reviews/9603/getty/fsrev.htm

Battleground: Ardennes
Tasos: http://www.nuke.com/compent/reviews/octarc/bga/tkrev.htm

Ted: http://www.nuke.com/compent/reviews/octarc/bga/tkrev.htm

Chaos Overlords

http://www.nwcomputing.com/chaos/

The official page from New World Computing on their computer strategy title "Chaos Overlords." Playing the Orcs in Warcraft II gave us a taste of being the bad guys and that's exactly what you are in this game determined to overrun and dominate this futuristic city (single-player or multiplayer play). This site has screen shots to view, game descriptions, and features—or download the demo for the Mac or Windows PC.

Chris's Harpoon Page

http://met.open.ac.uk/group/cpv/
harpoon.html

Download various custom-built scenarios for the game Harpoon—such as Battle of the Faeroes, Soviet Raiders, and The Bedford Incident. Grab the newest version of the game (linked to Games Domain) or get the latest patch. This British Web page also highlights other Harpoon-related pages around the world.

Chris's Warcraft II Home Page
http://www.tiac.net/users/efields/
chriswc2.htm

Chris's goal is to offer helpful hints for Warcraft II (WC2) and the expansion pack ("Beyond the Dark Portal"). Neat sections include showing how the computer scores you, learn how to edit the game so you can have your name in other colors, download WC2 (11MB), or print out the strategy and glossary sections. Cool music (from the game) and animations fill this frames-enhanced site.

Civilization Page, The
http://www.lilback.com/civilization/

Mark Lilback's Civilization Page is a repository of information on various games that are titled "Civilization." The first was Avalon Hill's adaptation of the strategy turn-based board game Civilization, called Advanced Civilization. Sid Meier liked the game, and created the computer game Civilization, which is published by Microprose. This site also pays homage to CivNet (the networked version of Civilization), Civilization II, and Avalon Hill's computer version of Advanced Civilization. This Web site provides info, patches, FAQs, and news on all versions.

CivNet and the Internet
http://www.iag.net/~jlehett/civtech.html

A no-frills site designed to provide help to both the beginner and experienced CivNet gamers who want to play over the Internet (TCP/IP connection). This guide, by John Lehett, goes into a little more depth than the MicroProse help page, and aids in helping reduce the number of crashes and other problems with the game.

CivNet at ICV.Net
http://www.icv.net/~williams/civnet/
civnet.html

The purpose of this mailing list is to get a group of people on the Net to play a game of CivNet one night a week. If interested, submit your name but you will need to have a SLIP/PPP account and a copy of Microprose's CivNet. Are you a Civilization II fan? Then join the Civ II e-mailing club instead (http://www.icv.net/~williams/civ2/civ2.html).

CivNet Challenge Board
http://www.wizweb.com/arena/civnet/

Dedicated to Civ fanatics the world over to "reach out and crush someone." This challenge board allows you to post and view the many worldwide CivNet players for some head-to-head action. The Modem List breaks up each country, and city, into area code if you wish to find someone in your neighborhood to play against (and save money by not playing on the Net). The much needed CivNet patch, FAQ, and real-time Java chat are also available.

CivNet Pictures, Icons, and a Map
http://www.wam.umd.edu/~tjsjr/
civpics.html

A listing of the 28 units used in Sid Meier/MicroProse's CivNet—the online sequel to Civilization. Copy each picture separately or download them all as one zipped set—16 have been made into Windows icons, too. You may also copy the custom Roman maps and start your game using T. J. Spahr's challenging designs.

Clay's Strategy Gaming Page
http://www.geocities.com/TimesSquare/
5559/

A page designed to give you files to get creative on your current computer strategy favorites. Games relevant here are Command and Conquer, Warcraft II, C&C: Red Alert, Starcraft, and others. In each gaming section you can expect a scenario editor, cheat editors/codes, unit and level editors, conversion tools, and builders.

Close Combat League
http://lasvegas.sisna.com/wraith/

The primary goal of the Close Combat League (C.C.L.) is to match gamers to play over the Internet. You will also find information on new releases, tactics to use in fighting, or chat with other members to collect strategy tips. Scores are noted and recorded and players are partially matched based on this accumulated point system.

Close Combat Page, The
http://www.JointChiefsPub.com/dow/
close.htm

Part of the larger Department of War site, this page looks at Microsoft's strategic war game Close Combat (CC). Sections include an online discussion board, a product review area, CC strategies and tactics, or read the multiplayer FAQ (to read up on how to play CC head-to-head via your modem).

Close Combat: Posted Challenges
http://www.wizweb.com/arena/
closeCombat/board/get.cgi

Part of the larger Arena: The Multiplayer Challenge Site, this is a posting board for Atomic Games/Microsoft's Close Combat (CC) game. Register yourself or view the players list to see who you would like to play in some fierce online TCP/IP combat. You may also read the CC FAQ or flip through the related links section.

Close Combat: Trial Version
http://www.atomic.com/ccmain.html

The official site at Atomic Games for the Close Combat game, published under Microsoft. Download the demo (Windows 95 or Mac), view screen shots, FAQs, and the thorough game description and features. Close Combat places you as the battlefield commander in a WWII tactical level simulation.

Command and Conquer:
Red Alert—The Ultimate Page
http://www.geocities.com/SiliconValley/
Park/9927/MAIN.HTML

This site is dedicated only to the Command and Conquer (C&C): Red Alert game due out the fall of 1996 from Westwood Studios. Areas include the Red Alert story, game features, full size pictures and screen shots, improvements over C&C: Tiberium Dawn, and a handy map of this site.

◎ AUTHOR'S PICK

Command and Conquer Game Page, The

http://www.pernet.net/~rlong1/
command.html

A graphically intense and Crescendo-enhanced page with much to see, hear, and do. Westwood Studios' Command and Conquer gets the royal treatment: game info, news and demo, a real-time chat room, a modem players list, videos and music, editors, patches, cheats and FAQ's, new missions, resource pages and Kali pages, a Q & A board, and more. A modern and resourceful award-winning site. Also check out Grommet's related Red Alert page (http://www.pernet.net/~rlong1/redalert.html).

Command and Conquer Stuff
http://www.globalnet.co.uk/~alpat/cc.htm

A sleek page from the UK with custom levels by Web page creator Al Paterson (with screen shots and descriptions for "Commando Threat," "Subversion," "Genocide," and "Infiltration"), and many files to download including Kali software (to play over the Internet), editors, and other utilities.

Other Related Command and Conquer Pages

(In no particular order)

Alex's Command and Conquer Page
http://mmm.mbhs.edu/~aberenga/cc.html

All Those C & C Notes
http://www.netcom.com/~moises/ccnotes.html

All You Can Harvest - Command and Conquer
http://user.nxus.com/apothos/c&c/c&c.html

Ryan's Command and Conquer Page
http://www.geocities.com/TimesSquare/4344/command.html

Andrea's Command and Conquer Page
http://ourworld.compuserve.com/homepages/Andreas_Peterschelka/

Brian's Command and Conquer Page
http://www.lookup.com/Homepages/69636/cc/cc_home.html

C & C War Games
http://www.netcom.com/~beatle9/index.html

Chaos's Command & Conquer Page
http://home1.gte.net/sbenitez/index.htm

Unofficial Command and Conquer Page, The
http://tahoma.cwu.edu:2000/~wilsonb/cc.html

David's Command and Conquer Page
http://www.innosoft.com/www_root/doc/davidb/cc.htm

Complete Command and Conquer
http://www.cybercomm.net/~tsansone/westwood/

George Tan's Command & Conquer Page
http://www.communique.net/~dream/

Conquerer Zone
http://www.ipoline.com/~kwanli/cc.htm

Institute Hall Base
http://www.wpi.edu/~miranda/cc/

C & C Outpost
http://www.io.org/~isarog/c-c/php.cgi/~isarog/c-c/c-c.htm

Tore's Command & Conquer Page
http://login.eunet.no/~torehaug/C&C/c&c.html

Fun One's Command & Conquer page
http://www.tyler.net/funone/F1C&C.htm

Complete Carriers At War

http://members.aol.com/SimnationT/index.html
Spanish Mirrored Site:
http://users.aol.com/simnationt/docs/spanish/spanishindex.html

One of the only pages dedicated to SSG's game Complete Carriers At War. Chris Wieczorek's site honors this PC CD-ROM game that contains Carriers at War I, Carriers at War II, the Carriers at War Construction Kit, new Atlantic and Mediterranean scenarios, and all Carriers at War scenarios from SSG's *Run 5* magazine. Download scenarios, view screen shots, patches, sound files, and links.

Conquest of the New World

http://conquest.interplay.com/

The official page from Interplay Productions providing Conquest of the New World screen shots, information, a Shockwave introduction movie, demos, strategy tips, playing tricks, patches, and more. A beautiful page but check to make sure you have the Shockwave plug-in and at least Netscape 2.0 before entering or your browser may crash.

Cool Cat's Games

http://www.superb.net/~blank/cat.shtml

Masters of Orion II (MOO2) and Command and Conquer (C&C): Red Alert are the topics of discussion at this site. The section on MOO2: Battle at Antares provides a downloadable preview of the game, news, screen shots, a game outline, and links. The C&C: Red Alert area has much of the same—a product description, news and rumors, screen shots, unit types, and related links.

Dan Meadows' Empire Deluxe Strategy & Tactics Page

http://www.unf.edu/~dmeado/

Dan's two pages (strategy and tactics) are intended to help the novice Empire Deluxe player, but experienced players may find some ideas useful here. In Empire Deluxe you control your cities in the production of various land, air, and sea units (roughly ten—each with their own advantages and drawbacks). Use the handy diamond-shaped clickable graphic to take you to the desired section, and learn how to develop and defend, and expand and conquer.

Deadlock Splash Page
**http://www.accolade.com/products/
deadlock/index.html**

The official Accolade page for Deadlock—the planetary conquest strategy game where you can play against the computer, two-player serial link, two-player modem, seven-player LAN, and seven-player Internet play via Windows 95. This Web page allows you to download the demo, read the Deadlock Odyssey weekly saga, system specs, or view a Shockwave preview of this futuristic warfare sim.

Deadly Games
http://www.sir-tech.com/coming/deadly/

Sirtech's official page for the Jagged Alliance sequel. Read the system specs for Deadly Games, along with a thorough description of the game and if it sounds good to you download the free playable demo. Various screen shots are listed along the right side of the page.

Deemon's Lair, The
**http://www.teleport.com/~deemon/
index.html**

A combo site for Stars! and VGA Planets by 27-year-old Jay Teague. Both the VGA Planets and Stars! areas have new, current, and finished game status listings, and a Network help file to get going. It's obvious Jay plays Stars! a lot more since he's in the middle of about ten games now.

Diplomacy Home Page
http://www.infersys.com/diplomacy/

A thorough list of guides to Avalon Hill's play-by-email game, Diplomacy. Rules, FAQs, Judge* info and Judge Hall of Fame, links to Web and FTP sites or download the text or HTML version of the introduction to the game.

*Most e-mail play focuses around a set of systems running Ken Lowe's Diplomacy Adjudicator software (often referred to as "the Judge").

AUTHOR'S PICK
Department of War, The

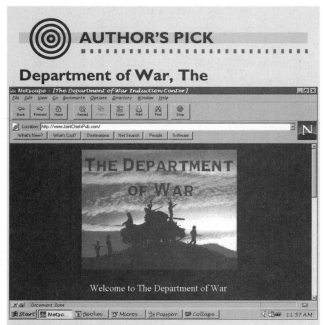

Welcome to The Department of War

http://www.JointChiefsPub.com/

A large interconnecting group of pages dedicated to computer war games. Up-to-date news, specialty sites on specific games, the Scenario Writer's Archive, a search engine and library (articles, reviews, stories, and more), and discussion groups make up the bulk of this mega site. The Scenario Writer's Archive contains additions for your Steel Panthers, Age of Rifles, Tanks!, Harpoon Classic, and Great Naval Battles games. A refreshing page with lots to read and download to supplement your favorite computer war games.

DM's CivNet Results Board
**http://www.ncweb.com/users/dm/
civnet.html**

A CivNet map repository of custom-built worlds, each with description, author name, or the option to download them all in one file. Read the CivNet FAQ and system requirements, view the player's directory (if you're looking for an online opponent), or check out the city of Ulundi getting nuked in a cool animated mini-movie.

Doug Woods Civilization 2 Page
http://www.webcom.com/drwoods/civ2.html
Doug provides novices or expert Civ 2 gamers with various unofficial and online FAQs, updates, patches/fixes, scenarios (30+), maps, other utilities, and game-related links. A cool scenario to check out is the U.S. role if Quebec separates from Canada!

Edmond's Command and Conquer Hint Page
http://www.cse.unsw.edu.au/~s2154869/cc.html
Gorgeous site from Edmond Gock in Australia, dedicated to helping you along with games Command and Conquer (C&C), Covert Operations, or Red Alert. Sections include: About The Game, Initial Hints, Leadership and Efficiency Ratings, Multiplayer Mode, Selling Units, Structures, Weapons, A Complete Walk-through, and Links. Click on the "Java Page" button and treat yourself to a mini-movie, straight out of the intro from C&C.

Empire Hall of Fame, The
http://web.mit.edu/madpit/www/empire/
The Empire Hall of Fame was created in 1992 by the Suboceanaen Arts and War Academy. It is maintained by Doug Pitters and recognizes legendary exploits of past rulers of the popular multiplayer strategic war game, Empire. To be listed here is a great honor and you, too, could be a winner of the illustrious (and real) Subby award, so point your browser to http://www.empire.net/~children/pea_pages/games.html, see who's playing, and join in.

Empire Info Pages
http://www.empire.net/~harmless/info/
A plain FTP-like site that is essentially a large list of terms used in the multiplayer war game Empire. Over 150 words are defined and used as strategy tips along with how to execute them in the game. A resourceful page for the novice Empire gamer. Example: this info page describes four different commands: "attack," "assault," "paradrop," and "board." These are the four

commands that you use to take something (ship or sector) from the enemy by force. A combat has 15 steps...

Fields of Battle
http://www.login.dknet.dk/~bvlstone/fob/fob.html
Download the free Windows or Amiga demo to this strategic warfare game that begins in World War I. View a detailed game description, screen shots, plus tips and tricks to conquering the game. For registered Amiga user, grab a copy of SNOW; the Fields of Battle mission editor.

Fight, Win, Prevail
http://www.geocities.com/SiliconValley/Park/6127/cc.html
This site provides info and files on the real-time combat strategy game Command and Conquer (C&C) by Westwood Studios. Game features, screen shots, editors, utilities, and an unofficial strategy guide are your options here. For more on C&C: Red Alert, go to http://www.geocities.com/SiliconValley/Park/6127/redalert.html.

GameChat Question Zone, The
http://www.vistech.net/users/kingn/wwwboard/wwwboard.html
From the creator of the Diablo page, comes the GameChat Question Zone—type in your query about any computer and you should have an answer back in no time! (Where was this site when I was stuck on Civilization?!)

Gamelord's Realm, The
http://www.gamelord.com/civ/
By the time you read this the page should be back from some construction work. It will highlight the Civilization II and Masters of Orion II: Battle of Antares computer strategy games. The Civ II section will offer many scenarios and maps to customize your game. Netscape 3, Microsoft Internet Explorer 3, and Crescendo are recommended for use with this page.

Gamespot's Close Combat Page

http://www.gamespot.com/features/
closecombat/index.html

This site is the Close Combat strategic operations guide by Kevin Mical. Cited as one of the best tactical-level computer war games, each side (American and German) is given strategy tips and tactics for each mission in order to stay alive and persevere. A very helpful page—one to bookmark if you're into this game.

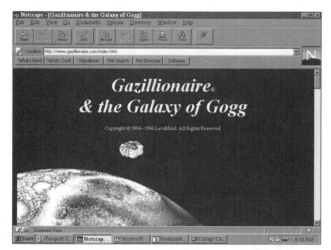

Gazillionaire & The Galaxy of Gogg

http://www.gazillionaire.com/index.html

LavaMind's strategic space Monopoly-style game of intergalactic trade, Gazillionaire, is offered here, so read some previews and reviews of the game, or better yet, download a free demo to try out yourself. The goal of the game is to sell the cargo out of your spaceship and strive to earn one million *kubars* before your alien competitors beat you to it.

General's Page, The

http://www.JointChiefsPub.com/dow/
generals.htm

This resouceful award-winning site highlights Mindscape/SSI's Panzer General and Allied General computer war games. Part of the larger Department of War mega site (war game pages, military history sites, and wargaming companies for the Mac or PC), this area focuses on the General's electronic strategy guide to Allied General and is quite a hot download here.

German World of Warcraft II, The

http://members.aol.com/laberkopf/
war2.html

This Warcraft II: Tides of Darkness page is written in German, for those of you inclined to understand it. But it's not too hard to figure out what is available: a Warcraft II demo, cheat codes (including a money cheat), a trainer (in English), info on playing Warcraft on Kali, and other Warcraft II links.

Goat Locker, The

http://www.mbnet.mb.ca/~moreau/
harpoon.html

Find out info on the computer and miniatures versions of the naval war game Harpoon created by Larry Bond. Learn more about, or subscribe to, the Convergence Zone (CZ) or download scenarios and back issues of CZ. (E-mail discussion lists based on Harpoon.) Related links are also available.

Great Naval Battles

http://www.JointChiefsPub.com/dow/
gnbattles.htm

A support page for the Great Naval Battles III and IV players (SSI's Advanced Simulation Series). There are four or five game and scenario editor updates/patches. Upload your own tactical studies (scenarios, battles) to the Department of War Archive Center for others to download and try on for size.

Grunge's Starcraft Page

http://pwp.starnetinc.com/grunge/
starcraft.html

Warcraft II in space! Blizzard's latest creation Starcraft is a real-time strategy game of interstellar combat. Choose which race to rule (Terran, Protoss, or Zurg)—and achieve galactic dominion, or freedom, through military expansion and/or defense. View many screen shots and previews to the game.

Grognard's Web Site - the place for Wargamers on the Web

http://grognard.com/

Grognard: a soldier of Napoleon's Old Guard; a veteran soldier; grumbler (French)—Oxford English Dictionary, 2nd edition. It also is slang for someone who likes playing war games. This huge site pays homage to the latter definition—all known war games are listed alphabetically (to access hints, strategies, tactics, screen shots, demos, patches, editors, etc.), but it doesn't stop just there. Trivia games (e.g. identify the war game by looking at the map…), links to war game companies, individual pages, magazines, news, and other downloads are accessible (many other war game add-ons such as scenarios, maps, units, and other extras. This site grew out of the now-defunct Grognards anonymous FTP archive (Joe Boeke's) but now relies on input from the newsgroup rec.games.board, The Virtual Wargamer Headquarters Discussion Board Web Site, and from individual contributions.

Harmless Guide to Empire, A

http://www.empire.net/~harmless/guide.html

Another no-frills Empire site designed for the beginner gamer. Empire is a real-time strategic war game—you can go at it by yourself or ally with whomever you choose. A game typically lasts for weeks or months and ends when a single player or a group declares victory with no resistance from others. The game can be very complex so this guide attempts to simplify its rules and tactics.

Harpoon II

http://www.customcpu.com:80/personal/sbond/

Welcome to the renovated Harpoon II (H2) home page, a site dedicated to the Naval warfare simulator and its fans. Subscribe to the H2 newsletter on scenario designing (taken over from creator Rodney Harper), engage in the H2 discussion group, or take a look through the related links.

Harpoon Classic

http://www.JointChiefsPub.com/dow/harpoon_classic.htm

Essentially a support page to give you access to the latest updates and demos for the Harpoon Classic game. DOS, Mac, and Windows files are available for download, as well as a FAQ file (v1.4), and a resource center for Harpoon Classic scenario writers and players.

Harpoon Deluxe II

http://www.rz.uni-frankfurt.de/~oweber/ h2.html

Tons to see and do here for the IntraCorp Harpoon II (H2) fan. Snag the final H2 update (to run scenarios created with H2 Deluxe MultiMedia), read the latest version of the official FAQ (provided by Three-Sixty), a document explaining several technical terms important to naval warfare (cool!), and the H2 Deluxe MultiMedia Scenario Magazine! The European mirror to the scenario page is http://www.rz.uni-frankfurt.de/ ~oweber/scenario.mirror.html.

Heroes of Might and Magic

http://www.nwcomputing.com/heroes/ heroes.html

New World Computing's official site for their award-winning strategy game (Computer Gaming World's "Strategy Game of the Year" and five-star rating [out of five], Computer Games Strategy Plus's "Turn-Based Strategy Game Of The Year," Computer Game Review's "Golden Triad Award," and PC Gamer's "Editor's Choice"). View many screen shots, read the operating system requirements (DOS, Windows 95, or Mac), game features, and links. For information on Heroes of Might and Magic II: The Succession Wars, point your browser to http://www.nwcomputing.com/ heroes2/.

Heroes of Might and Magic FAQ v1.1

http://www.users.fast.net/~ktolar/geoweb/ homm/homm.htm

This Web site is intended to offer tips and address some of the frequently asked questions (FAQs) on the computer strategy game Heroes of Might and Magic by New World Computing. Feel free to ask questions if the answers provided still don't answer your queries. There is a lot here to read but a shorter FAQ is available at http://www.nwcomputing.com/ faq/faq.html#Heroes.

Independent Player's Home Page

http://ourworld.compuserve.com/ homepages/Pode/

The Independent Player's Home Page for Wargames and Strategy Games provides strategy guides for hot war games and strategy games, read up on "new" and "cool" stuff, find out how to contact publishers, or use the handy built-in search engine to find what you want. Computes games such as Steel Panthers, Civilization II, Panzer General, Command and Conquer, TacOps, and the like, are all covered here.

J. Michael Tisdel's Warhammer 40,000 Web Resource

http://web2.airmail.net/jtisdel/w40k.html

Games Workshop's Warhammer 40,000 is a science fiction miniatures strategy game set in the 40th millennium. This page offers variations of the customizable game designed by J. Michael Tisdel or previously available from the Warhammer 40,000 mailing lists and the rec.games.miniatures.warhammer newsgroup.

Jagged Alliance Official Page

http://sir-tech.com/games/jagged/

Sirtech's main page for their computer strategy hit "Jagged Alliance." Read the reviews and awards or head straight for the free downloadable demo (2.4MB and an optional Speech Pack, 1.4MB). Read the official game description and features, or click to enlarge each of the screen shots. You may also order the full game online through the Sirtech Company Store with a valid credit card.

Jagged Alliance Strategy Page

http://www.gamesdomain.co.uk/walkthru/ ja.html

This is Games Domain's walkthrough page for Sirtech's hit strategy game "Jagged Alliance." There are over 30 pages of text to sift through here, so you may want to download it as a .TXT or .DOC file, and read it offline. Aside from the intro, the sections outlining different facets of the game are: Game Objectives; Hiring, Firing & Dealing With Mercs & Natives; Game

Tips; Breakdown of Game Items; If You're in a Money Bind; Cheats; and Tips for Saving Your Game. Resource page for beginners of the game.

Java Blackjack
http://www.atext.com/people/skister/ BJ.html

No downloading time is necessary here and you can enjoy the thrills of the age-old 21 on simulated green felt. The player can use either the mouse or the keyboard to hit, stay, double down, or split your dealt cards. No music or sound effects, however, but there is a clever high-score side-bar so others can see your name after you are gone from the site...that is, if you are good enough! Simple yet competent Java Applet you may want to visit often.

Jenga's Custom Warcraft II PUD Files
http://www.wincam.com/jim/Warcraft2/ index.html

Just as the Web site name indicates, pick up some custom-built PUDs (maps, scenarios) to use with Warcraft II. These are designed for 2 player use (via modem, network, or direct connect) in cooperative battles versus up to SIX computer opponents. Try out "Assault" or "Crossing." Screen shots are shown.

Jorg's Outpost Home Page
http://zeus.uni-duisburg.de/~stenger/ Outpost/

Although this site is fairly outdated, you can still access many important files to help you along with your game. Download Outpost patches (floppy or CD version), the official FAQ file (HTML and text version), strategy tips, saved games, and more.

LeadEaters PBEM Wargaming Club Site
http://205.180.52.4:80/leadeaters/

I think their own description of their page explains it best. "Leadeaters is a bunch of total computer war game maniacs, of which I am one. We love to neglect our household chores and families for a little play by

mail computer wargaming..." Their mission is to recruit more and more online subscribers into playing e-mail war games. This free club supports the following games: Atomic/AH's World at War series, SSI's Panzer General, Allied General, and Steel Panthers, and AH's Flight Commander II, and TacOps.

Lemmings Games Web Site
http://stud1.tuwien.ac.at/~e8826423/ Lemmings.html

Download demos, FAQs, patches, helpful tips, codes, solutions, cheats, technical assistance, and screen shots for the strategy game Lemmings and its sequels: On No! More Lemmings, Lemmings for Windows, OS/2, Lemmings—The Tribes, Christmas Lemmings 1991 and 1992 (demos), Holiday Lemmings 1993 and 1994, Lemmings 3 (All New World of Lemmings alias The Chronicles), 3D Lemmings, and Lemmings Paintball.

Other Lemmings Sites:

Tom's Spiffin's Lemming Page
http://www.halcyon.com/oatesjam/lemming.htm

Psygnosis O"nline
http://www.psygnosis.com/

Mac Wargame Support
http://www-leland.stanford.edu/~hills/ games.html

Matthew Hills provides editors, patches, custom scenarios, and other utilities for Macintosh versions of Mindscape/SSI's Allied General, Panzer General, Microsoft's Close Combat, and SSG's Warlords II. Many war game-related Web sites are provided as links.

Mark's Battleground: Waterloo Page
http://www.ndirect.co.uk/~mst/

This is Mark's "humble" attempt (his words) to provide information, tactical advice, and links to other sites of interest relating to TalonSoft's Battleground Waterloo CD-ROM computer war game. View tactics and tips, upgrade info, hints on playing by e-mail, and Napoleonic pictures (plus game-related screen shots).

Master of Magic 2 Web Page

http://www.aloha.com/~knightsoft/mom2/mom2.html

Master of Magic 2 (MOM2) is really just the name for a large program that you will install in your MOM directory. This program, while requiring MOM version 1.31 to work, will completely change most aspects of the game and will create almost an entirely new experience, although using the same engine. This site looks at the latest news, what exactly MOM2 is, why MOM2, who's in charge, where one gets a copy of it (and when), and links.

Masters of Orion Information Center

http://student.uq.edu.au/~s321643/mooic.html

In anticipation of the release of Masters of Orion II (MOO2): Battle at Antares, the folks here down under give news, rumors, screen shots, and a preview to the game as well as provide information and utilities for the original master of Orion (MOO). There is an online MOO strategy guide and a downloadable free game cheater.

Masters of Orion Macintosh FAQ

http://www.westol.com/~t2supprt/moomac.htm

Updated in the summer of 1996, this Mac FAQ is designed to provide info, tips, and answers to Masters of Orion (MOO) space strategy fans. This is part of the larger Take 2 Interactive Web Site. The official FAQ (for all versions) can be found at http://www.gamesdomain.co.uk/moo/moo13.html.

McDeth's Home Page for Warcraft 2

http://www.geocities.com/Hollywood/1955/

McDeth and associates have designed this page to provide Warcraft II PUD files (made by McDeth or others). Not much else is here but if you're looking for some custom-made scenarios for Blizzard's hit game—download what these guys have to offer and try 'em on for size. Doom and Doom II WADs are also up for grabs.

Mike Laver's Warcraft II Page

http://home.earthlink.net/~lavers/War2/war2.htm

The Warcraft II story outline, demos, news, cheats, strategy tips, game, and Kali patch (for Internet play), and other editors and utilities are available here. The PUD Palace contains custom-built single-player or multiplayer PUDs to download to use with your Warcraft II game.

Military Connection, The

http://www.accessone.com:80/~riccrowe/military.html

Essentially a links page taking you to *real* Military Web sites on the Net. But they're not about games, you ask? Well, visit a few of these Army, Navy, Marine Corps, and Air Force pages, and you'll be surprised how much it'll improve your next flight combat sim endeavor or strategic land-based military game.

Miniatures WWW Archive

http://www.cabm.rutgers.edu/~hooper/miniatures/miniatures.html

This plain page contains links to a number of resources, articles, and pictures related to the miniature war gaming hobby. Hot-link to the Historical Miniature Wargame Web Site, Man O' War Official Questions and Answers, view the Miniatures Picture Gallery, and more. E-mail queries to creator Britt Klein.

Modem Games Yellow Pages

http://www.azstarnet.com/~doomgod/

The Modem Games Yellow Pages (MGYP) were created to assist gamers in finding people in their area code to play computer modem games with. Strategy games such as Command and Conquer and Warcraft II are solid examples (next to the usual line-up of action games). This is a great idea since many of us would rather play for free in our area against someone rather than spending online time to play head-to-head with someone over the Net. Also, most of us don't have access to Networked stations either. Add your name to the list or search the large database for locals. You may also download a selection of Doom WADs while you're here.

Multiplayer Master of Magic Shell, Editor, and Scenario Generator
http://users.aol.com/mmoms/mmoms.html
This unofficial FTP-like site gives general game description and information on the multiplayer Master of Magic (MMOMs). You can download the latest shareware version of MMOMS (v4.2) or upgrade (get the patch to v4.2s), access support (for shareware and registered users), or upload/download scenarios. Other links to MOM sites are here, too.

Neggs Civilization II Web Page
http://zen.sunderland.ac.uk/~tb5nho/
Well, I can honestly say I've never been to a "Non-Smoking" Web site before. One of the UK's first Civilization II pages contains scenarios, maps, patches, and links. You may want to "borrow" the wallpaper at this site too (it's pretty cool). The scenarios section has some interesting downloads.

Nexus: Warhammer 40,000
http://www.aloha.com/~isaac/wh40k.htm
Graphics and animations fill the "high-bandwidth" section of Isaac Tobin's page. The Nexus is a home to supplement the popular Warhammer 40,000 strategy space game. Pictures of his Tyranids (clay, plastic and paint—before the codex and real Tyranids came out) are very impressive, and read the pages on new rules for Marines, Chaos, and Tyranids. And much more...

Novastar's Steel Panthers Page
http://www.vfr.net/~novastar/steel.htm
Here is the latest patch for Steel Panthers (v1.2 called steel12n.zip). This version corrects the problem which did not allow the campaigns to be played. View screen shots or read the synopsis of various add-on scenarios to purchase.

Officer's Club, The
http://www.shout.net/~freasoc8/
Welcome to the club where you will be able to find play-by-electronic-mail opponents for Mindscape/SSI's Panzer General and Allied General. As with many other multiplayer war game pages, they keep a ladder to measure your skills against the competition around the Net. Also download patches, scenarios, or get a free copy of Bill Haering's Allied General Scenario Generator.

Planet's Empire Archives, The
http://www.empire.net/~children/
Empire is one of the more popular strategy war games played by a number of people on the Net (usually between four and 100). Download software, documents, FAQs, operating system software, Mpeg movies, statistics, or go through the related links section. A different, randomly generated map for you to view appears with each visit here.

Planet Stars!
http://www.douzer.com/
A Web site about the Stars! multiplayer space strategy game. Visit the "Information Library" (what is Stars! anyway?), the "Literature Library" (new and famous Stars! stories), the "StarsoRama Mall" (shareware and screen shots), the "Gaming Center" (new and current Stars! games) and the "Stargate Warp Center" (other cool pages).

Prisoners of Warcraft

http://members.gnn.com/ClueEDM/pow.htm

Click on the picture if you want to enter the Humans or Orcs POW site (Prisoners of Warcraft). Once inside your desired race, read the POW guide to playing Warcraft II on Kali, download the demo, cheats, patches, news, expansion pack info or visit the PUD vault. Nice graphics from this Minnesota fan-related Web site.

PUDland

http://eggcite.com/pudland/

PUDland introduces the first online PUD Database! All PUDs (custom-made maps, scenarios, levels) on the site are now stored and are searchable by number of players, date of upload, type of game (single-player, multiplayer, cooperative, Deathmatch play), and author. Map images are now presented in a pop-up Javascript window for easy viewing. Submit a PUD, view other Warcraft II links, access cheat codes, or read Shlonglor's strategies.

PUD Page, The

http://www.acsu.buffalo.edu/~kazial/war2.html

PUDs, PUDs, and more PUDs. Download various custom-built maps and scenarios to use with your Warcraft II game—single-player, two-player, three-player, or PUDs by Rank (you can read up on the ranking system, too). Game strategies and links are provided.

Other PUD Pages for Warcraft II

UnderDark
http://http.tamu.edu:8000/~mjn0219/

Madman's Multiplayer PUDs
http://www.itsnet.com/~madman/puds.htm

Lord Red's PUD Page
http://www.geocities.com/TimesSquare/3001/index.html

Dark Portal, The
http://www.dawwn.com/warcraft.sht

EvilByte's Warcraft II Library
http://www.cuug.ab.ca:8001/~bereznii/war2.html

Lord Fett's Warcraft II Page
http://www.dragonfire.net/~dayton/war2.htm

Fragfest Warcraft II PUD Page
http://www.iblinc.com/fragfest/puds/misc/

Kenny Chong Warcraft Resources
http://www.geocities.com/Tokyo/2077/warcraft.html

Ian's Macintosh PUDs
http://www.axess.com/users/iano/pud.html

Jerry's Warcraft II PUD Page
http://www4.ncsu.edu/unity/users/j/jchinn/public/wc2pud.htm

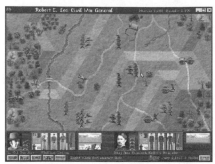

Robert E. Lee's Civil War General

http://www.sierra.com/entertainment/
civilwar/

The official page, by Sierra, for the Civil War General CD-ROM. This strategic war game puts you in charge of the Army of Northern Virginia through eight of the most famous battles of the Civil War. View screen shots, read an in-depth synopsis of the game, or purchase the game from Sierra's Online store.

Rob's Might and Magic Home Page

http://www.jagunet.com/~robertm/
homm.html

A fan-related page honoring New World Computing's hit fantasy empire builder game Heroes of Might and Magic (HOMM). Gaming news (and rumors on HOMM2), reviews and strategies are provided, along with new custom levels (DOS, Windows 95), and maps (Windows 95 only). Read up on past Might and Magic adventures (when they were still role-playing games) including solutions for almost all of the first five games. Killer wallpaper, too!

RYYT's CivNet Page

http://www.ualberta.ca/~wtsang/civnet.html

This Canadian Web page pays homage to CivNet and provides an introduction to the game, system requirements, game features, and a guide on how to network the game. Other noteworthy sections include cheat codes, screen shots, the FAQ file, and links to related Web pages, newsgroups, and #IRC chat.

AUTHOR'S PICK

RYYT's Unofficial Warcraft II Page

http://www.ualberta.ca/~wtsang/war2/
war2.html

A very nice-looking, well-organized, and resourceful center for Warcraft II info and files. As with his Civ-Net page, Edmonton's RYYT offers Warcraft II fans (or soon-to-be fans) a taste of the game and other game-related accessories. Download the PC demo, some Warcraft II Microsoft Plus! Pack themes, or extra PUD maps (by RYYT and others). Read the story behind Blizzard's hit game, system requirements, notes on Internet play, cheat codes or view various screen shots.

Saul's Harpoon Page

http://www.flash.net/~sjacobs/

Read the Harpoon FAQ, subscribe to the e-mailing list for the latest info (on Harpoon I, Harpoon Classics and Harpoon II war games), or download various utilities for the Mac or PC (IRC clients, unzippers, etc.). Also available: a related links area and an IRC section for chat.

Schwerpunkt
http://www.ghgcorp.com/schwerpt/
There ARE other computer game companies in Texas besides id and Origin, you know. This is the official page to Schwerpunkt—PC software for the serious historian or War buff. Games such as Rostov, Leningrad, Kiev, and Crimea focus in on little-known or neglected WWII battles with historically accurate maps. Read critics' reviews of Schwerpunkt's games or order them with a valid credit card ($29.95 each).

Shattered Steel: Index
http://www.bioware.com/ssindex.htm
A very modern-looking Web site devoted to Interplay's anticipated Shattered Steel CD-ROM. Download various demos to try out, read the Shattered Steel background story and game features, and preview the making of Shattered Steel.

Shlonglor's Warcraft II Page
http://www.andrews.edu/~fraizer/war2.cgi
This huge Warcraft II site relies on six computers to keep up and running. Geoff Frazier's page has many sections including "News and other stuff," "Warcraft II Kali players list," and "Who's Better: Orcs or Humans" (he argues for both). Lots more to read and download here: game features, spells, units, buildings, strategies, PUDs, utilities, FAQs, Kali info, and more.

Sid Meier's Civilization II
http://ftp.microprose.com/civII/
View various screen shots from Civilization II (Civ II), info and game specs, the patch (version 2.41), the official FAQ file, additional scenarios by Mick Uhl, and related links. The Official page to Sid Meier's Civ II also has a handy tech support area—fill in your name, e-mail address, and query.

Sid Meier's CivNet
http://www.microprose.com/civnet/
This is the official page at Microprose for their best-selling multiplayer sequel to Civilization. Get pertinent game information, the patch, read the official CivNet FAQ or the "CivNET and Internet Play" help file, and register with or peruse the Players Directory if you're looking for an online opponent.

Silent Service Wargamers Club
http://mypage.direct.ca/f/flatline/index.html
The fastest growing Wargaming Play-by-e-mail site on the World Wide Web. Headed by Canadian Ryan Shuttleworth, they support SSI strategy war games such as Panzer General, Allied General, Fantasy General, and Steel Panthers. Close Combat, The Battleground Series, and Age of Rifles are coming soon. Membership is free and read how it works at this site.

Silicon Wargamer, The
http://www5.palmnet.net/~tkm/
This site is dedicated to the avid computer war gamer. Close Combat, Steel Panthers, and Steel Panthers II are highlighted games for now although more are promised in the near future. Microsoft's Close Combat section contains a strategy guide, how to get hooked-up with another player, screen shots, or you can download the Windows 95 demo of the game.

Spanish Civilization II Page
http://www.ctv.es/USERS/aleal/home.htm
Antonio Leal's page is in both English and Spanish despite the name. Sections include The Scenario Dimension (downloadable custom-made scenarios and

maps), The Civ2 Solutions (mini FAQ and unknown facts), The Strategy Zone (tactical tips and helpful hints), and The Best Civ2 Links (game-related sources around the Net).

Starcraft Home Page

http://www.blizzard.com/star/star.htm

The official page to Blizzard's intergalactic real-time strategy game. View pages of screen shots and read the system requirements and game features. Starcraft is scheduled for a first quarter 1997 release for the PC and Mac and Warcraft II fans from around the world are waiting with bated breath for this space title.

Stars! Depot

http://www.plws.com/stars/findex.html

Alan's site is a tribute to the popular Stars! Space strategy multiplayer conquest game. Sections to mention include a news and current happenings page, a resource page, player's data base, and an area where you can download the latest shareware version (v2.6?). Many relevant (and resourceful) links are given. Check out the official Stars! home page at http://www.webmap.com/stars/.

Stars! +Zone, The

http://users.aol.com/corpwhore/index.htm

This is not a strategy site to aid you with your game, but is a good place for beginners that are interested in learning how to play Stars! This page is basically an introduction to the game, complete with screen shots and descriptions.

Steel Panthers

http://www.JointChiefsPub.com/dow/panthers.htm

As with the other computer war games highlighted in the Department of War site, you can access playing tips and tactics for Steel Panther (SP) and SP scenarios, read a review of the SP campaign disks (by Rodney Harper), join the SP e-mailing list, or download the many scenario development tools and resources.

German Steel Panthers Page
http://members.aol.com/vorsteher/simtest.htm

French and English Steel Panthers Page
http://www.infologo.ch/w_sphome

Another Steel Panthers Page
http://ally.ios.com/~oh2dogs9/steel.html

PC Review Magazine
http://www.megatoon.com/~t15/issue10/steel.htm

icon.john.com Web Page - Steel Panthers Review
http://www.iconjohn.com/category/pubsher/mc/mcsteel1.html

Steel Panthers (PC Entertainment)

http://www.pcentertainment.com/games/Dec95/steel1295.html

PC Entertainment's Steve Klett reviews and rates SSI's war game Steel Panthers by covering game play, setup, sound, and graphics. Strategy tips and company information is also available here.

Steel Panthers, by SSI

http://kumo.swcp.com/coach/vre/strategy/steelpanthers.html

A positive review of SSI's computer war game instant classic Steel Panthers. System requirements, game features, background story, screen shots are all included here. Andy Hardison awards Steel Panthers an overall 80% (with graphics and "fun" the highest ratings, and "interface" is rated the lowest).

Strategic Simulations, Inc.

http://www.ssionline.com/cgi-bin/start

The official page to such strategy/war computer favorites Steel Panthers, Silent Hunter, Panzer General, Allied General, and Fantasy General. Choose your browser and download demos, patches, FAQs, and hints, or read up on SSI info, news, tech support, previews, and more.

Strategies For a Deity

**http://ourworld.compuserve.com/
homepages/Pode/civ2.htm**

Strategies For a Deity is an unofficial strategy guide
written by avid players—for avid players—of Civilization II. It is an "interactive" electronic book for Windows 3.1, 95, or DOS, focusing on winning strategies
at deity level. It's designed for both beginners and hard
core Civ2 veterans. Read about the program here or
order it online for $10.00 U.S. (it gets sent attached to
an e-mail message). This is one of Pascal Ode's pages
(Independent Player's Home Page).

TacOps Info

http://www.why.net/users/wes/TacOps.html

An introduction to the 1994 winner of many Mac strategic game awards. Now available on Windows too,
TacOps is a strategic tactical level war game which
simulates armored combat on the modern battlefield.
Get the PBEM list, download strategy tips and tricks,
scenario guide and maps, and more. Note: most files
are for the Mac operating system.

TacOps Page, The

**http://www.JointChiefsPub.com/dow/
tacops.htm**

Download the TacOps demo for the PC or Mac. The
CPX section includes downloadable files offering advice on using the TacOps game engine to set up a multiplayer club-style game or military-style Command
Post Exercise. Other notables are the TacOps FAQ,
game description and information, updates, bug fix
patches, and strategy tips. This is part of the much
larger Department of War site.

TANKS!

**http://www.JointChiefsPub.com/dow/
tanks.htm**

If you own TANKS!—the Wargame Construction Set
II, then download the 1.3 update or visit the archive
center that provides user-built and submitted scenarios
available for download (by Trey Marshall and Jim Miles).

AUTHOR'S PICK

TalonSoft Web Page

http://www.talonsoft.com/

Welcome to the official site of TalonSoft—creators of
historical strategy games developed for Windows (3.1
and 95). Successes such as the Battleground series
(Gettysburg, Waterloo, Shiloh, Ardennes) have put
this company on the war gamer's map of excellence.
This terrific page contains many "rooms" divided up
into: The Enlistment Room (add yourself to the e-mail
list, post a message on the discussion board, or do online ordering), The Briefing Room (info on current
games, screen shots, upgrades), The Intelligence
Room (info on upcoming games, screen shots), The
Recon Room (how to contact TalonSoft and links to
other cool Web sites), and finally, The Debriefing
Room (e-mail links for suggestions and comments
about the games, FAQs, modem game set-up instructions). A very resourceful company site with lots to
read and download.

Unfortunately there's nothing here at the Department
of War for those of you who are curious about the
game and want to read more before purchasing.

Tanker's Home Page

http://www.rapidramp.com/tanker/

Meritorious of *The Net* magazine's "Site of the Month" honor, the Tanker's Home Page is a strategy and military historian's dream. Created by Paul J. Calvi Jr., a graduate of the U.S. Army School and the Ft.Knox Armor Officer Basic Course, this Web site is an appreciation to war games and land, sea, air, and space battle simulations alike. Numerous insightful departments can be found here including "At Ease" (war-related films and video snips) and "The Discussion HQ" (The Tanker's forums). Veteran stories, book reviews, an online store, real military articles and other related links are all at this unique and resourceful Web site.

Tariq and Marc's 2Cool Warcraft2 Page

http://www.eburg.com/~chandlel/war2.html

This page provides a description and pictures of all of the characters, buildings, and towers in Blizzard's hit Warcraft II. If you like what you see, click on the logo and download the demo from the Blizzard home page. Tariq and Marc's Warcraft II Air and Water page is at http://www.eburg.com/~chandlel/war22.html.

Temple of the Conquerer

http://www10.torget.se/temple/

A nicely designed frames-enhanced Command and Conquer (C&C) page for the advanced gamer. The layout is refreshingly different and is divided into sections: The Construction Yard, The Temple, Library of Conquest, Press Center, Tech Center, Barracks, Intelligence Center, and Airport. Each serves their own function but I found the Construction Yard the most resourceful: editing and construction tools, mission packs, modified game.dat files, patches, saved games, trainers, the C&C scenario, and map and structure editors. There are many levels and mission packs to try out as well as other miscellaneous downloadable goodies.

Mirrored Sites:
http://www-personal.umich.edu/~vecna/temple/
or
ftp://ftp.arkham.be/pub/temple/

Tim's Civ 2 Page

http://www.swlink.net/~milo/

Heavy on downloadable custom maps, this site offers most of what is available at other Civilization II Web pages: scenarios, maps, strategy FAQ, MOD packs, hints and tips, and links. There are a good two dozen maps to try out including Quebec Canada, a set of Maps For Navy Folks, and Vietnam.

U.F.O./X-COM - The Terran Defense

http://www.franken.de/users/speedy/hakan/
hobbies/daddel/xcom/Welcome-e.html

An English and German FTP-like Web site gives information about MicroProse's hit game X-COM (originally called U.F.O. but was changed when released in the U.S.). Download some stories and editors for the game or hot-link to Hakan's X-COM sequel page: Terror From the Deep (another bilingual page) at http:// www.franken.de/users/speedy/hakan/hobbies/daddel/ tftd/Welcome-e.html.

Ultimate Warcraft Page, The

http://www.teleport.com/~cschaye/
warcraft.html

Contrary to the title, all this page offers are a few Warcraft links around the Net. If you need to find some cool sites to satiate your Orc or Human hunger, check these links out but don't bother visiting here for any other reason.

Unofficial Close Combat Headquarters

http://www.worldvillage.com/~tmurff/cchq/
cchq.cgi

This site is designed to assist Close Combat players with the difficult task of locating other Internet players. Resister your name, IP address, what side you're on (American, German, Either), Maneuver, and Battle, then click on the "Check For Games" button to display who's playing.

Other Civilization II Pages of Interest

Civilization II Page!
http://www.goodnet.com/~snitz/civ2/
civindex.html

Anxiety's Civilization II Page
http://www.serve.com/anxiety/civ2.shtml

Sid Meier's Civilization II Page (Official Page)
http://www.microprose.com/civII/

Sun Tsu's War Academy
http://www.serve.com/anxiety/civ2stgy.shtml

Unofficial Civilization II Page, The
http://www.xpoint.at/datcom/matthias/civ2/

IP Homepage For Civilization II Page, The
http://ourworld.compuserve.com/homepages/
POde/civ2.htm

Justin's Civ 2 Page
http://spruce.evansville.edu/~jg22/civ2.html

Paul's Civilization page
http://www.clark.net/pub/pgilbert/civ2.html

Unofficial Master of Magic Homepage, The

http://www.proaxis.com/~jarvinen/magic/
magic.shtml

An attractive page designed for the Master of Magic (MOM) fan, MicroProse's computer fantasy strategy game. View or download current news and articles, links to other MOM pages, editors, patches (v1.31), Cup Challenges, hints, the Hero's List, and other miscellaneous stuff. Popular reading here is The Saxon Diaries—the literary Saga of Master Wizard Dan Saccavino.

AUTHOR'S PICK

Ultimate Civilization II Web Site, The

http://www.dreamscape.com/overlord/civ2.html

Make sure you view the following pages in Microsoft's Internet Explorer 3.0 or Netscape 2.02 or higher (with the Crescendo plug-in). This is a beautifully designed page chock-full of great info and downloads for Civilization II (Civ2). Areas include a What's New section (current news), a message board, chat room, hints and tips, scenarios, maps, MOD files, tournament games, a Hall of Fame, and links. Lots to do, see, hear, and download here.

AUTHOR'S PICK

Ultimate Command and Conquer File Collection, The

http://www.k2.org/

There are hundreds of Web sites dedicated to Westwood's hit real-time strategy game Command and Conquer (C&C) and it's inevitable that some will rise above the rest. This is the case here with the many map packs, single-player and multiplayer mission packs, bonus levels and campaigns, saved games—for both GDI and NOD sides. There are also editors, mission builders, patches, and other utilities available for download. This page is attractive, conveniently organized, and extremely resourceful housing hundreds of free files to last you ages.

Unofficial Warcraft II Homepage
http://www.spods.dcs.kcl.ac.uk/~jessie/
UK's Jessica and EZRhino's site offers the Warcraft II (WC2) fan cheat codes, strategies, custom-built PUDs to download, a Campaign page, links, a money crack, trainers (two types), and the Kali patch for WC2 and how to set up Kali for IPX or modem play. Although unrelated to the game—check out Nam Tran's Random Art Gallery of fantasy and science fiction drawings (press the "Reload" or "Refresh" button to see a new one...cool!)

Unofficial X-COM/UFO Web Page, The
http://www.surfchem.kth.se/~aa/xcom/xcom.html
A large site that was unfortunately abandoned on October of 1995. So I guess no X-COM III, eh? Well, it may not be great to look at but there is a lot here—X-COM and Terror From The Deep (TFTP) utilities, nine of Russ Brown's excellent XCOM sagas are available for download, patches, cracks, and more.

Viable Software Alternatives: World Empire III

http://viablesoftware.com/wewpage.htm

Download an evaluation copy of World Empire III: The Strategy Game, for free. Play against human or computer opponents in this award-winning shareware game (Computer Gaming World magazine's "Best Shareware Strategy Game of 1995"). This Web site shows screen shots, discusses game features, and allows you to order the full seven-player version if interested.

Vikings Warcraft II (and Command and Conquer) Page

http://www.descom.se/~lazze/

Designed for either Netscape 3 or Explorer 3, you can grab a Warcraft II (WC2) demo, patch, Desktop theme (and Command and Conquer, too!), cheats, how to change your colors on your alias, current info (mainly on Command and Conquer's Red Alert), and links (including the game companies).

Wages of War: The Business of Battle

http://www.nwcomputing.com/wages/

This is the New World Computing official page for its upcoming "Wages of War"—an intense strategy war game involving discerning business bargaining and futuristic squad-level, commando-style warfare. Read the game features, view the system requirements for the Mac or Windows 95, and click to enlarge the screen shots for a closer look.

Warcraft II

http://www.imsa.edu/~reptile/warcraft2/index.html

Welcome to Bob Ramashko's page on Blizzard's Warcraft II computer strategy game. Read up on Human and Orc unit descriptions (very useful—and thorough), game strategies, cheats, and of course, links to other Warcraft II sources on the Net. To use the cheats during game play, press the Enter key and type in the corresponding word(s) to activate the given cheat listed here.

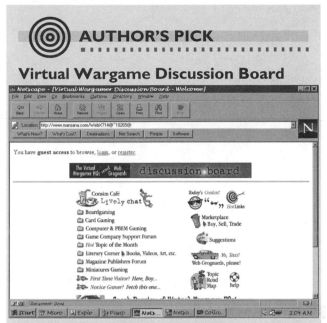

AUTHOR'S PICK

Virtual Wargame Discussion Board

http://www.manzana.com/WebX?18@@14@.ee6bzf3

The Virtual Wargamer HQ and Web Grognard's bring you The Discussion Board—a very hip and comprehensive place to talk about your favorite games whether it be computer, PBEM gaming, board, or card gaming. Once you're in the particular category, click on the game you're interested in and read or interact with the postings. An attractive and easy graphical interface lets you navigate freely. Many other areas make this an excellent, all-in-one place to go for tips, strategy tactics, or to arrange for an online head-to-head or multiplayer game.

Warcraft II Home Page

http://www.sbox.tu-graz.ac.at/home/elsnercl/wc2.html

Download up to three Warcraft II Plus Packs! for Windows 95 to snaz up your desktop, or choose up to 18 or so PUDs to try out (including Besieged, Daemon's Forge, Wastelands of Gold-Isle, and The Great Lake).

Still Interested In More Warcraft II Sites? Try These On For Size

(In no particular order)

The Warcraft II Domain.
http://home.earthlink.net/~knickrehm/warcraft2.htm

Dave's Warcraft II Page
http://www.teleport.com/~conrad/war2/war2.shtml

ReG's Warcraft II Page
http://www.magg.net/~regulate/war.htm

Warcraft II Alliance
http://ourworld.compuserve.com/homepages/ternovsky/warcraft.htm

Stallion's Warcraft II Page
http://www.geocities.com/TimesSquare/3488/war3.htm

Warcraft II: Face to Face
http://www.iepsnet.com:80/personal/wlungren/WAR2.HTM

Warcraft II
http://members.aol.com/formula73/webpg/wrcrft.htm

ACE's Warcraft II Archive
http://mmm.mbhs.edu/~achen/games/warcraft2.html

Jeff's Warcraft II Page - Unauthorized and Unofficial
http://www.smartlink.net/~jeffrey/warcraft_2/warcraft.html

Warcraft II
http://www.tgx.com/~kenity/frame.htm

Golfa's Warcraft II Page
http://www.bluefin.net/~golfer/war2.html

Warcraft II at Planet Stratos
http://members.tripod.com/~jenex/WarcraftII.html

Jeff and Dave's Warcraft II Page
http://www.eecs.uic.edu/~ddurham/war2.html

Warcraft II: The Homepage
http://www.igs.net/~tinker/wc2/index.htm

Ian's Warcraft II Page
http://nueva.pvt.k12.ca.us/~ianwesl/

Longsword's Warcraft II Page
http://www.geocities.com/Athens/1887/warcraft.html

Warcraft II Tournament Page
http://www.geocities.com/TimesSquare/3439/

IWL - International Warcraft II League
http://www1.ridgecrest.ca.us/~bgeorge/iwl/iwl.htm

Shafe's Warcraft World Wide Web Page
http://www.gprep.pvt.k12.md.us/~mikes/warcraft.html

Warcraft II Modem League
http://members.aol.com/NickW2ML/W2ML.htm

In the 35-member Warcraft II Modem League, people from all around North America compete in modem head-to-head games (directly over modem or Kali). Visit the New Headlines area, the New Members Lounge, or the PUD of the Week section. Fill out the membership form if you wish to join.

Warcraft II Page
http://www.primenet.com/~ranma/wc2.html

Read the helpful strategies (money management, wizard uses, fighting over waters), copy down the cheat codes, or peruse through the many other Warcraft II pages around the Net. Large graphics and sound clips add an extra touch to this fan-related site.

Warcraft II Resource Page, The
http://www.halcyon.com/mage/war2/war2.htm

Another interesting site (with neat wallpaper!). Read the Warcraft story, system requirements, and news or download multiplayer maps (lots!), utilities, and patches. Check out the related-Warcraft related links including Kali's home page.

Warcraft II: Tides of Darkness
http://www.amherst.edu/~krichard/war.html

13-year-old Chris designed this page to give a new map every day for Warcraft II fans, and illustrate the air units (human side) and magical elements in the game. Each contains a screen shot, or two, and a description of its design and uses. Good job!

Warcraft II: The Tides of Darkness FAQ

http://www.teleport.com/~kav/WarCraft2.faq

This is the official Warcraft II FAQ (v1.2) written by Kav Latiolais—an excellent starting place for those who want to learn more about Blizzard's awesome computer strategy game. This FAQ covers basic information, features, the Human and Orc story outline, and strategy tips and tricks. No screen shots or downloadables here—just the FAQs, ma'am!

Warhammer 40,000 Info Page

http://vms.www.uwplatt.edu/~kienbaum/40k/40k.html

Warhammer 40,000 is a miniatures-based tactical combat game which takes place in a dark and gothic future. Space Orks, Eldar, Chaos, and other enemies are threatening Mankind's existence. The unmerciful Tyranid hoards are invading our Milky Way galaxy in search of fresh genetic material for their bio-engineered race. You can't just sit there and let this happen! Want to read more about it, or what you need to play? Visit this site for all pertinent details to get going.

Warlords II

http://www.teleport.com/~stiltman/warlords.html

A brief introduction to the game precedes the real substance of this site—custom made scenarios by The Stilt Man himself. He used the Scenario Builder to construct these including the Arghan scenario—Deluxe Edition, Stilte's Inferno (move over, Dante), and more. Each accompany thorough descriptions.

Warlords II ands Warlords II Deluxe

http://www.cs.uiowa.edu/~schikore/Warlords2/

This site pays homage to SSG's Warlords II and Warlords II Deluxe for the PC and Mac. Each of the four areas offers reviews, scenarios, army sets, utilities and upgrades, and links. Be forewarned there is a lot more here for the PC version of the game.

Warlords II Player's Web Site

http://www.princeton.edu/~rfheeter/w2home.html

A FAQ-like page giving a broad overview of the various ways to play SSG's fantasy war game Warlords II. Read sections on new features and recent game news, the Warlords series info and reviews, screen shots, other info, hints and tips on the game, play-by-e-mail info, scenario builder information, and more. Visit the SSG official Home Page at http://www.ssg.com.au/.

World At War

http://www.engr.usask.ca/~nnc250/w@w20.html

The World at War Support Site was created as a resource center for the World at War series of games designed by Atomic Games (of recent Close Combat fame). Information and files are provided for both the PC and Mac platforms and there are three games in the series so far: Operation Crusader, Stalingrad, and D-Day: America Invades. The left frame bar has all the standards, including strategy tips, PBEM notes, an art gallery, game ladder, news section, multiplayer gaming, links, etc.

World of Warcraft, The

http://www.voicenet.com/~warden/warcraft.html

Killer wallpaper! Christopher Warden's site provides info and files on the original Warcraft, Warcraft II: Tides of Darkness, and the expansion set Warcraft II: Beyond the Dark Portal. FAQs, patches, cheat codes, demos, editors, PUDs, and links are offered.

X-COM: Apocalypse

http://www.geocities.com/TimesSquare/2777/xcom3.html

The long overdue third installment in the MicroProse series has been highly anticipated for a long time. X-COM 3 is slotted for a "first half 1997 release" (whenever that means) but this Web site will be enough to whet your appetite until then with its up-to-the-day news and rumors, many screen shots, previews, game features, and an X-COM 1 and 2 overview. A nice, colorful, informative page with good writing.

XPilot Page, The

http://www.cs.uit.no/XPilot/

Welcome to the world of XPilot—the strategic 2D game of space combat you can play on the Internet. Learn how to get set for one-on-one or multiplayer play, research the many weapons, how to activate them, and how to use them effectively. There are discussions on maps, strategies, compiling, and more. Whether you wish to start to learn the game or are a seasoned pilot, this site may answer your questions. Read through the FAQs, tutorials, references, activities, services, and more.

Yujun's Heroes of Might and Magic Pages

http://www.egr.uh.edu/~yxq60120/hero/hero.htm

An award-winning page that contains some neat files along with the usual standbys (screen shots, strategy guide [v0.2, March 1996, written by Yujun], FAQs, etc.). How about spicing up your Windows 95 desktop with Yujun Qin's own Heroes Plus! Pack Theme? Or download more maps as well as Hero, Combat, Troops, Artifacts, Spells, and Dwelling info. Nice-looking frames-enhanced page with cool animations and fonts.

Zamllo's Starcraft Home Page

http://members.icanect.net/~zamllo/starcraft.htm

Updated quite frequently from what I can tell, this site provides "waiting material" until Blizzard's highly anticipated real-time space strategy title ships early in 1997. Starcraft race information, units, buildings, weapons, and screen shots are offered—future sections will include a downloadable demo and strategy tips. Associated with the International Starcraft League (ISL) at http://members.icanect.net/~zamllo/isl.htm.

8

SPORTS GAMES

BASEBALL GAMES

FRANK THOMAS BIG HURT BASEBALL

Frank Thomas Big Hurt Baseball
**http://www.acclaimnation.com/
acclaimnation/twitch/interactive/big-man/
FTbighurt.html**
Two-time winner of the Most Valuable Player award, Frank Thomas lends his name to this state-of-the-art motion-capture baseball experience. Play ball with Frank in twenty-eight stadiums and against over seven hundred major league players, either in exhibition games or a full season schedule. Find out more about the game and the powerful Frank Thomas at this promotional site hosted by Acclaim.

ReadMe File for Frank Thomas Big Hurt Baseball
**http://www.gamespot.com/sports/bighurt/
readme.html**
Those with technical questions about Frank Thomas Big Hurt Baseball can find the game's readme file posted to this page. Installation, reconfiguration, and troubleshooting all receive attention.

FRONT PAGE SPORTS: BASEBALL PRO '96

Front Page Sports: Baseball Pro '96
**http://www.sierra.com/entertainment/
bball96/**
Batter up for true-physics play action with a complete lineup of Major League Baseball players. Sierra promotes its motion-capture-based sports simulation that takes players from spring training all the way to the

"big show." Read the company's overview of the game and its features, download screen shots, or link to other company pages for the game's troubleshooting guide and tips for better play.

HARD BALL 5

Hard Ball 5
**http://www.accolade.com/products/
hardball5/index.html**
Picking up where its award-winning predecessors left off, this sports simulation offers ten skill levels (from arcade to full simulation), play-by-play calls by Al Michaels, forty man rosters, over eight hundred MLB-PA players, head-to-head modem play, a variety of camera angles, and a complete stat construction set. Learn more about this fifth-generation game at the official Accolade site, check out screen shots, even download demos. Technical details and game reviews are also available online.

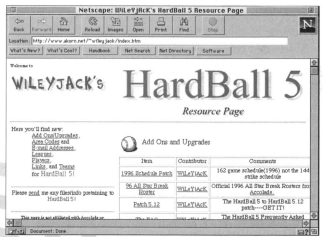

Hard Ball 5 Resource Page
http://www.akorn.net/~wileyjack/index.htm
Baseball enthusiast Wiley Jack hosts this Hard Ball 5 info page for fellow gamers, especially those interested in head-to-head play. Along with patches, add-ons, and the FAQ, you'll also find a roster of players eager to take on all comers in over-the-line play. Those who'd

like to add their name to the list can do so. Also, keep your eyes open for a stray tip on getting more out of the game.

Unofficial Hard Ball 5 Page
http://www.rain.org/~ssa/sean/hardball.htm
Download Hardball 5 demos along with leagues, teams, and players created and contributed by folks who enjoy the game. Pick up a few tips to improve your game. Link to other game and topic-related pages on the Web. This unofficial page is another offering from Sean Ohlenkamp, the author of Sean's Ultimate Baseball Page. Follow the link; that ball page is pretty ultimate.

OLD TIME BASEBALL

Old Time Baseball
http://www.ea.com/oldtime.html
This offering from Entertainment Arts (EA) provides little more than a chit sheet detailing the features found in the game Old Time Baseball from Stormfront Studios. Two screen shots add to the presentation. Links point to the EA Store and information on the company's affiliated labels.

Old Time Baseball
http://www.stormfront.com/oldtime.htm
Leave it to the company that designed Old Time Baseball to properly pitch the game. Stormfront steps up and delivers both the facts and best features about its 1995 game, which pits the great baseball players of yesteryear (more than twelve thousand players from the years 1871 through 1981) in fantasy "what-if" match-ups. Quotes from customer cards and letters are offered in support of the game, as is a collection of press clips.

TONY LA RUSSA BASEBALL 3

Tony La Russa Baseball 3
http://www.ea.com/tony3.html
Co-designed by and good enough to carry the name of five-time pennant-winning manager Tony La Russa, this fantasy baseball game offers stunning animation, a choice of three announcers, a full fantasy draft feature, and more. Visit this official EA Sports page for the game's stats and a look at screen shots, and to listen to audio files.

Tony La Russa Baseball 3
http://www.stormfront.com/tony3.htm
Stormfront Studios leads the collective cheer for its award-winning baseball simulation game. Find out what awards the game has won and what nice things the critics have to say about it. Also read a general overview of the game and the features that helped make it an instant winner upon its May 1995 release.

Ultimate Utilities for Tony La Russa and Old Time Baseball Games
http://ourworld.compuserve.com/ homepages/NickKeren/
Nick Keren presents this collection of shareware add-ons he has designed to complement Stormfront's Tony La Russa series of baseball sims and its Old Time Baseball game. Add-ons include Ultimate Utilities (a bundle of four scouting, scheduling, and managing utilities), the computerized general manager, remote league manager, and custom league reporter. Find out what each of these programs can do and where to download the shareware version. Other site features include technical support, latest updates, and a look a Nick's drawing board.

TRIPLE PLAY '97

Triple Play '97
http://www.easports.com/trplay/
window.htm
Download the playable DOS and Win95 demos for this EA Sports baseball sim. While you're at it, download extra game sounds and play-by-play, too. It's all part of the official promotion for Triple Play '97. Other site features include screen shots, Quick Time clips, and a rundown of the game's features, such as six-player multi-play action, three batting and five fielding views, real-physics action, five game modes, and a multi-player home run derby challenge.

Triple Play '97
http://www.cu-online.com/~solso/tp97.html
Stan Olson sings the praises of EA Sports' first PC baseball game, Triple Play '97, and offers a place for fellow fans to brag about their skill with the game and pick up a little ballpark action. Access the Home Run Derby records database to post your record-breaking hit or to review the records waiting to be broken. In the modem players database, find players looking for a little head-to-head gaming action.

BASKETBALL GAMES

COLLEGE SLAM

GameSpot: College Slam at a Glance
http://www.gamespot.com/sports/colleges/
Acclaim Entertainment's arcade-style basketball romp, College Slam, stands center court in this GameSpot report. Read the official company line on the game and find out how well the critics enjoyed the hoops action. Check out screen shots, download a sound file, pick up

some neat cheats, and follow pointers to official and topic-related pages. The technical information on file includes the game's readme file and a player's discussion forum.

NBA LIVE '96

NBA Live '96 Online Player's Guide
http://www.gamespot.com/sports/nbaliv96/
hint_lb_bcf2.html
Need hints for playing NBA Live '96? Visit this GameSpot page and find a guide to the fundamentals of play. Get pointers on shooting different shots, driving to the hoop, avoiding getting stuffed, and dunking the ball. Also learn how to coordinate a fast break and how to mount a basic defense. Those who like a few sneaky tactics in their kit won't be disappointed, either. The guide tells out how to thwart a ball handler and shoot an extra long three-pointer. To get the crowd going, there's even a section on starting the wave. Pointers on the page lead to audio and video clips and access the readme file from the game.

NBA Live '96 Page
http://www-users.informatik.rwth-
aachen.de/~timt/nba96.html
Tim Tschirner declares that he loves this game. He proves his devotion with this impressive posting that will have other NBA Live '96 fans loving Tim. Visit the download area for roster patches, editors, and FAQs he has assembled. Pick up some game-winning strategy in the tips section. Browse the links for pointers to official and fan pages, plus sites of related topical interest.

NBA Live '97
http://www.easports.com/nba97/index.html
Forget '96. The '97 season is almost here and with it will come the updated NBA Live game from EA Sports. Visit this promotional page for the official announcement and details on what EA Sports has in store for its hoops-hungry fans.

FOOTBALL GAMES

ALL-AMERICAN COLLEGE FOOTBALL

All-American College Football
http://www.cdrom.ibm.com/allameri.html
It's college gridiron gaming action from IBM. You're the coach and call the plays for any or all of over 80 Division I-A universities and over 340 of the greatest college teams. Visit this promotional page to review the game's features and system requirements. A few screen shots help illustrate the game's layout. Those who are so inspired can link-out to order online or check out other IBM games.

FRONT PAGE SPORTS: FOOTBALL PRO '96

Front Page Sports: Football Pro '96
http://www.sierra.com/entertainment/fb96/
Front Page Sports Football Pro reportedly has been the highest-rated football game by *Computer Gaming World* for three years running. Read Sierra's promotion for the game, check out the features that set this game apart, and admire the series awards the game has garnered since its introduction. Screen shots are available for review. Links lead to patches and the official troubleshooting guide, as well as game-play tips.

MADDEN NFL '97

Madden NFL '97
http://www.easports.com/easports/preview/madden/index.html
Check out the stats for EA Sports' football simulation, co-designed by John Madden. Game features include options for modem and network play, the Madden University interactive tutorial, and illustrated NFL films footage. The game offers exciting play action with more than 100 teams, including 69 all-time great and Super Bowl teams, plus superior graphics and animation. A look at the screen shots and QuickTime movies featured will illustrate that point, and the downloadable demo will drive it home.

Madden NFL '97 Downloadable Demo
http://www.cdmag.com/demos/pages/madden97.html
Looking for a little pigskin action? Download the demo of Madden NFL '97 here. The full game features more than five hundred offensive and defensive Madden-designed plays, unlimited camera angles, play-by-play, stat features and much more.

NFL QUARTERBACK CLUB '97

NFL Quarterback Club '97
http://www.acclaimnation.com/acclaimnation/twitch/interactive/nfl97/NFL97.html
Capturing the sport in all its NFL glory, Acclaim/Nation's NFL Quarterback Club '97 gets into the action at this promotional site. Check out the game's features, review screen shots, and read excerpts of what the critics had to say. A demo is promised for the near future.

NFL PRO LEAGUE FOOTBALL

NFL Pro League Football
http://www.cdrom.ibm.com/nflprole.html
Here's more IBM football action. This time, however, it's professional ball, and you can experience what it's like when you're the coach and the game is on the line: You're at the five-yard line and a field goal will only tie the score. Visit this promotional page to find out what other excitement this coaching simulation has to offer, including an option for head-to-head modem action.

NFL Pro League Football
http://www.pcentertainment.com/games/Nov95/nfl1195.html
Andrew Miller tallies the stats and rates IBM's football coaching simulation games, NFL Pro League Football and All-American College Football, a solid B. Offering enough hands-on control for those fond of the Madden series but enough field maneuvering to satisfy coach wanna-bes, the games seem to strike a happy medium for the reviewer. Read the text of this November 1995 review for a critical look at how the games play, plus find a link to a few gaming hints.

UNNECESSARY ROUGHNESS '96

Unnecessary Roughness '96 FAQ
http://www.accolade.com/UR96-faq.html
In support of its NFL football sim, Accolade posts these answers to the most frequently asked questions about the game. Topics receiving attention include hardware requirements, installing and running the game, troubleshooting potential problems, and game patches. Links lead to other Accolade pages

GOLF GAMES

GREG NORMAN ULTIMATE CHALLENGE GOLF

Greg Norman Ultimate Challenge Golf
http://www.Grolier.com/interact/products/golf/docs/greghome.html
Play golf like Greg Norman, or just play his home course in Hobe Sound. Either way you also manage course play, and it's course management that separates the bait from the sharks. Find out more about Greg Norman's Ultimate Golf Challenge at this official Grolier site offering an illustrated tour of the game. Those curious about what the critics said about the game can read the reviews, and the technical information section offers an overview of system requirements. Online ordering is available.

Greg Norman Ultimate Challenge Golf Hints and Tips
http://www.gamespot.com/sports/gregnugc/hint_lb_c2e2.html
Stop by this six-tip golf clinic hosted by GameSpot to help ensure that you only play Ultimate Challenge Golf like Greg Norman himself. Also on this page, find links to a sampling of game screen shots and downloadable trailers, a collection of pointers leading to official and golf-related sites, and a selection of technical information about the game.

JACK NICKLAUS SIGNATURE EDITION

Bob's Favorite Jack Nicklaus Signature Edition Utilities

http://www.primenet.com/~rnovello/jn0.htm

Bob Novello treats Jack Nicklaus Signature Edition (JNSE) golf fans to a nice selection of utilities that can be downloaded and used with the game. The Power Bar utility slows down the power bar speed; the Mousekey utility aids the creation of key files using your computer's mouse; the Special Effect Generator adds unique effects to course designs; and the Great Shot Recorder does just that—records great shots made with the game.

Jack Nicklaus Signature Edition Courses

http://www.cae.wisc.edu/~seth/jnse.html

Here's an extensive archive of downloadable JNSE golf courses to play and master. Other features include JNSE golf course design aids and links to other pages offering game-related content. Hosted by Seth Johnson, the site is available in Java and non-Java versions.

Jack Nicklaus Signature Edition Fantasyland

http://users.aol.com/td4732/pinecl.zip

Tom Duffy, Pete Broad, and Charles Whiddon maintain this golfer's paradise, offering dozens of fantasy courses to download and play with the Jack Nicklaus Signature Edition golf game. (There are so many available, new courses are rotated on a bi-weekly basis!) Other site features include downloadable backgrounds, screen shots, and the JNSE Designer Toolkit. What golf site wouldn't be complete without links? About a half-dozen are offered, pointing to sites of interest to JNSE enthusiasts.

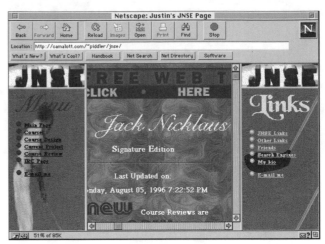

Justin's Jack Nicklaus Signature Edition Home Page

http://camalott.com/~piddler/jnse/

Jack Nicklaus Signature Edition game fans looking for new golf courses to conquer should visit Justin Williams' page for his links menu. Not only does he post a few courses of his own design, but he also points to other sites where courses are available to download. Stop by his course review section if you're curious about what Justin thinks about the courses he's played.

LINKS LS

Links LS

http://www.accesssoftware.com/golf/golf.html

Access Software promotes its line of improved golf simulators via this official page. Check out the various sims' features, system requirements, and screen shots. Those who'd like other holes to play can stroll through the add-on courses available. Other site features include a listing of the PGA Tour schedule, information about golf tournaments on the Web, and links to other sites for golf fans.

Links LS Hacker's Corner
http://www.emperor.com/www/gulley/ls/ls.html

Ray Gulley hosts this graphically intense page for fellow hackers and fans of Access Software's Links LS golf simulator games. Features include a bulletin board where players can find partners for modem play, recorded rounds to download and play against, and an annotated list of all the Links LS courses available. Pointers to other fan and game pages are also included, as is a downloadable sound patch for the game.

MICROSOFT GOLF

Microsoft Golf
http://198.105.232.5/sports/golf/default.htm

Download the Microsoft Golf Theme Pack with sights, sounds, and images from the Microsoft Golf game. Find technical support for Microsoft Golf 2.0. Preview the upgrades and improvements coming in Microsoft Golf 3.0. Comments or tips to share? Stop by the Feedback Forum. Looking for tips? Check out the Game Tips section for the Tip of the Month.

Microsoft Golf Hints
http://www.gamespot.com/sports/msgolf/hint_lb_c002.html

Here's an online clinic for golfers driving the fairways of Microsoft Golf 2.0. Hosted by GameSpot, this six-tip tutorial helps players get the most from their game. Be sure to jump to the demos and downloads that are offered. They have plenty to make the jump worthwhile, including patches and add-on rounds.

PGA TOUR GOLF '96

PGA Tour Golf '96
http://www.easports.com/pga97/index.html

Here's the official EA Sports' online promotion for its PGA Tour series. Download a playable one-hole demo, check out the online excerpt from the PGA Tour '96 Player's Guide, link to Electronic Arts' technical support pages, and check out the new course add-ons that are now available. Also, find a game overview offering a list of key features, sample screen shots, and a look at system requirements.

CGR Reviews: PGA Tour '96
http://www.nuke.com/cgr/reviews/1195/pga96/pga.htm

Read this November 1995 review of EA Sports' PGA Tour '96 golfing sim for a critical perspective on the game. With more good than bad to say, the reviewers rate the game above par.

SPORTWARE GOLF

SportWare Golf
http://www.harpercollins.com/hci/edu/golfh.htm

Though this is not a game, it's designed to help users play better golf. Basically, the software offers an interactive golf tutorial featuring Jim McLean, 1994 PGA Instructor of the Year. Learn more about the program—its features and system requirements—and see sample screen shots at this official HarperCollins site.

HOCKEY GAMES

NHL HOCKEY '95/'96/'97

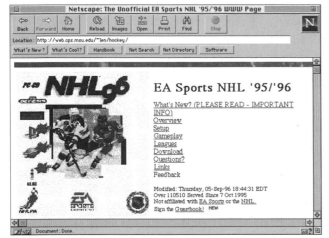

EA Sports NHL '95/'96: The Unofficial WWW Page

http://web.cps.msu.edu/~len/hockey/

Hockey fan Nguyen-Anh D. Len tends to the action found in EA Sports' NHL hockey sim series by offering this well-crafted resource of game facts, tactics, and tricks. Find overviews and reviews, setup assistance, game-play tutorials, and a generous assortment of downloads that include player editors, updated rosters, patches, and utilities. Links lead to other unofficial fan pages devoted to the game.

Daniel's Unofficial Site for NHL Hockey

http://www.geocities.com/SiliconValley/ Park/6431/nhl96.html

Download editors, patches, rosters, and extras from the impressive collection of NHL Hockey programs assembled and presented by Daniel Gothe. Those needing hints to get past virtually unstoppable goalies will find a little comfort in that regard. Links point out other NHL Hockey fan pages and sites devoted to the real sport. A section that previews what's ahead for the EA

Sports' NHL Hockey gaming series offers general comments from the visitors who have dropped by.

NHL Hockey '96 Downloadable Demo

http://www.cdmag.com/demos/pages/ nhlh96.html

There's no reason to visit this site except one: to download a 3MB demo of Electronic Arts' NHL Hockey '96 sports sim. Stop by and check out the action.

NHL Hockey '97

http://www.easports.com/nhl97/index.html

Forget '96; that's one for the record books. It's a new day and a new season, and here's the latest in the EA Sports hockey series to prove that the world keeps turning. Check out NHL Hockey '97—offering more of what made the previous games in the series such a hit. Review the game's features, system requirments, and screen shots at this official EA Sports site.

RACING GAMES

AL UNSER, JR. ARCADE RACING

Al Unser, Jr. Arcade Racing

http://www.mindscape.com/msgames/ AlUnser/index.html

Take to the track alone or lay rubber against a hungry pack of ten Indy-style drivers ready to vie for the title King of the Road. Here's Mindscape's official page for the arcade action game. It's good enough to carry the name of two-time Indianapolis 500 winner Al Unser, Jr. Stop by to check out system requirements, read reviews, and get a load of the screen shots.

Al Unser, Jr. Arcade Racing

http://www.pcentertainment.com/games/
Dec95/unser1295.html

Bill Meyer rates Al Unser, Jr. Arcade Racing a solid B in this December 1995 review. Find out why the play action rates so highly, as the reviewer ticks off some of the game's more outstanding features.

BIG RED RACING

Big Red Racing

http://www.domark.com/brr/brr.html

This is no ordinary road race. In fact, it's an off-road race where almost anything goes—players need only get in and drive it away! Download a demo of the game to see what kind of mayhem can come from a racing game that features twenty-four all-terrain circuits and a sixteen-vehicle motor pool offering everything from lunar buggies to hovercraft. Other site features include system requirements, game reviews, and screen shots. Links lead to the Big Red Racing owners technical support page and the home page of the unofficial fan club.

Big Red Racing Ladder

http://www.oz.net/~kerhop/brr/
brr-ladd.html

Here's another opportunity to download the two-track demo of Domark's Red Racing game. What's more, here's an opportunity to join an unofficial racing club that allows players to compete against each other over the Internet. Find out what's required to join, and check the leader board to see who to beat. The page is a service of Frank Laughlin.

GRAND PRIX II

Grand Prix II

http://www.microprose.com/gp2/index.html

MicroProse posts this promotion for the game it describes as the "ultimate Formula One racing simulation," offering players either a quick ride around the track or a full season on racing circuits around the world. Find out what else the game offers, check out the screen shots, and browse the official FAQ.

Grand Prix II Forum

http://ixtas.fri.uni-lj.si/~mitjag/gp2/

Combining their time and talents, Matt Wright and Mitja Golob present this collection of forums for fans of the Grand Prix II racing game. Post messages or stop by to find out what others are saying. Featured forums cover topics such as game utilities, GP2 Web pages, racing records, problems with the game, and much more. A site FAQ helps first-timers acquaint themselves with the format of the page and the protocol for posting messages.

The H.P.S. Grand Prix II Pages

http://www.xs4all.nl/~pidi/ie/gp/
hpsindex.htm

Here's the collective home page for three guys—Henk, Pieter, and Seth—who have combined their talents and their Grand Prix II pages into one fairly comprehensive resource. Visit Henk Emmelot's page for tips, tricks, and help to configure the game. Stop by Pieter van Dieren's page for hotlaps, crashes, screen shots, and utilities. Pull into Seth's Myst Grandprix 2 Championship site to look into competing for the unofficial Grand Prix II world title. Plus there's plenty more at these sites, including IRC chat and tons of links to other GP2 and related pages on the Web.

VIRTUAL KARTS

Virtual Karts
http://www.holobyte.com/virtkart.html
Download a demo and test drive MircroProse's virtual go-kart racing sim to see just how smoothly and easily it handles. Screen shots are online for a quick peek at the graphics, as is a Virtual Karts slide show. Game specs and features are detailed for those with an interest in reading more about what the game has to offer. Links lead to other MicroProse pages.

WHIPLASH

Whiplash
http://www.interplay.com/games/
whiplash.html
Loop the loop, rip through corkscrew turns, jump traffic, and beat the raising draw bridge in this wild and wicked racing game from Interplay. Download a demo to see how the engines scream, the tires squeal, and the metal crunches when drivers misjudge the insane tracks' demands. Other site features include screen shots and an overview of the game and its key features. Links lead to other Interplay pages, where the games, cheat codes, and current patch are located.

Whiplash Demo
http://www.websolutions.mb.ca/realm/dos/
whipdemo.html
The Gamers Realm hosts this link to the FTP sites where the Whiplash demo can be downloaded. A brief look at system requirements is also featured.

SOCCER GAMES

FIFA SOCCER '96

FIFA '96
http://www.msilink.com/~solso/fifa96.html
Stan Olson does a nice job enticing the readers of his page into finding as much to like about FIFA Soccer '96 as he does. Read the "Byte This" review that raves about the game, learn about online tournament and league play, pick up game tips and hints for scoring big, and check out the unofficial FAQ by Guy Saner. Other site features include a registry for modem players and troubleshooting tips. Finally, there's a huge 46MB playable demo available for downloading.

FIFA '96 Online Technical Support
http://www.ea.com/techsupp/fifa96.html
EA posts this online help page for players seeking answers to technical questions concerning FIFA Soccer '96. Find help for about a dozen of the most common game problems reported.

FIFA Soccer '96
http://www.ea.com/fifa5.html
EA posts this look at its FIFA Soccer '96 sports simulation. Read a game overview, check out the sim's features and system requirements, and enjoy a collection of screen shots.

FIFA Soccer '96 Page
http://www.students.uiuc.edu/~mmkoenig/
fifa.html
Here's the home page of the official, unofficial FIFA Soccer modem players league, set up by Matt Koenig. Check into league action and find out how to get involved. Site features include rankings, score reports,

stats, and tournament news. Also find playing tips and a link to the site where a demo of FIFA Soccer '96 can be downloaded.

PLANET SOCCER

Planet Soccer
http://www.interplay.com/website/sales/planetso.html
Interplay uses this page to promote its simulated soccer game that combines realistic play action and "a multitude of game options." Check out the game's strategic and user-friendly features and review its system requirements.

OTHER SPORTS GAMES

BRUCE JENNER'S WORLD CLASS DECATHLON

Bruce Jenner's World Class Decathlon
http://www.imagicgames.com/decathlon.dir/decathlon.html
What does it take to be the world's greatest all-around athlete? Interactive Magic helps players answer the question for themselves (sort of) with this virtual decathlon competition. Read an overview of the game, review its features and sytem requirements, then download a demo and give the game a try. You'll find ordering information online as well.

Decathlon Hints & Tips
http://www.gamespot.com/sports/brucejen/hint_lb_29fea.html
Every player needs a coach, and here's an online coach to help you succeed with Bruce Jenner's World Class Decathlon game. Find tips for approaching the various competitions and improving skill performances. Hosted by GameSpot, this page also offers links to a playable demo and the game's readme file.

HYPERBLADE

GameSpot Review of HyperBlade
http://www.gamespot.com/features/activision/hyper/index.html
Players who want to learn more about Activision's new futuristic sport simulation, HyperBlade, can learn a little something about the game in this overview presented by GameSpot. Illustrated with screen shots, the page also features an AVI trailer. Those who follow

links to GameSpot's What's New section will be rewarded with a downloadable demo of the game.

HyperBlade
http://www.activision.com/hyperblade/index.html

Cross hockey with roller derby and you get a vague idea of what HyperBlade is all about. Better download a demo of this one to find out if you have what it takes to win in what Activision is promoting as the "most brutal" competitive sport in history.

PBA BOWLING

PBA Bowling
http://www.bethsoft.com/html/pbabowling.html

Now everyone can be a virtual PBA pro, thanks to this sports sim from Bethesda Softworks. Offering realistic physics, three levels of play, and dozens of other features, the game makes players feel as if it's Friday night at the local alley. Read about the game, view screen shots, and try a demo. Players with registered copies can also download the latest game update.

PBA Bowling Hints
http://www.gamespot.com/sports/pbabowli/hint_lb_77c2.html

The only thing that helps players win at PBA Bowling is the same thing that helps real PBA players win: practice. Still, players may want to stop by this GameSpot site for a quick review of bowling basics as they relate to the Bethesda simulation of the sport. Links lead to a demo and an add-on that can be downloaded, as well as the latest game patch.

AUTHOR'S PICK

Computer Sports Edge
http://www.compsportsedge.com/index.html

Stay on top of the action in the world of computer and tabletop sports gaming with this electronic magazine. Contents include product reviews, industry news, and sneak previews. But that's only the beginning. The site also offers strategy tips, hosts competitive league action, and provides a chat area for casual talk. On-site surveys register reader opinions, contests add extra excitement, and an FTP site is in the works. The features and services presented are free, so anyone interested in playing sports simulation games can't go wrong by enjoying the extras that come with the Edge.

TROPHY BASS

Trophy Bass
http://www.sierra.com/entertainment/tbass/

For when the weather won't let you get out or the fish just won't bite, here's a photo-realistic sports sim from Sierra that lets players fish five top bass lakes. Check out the game's features, including a multimedia guide to bass fishing, and download a fishable demo.

Hints and Tips for Trophy Bass
http://www.gamespot.com/sports/trophyba/hint_lb_7026.html

Cindy Vanous offers players Trophy Bass tips to help make their virtual fishing expedition a winner. She has proven herself a virtual fishing pro and offers the tricks that took her to the top of the tournament totals board.

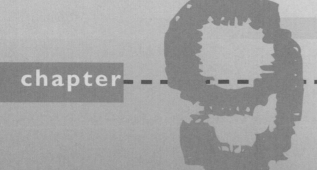

BOARD GAMES, CARD GAMES, AND PUZZLES

BOARD GAMES

ABALONE

Abalone
http://suppnet1.support.nl/clickhere/
abalone/

Select a browser type (fanciest browser listed in Netscape 1.1) and enter the gaming area to play the computer in this game of strategic maneuvering. On-line help aids those unfamiliar with the board game and explains how to move pieces.

A.R.E.N.A.

A.R.E.N.A.
http://www.cis.upenn.edu/~bhou/Arena/

A strategic board game based on the kill or be killed, live, and die action of the gladiator's arena. The key to winning is anticipation: What is my opponent thinking I'll do and how would he react if I did? The acronym of the game's name means All Right, Enough Napalming Already. The rulebook, background notes, and game components are available for downloading. Because it is a board game and not a computer game, some assembly is required.

AXIS AND ALLIES

Axis and Allies
http://web.nmsu.edu/~jwebb/AxisAndAllies/
aanda.htm

In this Milton Bradley World War II simulation board game, players assume control of the five major powers of the war and devise strategies to exploit the weak-

nesses of their enemies without revealing their own. Visit this online resource for an overview of the game and the problems each of the major powers must overcome. Discussions of strategies are also featured.

Axis and Allies Alternate Scenarios
http://member.aol.com/pj1701/scenerios/
war.html

Developed by an Axis and Allies gaming enthusiast, the three additional scenarios presented move the time frame for play action from the past into the next century. According to the developer, all three scenarios have been play-tested and lead to large-scale battles quickly.

Axis and Allies Odds Calculator
http://members.aol.com/PhilipHall/aanda/
aamain.html

A shareware program that allows players to calculate the odds of winning an Axis and Allies battle is available for download at this site. The program runs on Windows 3.1 and Windows 95. Though two versions are available, the latest version is only available to registered users of the first.

BACKGAMMON

Backgammon Frequently Asked Questions
http://www.cybercom.net/~damish/
backgammon/bg-faq.html

Edited by Mark Damish, this FAQ has been compiled to answer the questions most often posed by new visitors to the Usenet newsgroup rec.games.backgammon. Section headings include: Essentials; Electronic Backgammon: VS Other Humans; Electronic Backgammon: VS Machine; Resources; and Miscellaneous. Beginning with the basic rules of play, the FAQ then proceeds to explore the world of online and computer-based gaming. A list of topical books and newsletters is also included, as is a review of other games that can be played on the backgammon board.

Backgammon Galore!
http://www.io.org/~takeith/bg/main.html
Learn the game rules, review the terminology of play, and read about "doubling" strategies for winning big at backgammon. Related articles and annotated matches are also online for further study. Those eager to play online and who have a Java-capable browser can access an onsite game and play the computer. Others may want to follow the pointer to information about FIBS—the First Internet Backgammon Server.

FIBS—Backgammon on the Internet
http://www.cybercom.net/~damish/
backgammon/mike_quinn/fibs.htm
Compiled by Mike Quinn, this unofficial page provides a general guide to playing backgammon via Telnet connection with the First Internet Backgammon Server (FIBS). Find out exactly what FIBS is and how to connect, download a list of FIBS commands, and look into improving the enjoyment factor of online play by downloading and setting up a graphical browser.

JavaGammon
http://www-leland.stanford.edu/~leesmith/
JavaGammon.html
Backgammon players with Java-capable browsers can test their skills against other players via this interactive game. To start, players must load the applet and board image, then wait to be paired with an opponent. Players are matched on a first-come, first-served basis. If no challenger connects, waiting players can open another window on their browser and play themselves.

Lou Poppler's Backgammon Page
http://www.msen.com/~lwp/bg.html
The Webmaster invites players to try his New Other Backgammon Server (NOBS), an alternate online gaming source written during periods when the First Internet Backgammon Server (FIBS) site was unavailable. NOBS imitates FIBS in its structure, and players can link via standard Telnet or with the FIBS client.

NetGammon
http://www.nordnet.fr/netgammon/index_
usa.html
Download the software and connect to the International Backgammon Server (IBS) to play and compare skill levels with other players from around the world. Windows 3.1 or Windows95 required for the software. Web site available in French and English.

The Unofficial FIBS Players' Directory and Photo Gallery
http://flemingw.flemingc.on.ca/~bmouncey/
fibs.html
Meet a few of the folks who play backgammon online at the First Internet Backgammon Server (FIBS). Player profiles, e-mail addresses, user handles and real names are featured. Online registration encourages all who access FIBS for fun to list themselves in this growing directory. Links to general FIBS resources, including Telnet client download sites, add to the overall presentation.

Worlwide Backgammon Federation
http://alpha.science.unitn.it/students/
roberto/WBF/wbf.html
Working within the Internet backgammon community to transform the board game into a "Sport of the Mind," the Worlwide Backgammon Federation (WBF) posts official rules of play and propriety to which it insists its members adhere. The organization also organizes individual and team events for online international play. Visit the federation's home page to review its official tournament rules and look into becoming a supporter. Results from recent gaming events are also posted.

The WWW Backgammon Page
http://www.statslab.cam.ac.uk/~sret1/
backgammon/main.html
Stephen Turner's extensive look at backgammon resources on the Internet points players to game basics, online action and graphical interfaces, computer programs, related publications, clubs, and competitions.

Among the resource collections featured, find a back-gammon FAQ, a matches archive, book reviews, and a list of clubs worldwide. Originated in the United Kingdom, this popular site is mirrored in the U.S. and Russia.

BATTLESHIP

Battleship
http://www.bu.edu/~aarondf/java/battleship.html

Aaron Fuegi presents this Java applet for playing the classic board game Battleship. Be sure to read the instructions and Help file to ensure a good game, and be patient while the images load. Those wishing to compete for a place on the High Score List must register. A Java-capable browser is required.

Battleship—Interactive Web Game
http://godfather.ifs.univie.ac.at:8080/~apo01/

Presented by Thomas Winkler together with Thomas Bernhart, Karl Bacher, and Markus Beiber, this interactive version of Battleship allows players to set game parameters. Those unfamiliar with how the game is played can refer to a brief overview of the rules and game objectives. For those more interested in how the game works than how it's played, the computer code is available as well.

Sink the Bismark
http://polaris.biology.ucla.edu:8088/ships/Home.shtml

In this "playground" rules version of Battleship, opponents don't know which ships have been hit or sunk. For clarification on the rules, check into the briefing area. The game's programming is best accommodated by Netscape browsers.

WebBattleship
http://info.gte.com/gtel/fun/battle/battle.html

Steve Belczyk invites players to test themselves against the computer in his Web version of the Battleship board game. Easy to understand instructions aid those unfamiliar with the game and acquaint first-timers with the symbols used in this version. The game's programming is best accommodated by Netscape browsers, though others may work.

BINGO

Bingo Card Maker
http://www.interlog.com/~dmick/bingo/bingo.html

If there's a party and the gathered want to play Bingo, this site will be more than handy! It randomly generates BINGO cards.

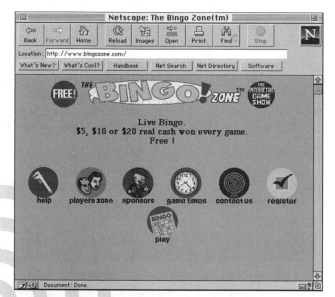

Bingo Zone
http://www.bingozone.com/

Play Bingo live, on the Web through any browser, up to 24 hours a day and win $5.00, $10.00, or $20.00 cash jackpots. Play is free, but all players must register before logging on to play. Eight types of games are featured; online help aids newcomers into getting settled. Must be 18 or older and have a valid e-mail address to register.

The Las Vegas Bingo Club
http://www.accessnv.com/bingo/
PC users can download the latest version the Las Vegas Bingo Club software and play games which pit users against the computer. The program features seven different types of Bingo games. The registered version requires a $10.00 fee.

BLOOD BOWL (FANTASY FOOTBALL)

Blood Bowl
http://www.cabm.rutgers.edu/~hooper/
miniatures/bill/bludbowl.html
Combine the orcs, goblins, elves, dwarves, and humans found in the Warhammer Fantasy world with the rules of U.S. football and the board is set for this fantasy sports game using miniatures. Teams are allotted 16 turns in which to score as much as possible, all the while preventing opposing teams from scoring. Visit this player's resource for a detailed description of the game, links to online rules indices, and tips for starting and managing successful leagues.

Blood Bowl: The OBERWALD
http://www.teleport.com:80/~matasar/
bb.shtml
The Online BloodBowl Enthusiast Reference With Assembled League Doctrines (OBERWALD) site serves as the official unofficial archive for rulings governing Blood Bowl play. Sources for rulings are credited and originated from the game's designer, Jervis Johnson; the game's publisher, Games Workshop; or the FAQ presented in White Dwarf 182. The site's features unrelated to rules include a look at the future of the game, information detailing where to buy merchandise,

and links to topical resources including the Blood Bowl mailing list and related newsgroups.

Triple Skulls: Andy Cowell's Blood Bowl Page
http://www.cs.utk.edu/~cowell/min/bb/#IRC
Letters originally posted to the Blood Bowl mailing list by the game's designer, Jervis Johnson, are archived here, along with instructions for joining the mailing list. Other site features include links to online rules references (official and unofficial), a painted miniatures gallery, and a report on which miniatures are available from where. Gamers interested in challenging players via IRC will also find useful facts, ideas, and pointers.

CHECKERS (DRAUGHTS)

Chinook
http://web.cs.ualberta.ca/~chinook/
Hosted by the Department of Computing Science at Canada's University of Alberta, this site treats players to an online checkers challenge. Visitors can test their game skills against a world championship checkers program developed as a by-product of research into gaming strategies. Those more interested in boning-up for future play can view the endgame database and review world championship matches. Or if inspiration is desired, a visit to the WWW Wall of Honor or International Checker Hall of Fame might be in order. Other pointers lead to free checker software, commercial programs, and related items for sale.

Jim Loy's Checkers Pages
http://www.mcn.net/~jimloy/checkers.html
Exhibiting his love for the game, Jim Loy presents this directory to the various checkers-related Web pages he's authored. Explore the Standard Laws of Checkers, read a history of the game, and browse recaps from famous checker games of the 19th and 20th centuries. Tips for good openings and expert endings are also featured along with links to player federations in Great

Britain and the U.S. And of course, eager players will find jumps to sites where online play is available.

Draughts (with Harry also Dammen and Jouer aux dames)
http://www.noord.bart.nl/~damnet/draughts.html#Summary
Learn the international rules of Draughts, a European version of Checkers which uses a 10x10 checkered board instead of an 8x8 board. Find a general game summary, detailed rules, and a section on terminology. Links to draught-related sites and information on playing by e-mail are also featured. The site's text is available in English, French, and Dutch.

CHESS

British Internet Chess Server
http://www.warwick.ac.uk/~suaaw/
Hosted by the Chess Club at the United Kingdom's University of Warwick, the British Internet Chess Server (BICS) welcomes players of all abilities. An account is needed for play via Telnet, but all are welcome to review the BICS information and help files, articles, and member directory. Links to chess newsgroups, other Telnet chess sites, and a downloadable software archive round out the offerings.

ChessLive!
http://oasi.shiny.it/chess/index.html
As the site's title suggests, visitors can play chess live on the Web with this Java applet hosted by Francesco Bosia. Play features include the ability to privately chat with opponents during games and to suspend play and resume at a later date. An automatic rating system lets players know where they stand, a chat area lets bolder players issue public challenges, and the spectators' gallery affords lurkers dynamic viewing of all games in play. If you've got the plug-in, this site's jumping!

AUTHOR'S PICK

BU's Interactive Game Server
http://www.bu.edu/Games/games.html
Find out what computer scientists are musing over when they're not playing with programming code. The Scientific Computing and Visualization (SCV) group within the Office of Information Technology at Boston University hosts this outstanding online games arcade, offering a few of the standards like Tic Tac Toe, Minesweep, and Pegs. A special treat is the multiplayer Hunt the Wumpus game, in which players scour a maze of caves dodging bats, bottomless pits, and other players' arrows to shoot the wumpus. These games can be played with almost any browser, and for those who have Java, a few Java applets are online as well. The site is good fun, and fun is good.

Chess Space
http://www.chess-space.com/
From archives to Usenet, if it's on the Internet and involves the game of chess, there's probably a pointer to it from here. With a total of 713 links organized into obvious, easy-to-understand categories, this directory serves as a superior resource for chess players of every level. Find FAQs, organizations, online gaming sites, playing strategies, publications, even links to the home pages of masters and novices around the world. For anyone serious about the game of chess, this site's a must-see.

CyberChess
http://www.newgalaxy.com/cyberchess/
An automated play by e-mail chess server, CyberChess matches players of the same skill level for play, keeps track of game boards, and notifies cyberplayers when it's their turn to move. Play can be fast or slow depending on the opponents in a given match and how often they check their e-mail. Other online features include automatic player rating, a conference room, and an

observation area to view games in progress. Player registration is required.

Demeter's Chess Page
http://members.tripod.com/~demeter/Chess
This site is for those who've always said, "Some day I'm going to learn how to play chess." Find a clear, concise description of the board and the manner in which each chess piece may be played. Special maneuvers like castling, promotion, and *en passant* capturing are covered, as is standard play notation. Those who'd like a little help with their first game can find that, too. A variety of standard openings are featured.

EERIE Chess Servers
http://www.eerie.fr/~echec/chess/
Hosted by France's School for Engineering and Research in Computer Science and Electronics, this site presents two chess options: one Telnet, the other Java. The site's text is in French only.

GNU WebChess
http://www.delorie.com/game-room/chess/
Step on up and challenge the computer to a quick game or two of chess. Variable options allow players to enrich the display features and increase the challenge level. And this old site has even been updated for Java. Gamers more interested in the GNU program and its workings will find plenty to ponder in the FAQ. Along with the standard answers, the FAQ also supplies pointers to GNU-designated newsgroups and an anonymous FTP site where the program can be downloaded.

iChess
http://www.ichess.com/
Play live or watch live play at this Java-based, interactive chess site. Players can communicate with one another during matches through a special chat window, and if one player gets called away, the game can be suspended, saved, and then resumed at a later date. Registration is required, but the server is free. An FAQ assists new players in becoming acquainted with the server and match play.

Internet Chess Library
http://caissa.onenet.net/chess/
Offering visitors a wide variety of fact and fancy, the Internet Chess Library caters to the interests of true chess enthusiasts. Browse the FAQ (Parts 1 and 2) from the Usenet newsgroup rec.games.chess for answers to all manner of questions detailing what's what in the world of chess, online and off. Study the games databases, which archive the winning moves of masters and champions. Review the ratings information, which explains how the different systems work and profiles who's where in the standings. Or, stop by the art gallery for a look at some exceptional boards, gaming pieces, and chess celebrities.

The Internet Chess Servers
http://www.onenet.net/pub/chess/HTML/ics.html
Looking for a rousing game of chess? Here's an excellent beginner's resource with quick facts and pointers to Internet Chess Servers (ICS) offering interactive play. Link to Telnet sights in the U.S. and abroad, some free, some for pay. Also find a directory of fellow ICS enthusiasts and a history of the game's evolution in cyberspace. A pointer to the newsgroup devoted to ICS issues rounds out the useful offerings presented.

Steve Pribut's Chess Page
http://www.clark.net/pub/pribut/chess.html
Here's a standard mega-resource for chess players of every rank. Stay abreast of player ratings, current chess news, and the page author's reviews of chess products. Players searching for FAQs can find these as well.

Swedish International Chess Server
http://www.mds.mdh.se/nojen/schack/
Another site suited for novice online players, the Swedish International Chess Server (SICS) serves up a list of sites around the world where online play is available free via Telnet. Those needing a client (or graphical interface) to connect will appreciate the link leading to an FTP archive offering help and software. The SICS supports various game types and variants, including bughouse.

WebChess

**http://www.willamette.edu/~tjones/
chessmain.html**

Play chess against a real-live opponent in real time with
no special interface, just a Web browser that's forms-
capable. Simply let WebChess know you're online by
signing in, then select an opponent from the players
available, or "start a new game" and wait for someone
to select you. Up to five games, with ten different players, can be run simultaneously. Be sure to read the instructions for play to ensure every experience is good,
beginning with the first. An onsite BBS lets players post
when they'll be online for play.

CONNECT FOUR

Connect-4

**http://www.castrop-rauxel.netsurf.de/
homepages/sven.wiebus/applets/connect4/**

Written and presented by Sven Wiebus, this Java applet presents an online version of the Connect Four
game. According to its creator, the game is quite beat-
able, but if you couldn't win, what would be the point
of playing? Those interested in the source of the game
will find a link to see how the applet works.

Connect Four

http://csugrad.cs.vt.edu/htbin/Connect4.perl

Play with or without graphics at this browser-friendly
site offering a Web version of the Connect Four game.
Rules are available for those who need them and a high
score list keeps track of the latest winners and losers.
Registration is required for scoring purposes. Presented by Joe Hines and Brian Roder.

Connect Four

**http://www.dbai.tuwien.ac.at/cgi-bin/rusch_
four/aanqdcbk/large/**

Peter Wansch and Klaus Johannes Rusch host this
browser-friendly Connect Four game. Select text
mode, small graphics, or large graphics. Rules of the

AUTHOR'S PICK

Fun House: Play Now

**http://starcreations.com/abstract/funhouse/
ga-pln01.htm**

Anyone looking for online action can't go too far afield
by consulting this index of some of the best interactive
entertainment the Web has to offer. Organized in three
groupings (A to L, M to P, and Q to Z), the online games
listed run the gamut from adventures to manipulative,
and from puzzles to virtual reality. Enjoy Web classics
like S.P.Q.R., where players search ancient Rome for
hidden secrets. Sweep for mines, sink battleships, and
hang men who can't spell. Look into the future with the
Magic Eight Ball, or just Ask Bob. And ponder over puzzles, mazes, and other mind games. There's fun here for
the whole family, or just one member at a time. Maybe
that's why they call it the Fun House.

game are close at hand, the skill level is adjustable, and
simple directions help players begin the game quickly.
Play is against the computer.

Connect Four—On the Web

http://www.iaw.on.ca/rickb/connect4/

Perhaps it should be called Connect Two because unlike other Web incarnations of this game, two people
can play this version against one another. Visit the instructions for a quick look at how things work, then
you and a partner are ready to Connect Four. The
game is hosted by Rick Byers.

For other Connect Four Java applets, see:

Connect4
http://dmawww.epfl.ch/~kuonen/Java/4.html

Connect Four
**http://server.snni.com/~mfo/java/connect4/
index.html**

DIPLOMACY

Diplomacy
http://www.tkblack.com/Diplomacy
Vie for control over pre-WWI Europe through skill, cunning, and international negotiation in Diplomacy, a board game from the folks at Avalon Hill Game Company. Interested? Stop by this site hosted by Thaddeus Black for an introduction to the game. Find a game overview, words of caution for e-mail newbies, a strategy session with Jake Orion, and links to a variety of Diplomacy sites and resources on the Web.

Diplomacy Central
http://home.sn.no/~arannest/dip/dip.htm
Anund Rannestad invites games enthusiasts to play Diplomacy via e-mail. Find a brief introduction to the game itself and step-by-step instructions for joining an e-mail game. A section on utilities and maps for e-mail play offer even more assistance. And for Diplomacy newbies, a strategy page offers insight into how the different countries might best be played.

Diplomacy E-mail Information
http://www.infersys.com/diplomacy/
Josh Smith hosts yet another "here's how to do it" for folks interested in joining the growing number of e-mail Diplomacy players. Features include a newbies guide, help files, and house rules. A guide to real-time play suggests this method isn't quite up to par with the e-mail games, but worth a shot. Also find a Diplomacy hall of fame, a subject index, and an FAQ among other topical FTP and Web sites.

Diplomacy Subject Index
ftp://ftp.ugcs.caltech.edu/pub/diplomacy/WWW/dip/dip_index.html#Z
Intended for both novices and experts involved in playing Diplomacy via e-mail, this exhaustive index of pointers, arranged alphabetically by subject, helps answer players' questions by linking to correct and up-to-date information concerning the game. Find everything from acronyms to Diplomacy zines and everything in between. Notes on using the index are available if needed.

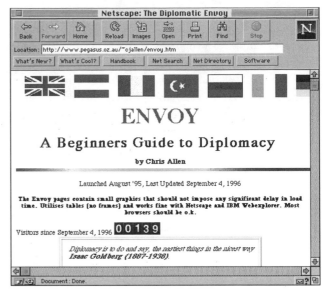

Envoy: A Beginners Guide to Diplomacy
http://www.pegasus.oz.au/~cjallen/envoy.htm
Chris Allen hosts this introduction to the game where honesty isn't always the best policy. Read a general overview of Diplomacy, review rules and strategies, and find out how to get started playing via e-mail. Information on face-to-face tournaments are also online, along with links to other players' home pages and game resources. For anyone curious enough to learn the playful nuances of international negotiation, here's an excellent place to begin.

Jake Orion Teaches Diplomacy
http://www.uidaho.edu/~blac9512/Orion/
A master at the game of Diplomacy, Jake Orion trains others via this ongoing series of articles written to help "warriors and diplomats" rise to new heights and levels of play. Currently available: Opening Strategy Part I and Part II.

The Labyrinth

http://www.new3.com/labyrinth/

No need to get out those Greek mythology books, even though this game uses the story of Theseus and Minotaur as its theme. Here's the quest: Navigate the maze of interconnected rooms known as The Labyrinth and search out the monster's lair. Those who successfully find the hiding place of Minotaur are eligible to win prizes and have their name posted in the Hall of Theseus. A counter details how many players have entered the maze that day and how many have succeeded in their task. (And by the numbers' indication, this game is harder than it sounds.) New players may want check out the Rules & Tutorial page for a better understanding of the game and for some of the secrets of the labyrinth. Players curious about the Minotaur legend will find a retelling of the tale available as well.

Judge Openings

http://www.ii.uib.no/~bjornts/openings/
openings.html

Diplomacy players looking to join an e-mail game need only consult this list of game openings at different Judges to find a spot. Check carefully though and read the full game listing. Not all games are in English and players should be fluent in the "official" language of the games they join.

The Newbies' Guide to the Judge

http://nurk.com/andy/main.html

Join Andy Schwarz for a step-by-step tutorial on finding a Diplomacy e-mail server (or Judge), registering with The Judge, then signing up for and playing games. All totaled it's a twelve-step program and quite easy to understand.

For more on Diplomacy, see:

Diplodocus

http://pages.prodigy.com/koehler/diplod.ht

An electronic zine for Diplomacy e-mail players.

DOMINOES

DominoNet

http://neon.ingenia.com/dominet/

Replete with its own theme song and a Fellini movie, this multimedia adventure into the world of dominoes offers something of interest for the novice and master gamer alike. Learn the essentials of play, become familiar with the correct use of terms, and gain insights into the strategies of play. A look at dominoes in society treats players to drinking games associated with the numbered tiles and inspects dominoes for sale. Links lead to newsgroups, a search utility, and the Domino-Net FTP site.

GO

American Go Association

http://www.usgo.org/

Go is an ancient Chinese board game of skill and strategy whereby two players compete turn-by-turn to "surround territory." Stop by the official home page of the association of Go players in United States to find out more about the game and sanctioned play, or to browse the AGA's online resources, including tips for improving play. Application for membership in the group can also be completed online.

Go Game Client

http://www.csun.edu/~hbcsc500/GoClient/
load.html

Play Go via this Java applet hosted by Roger Zou. Players should be familiar with the rules of the game before arriving to play; little instruction is available.

The Go Teaching Ladder

http://hyperg.iicm.tu-graz.ac.at/GTL

Thanks to Arno Hollosi, Go players who seek to reach new levels of play now have access to a venue for improving game performance. Players can submit their games for review by stronger players. Curious? Check

AUTHOR'S PICK

Piercing Mildred

http://streams.com/pierce/

What do you get when you cross the 90s fashion fetish for body modification with the wizardry and wonder of the World Wide Web? Here it is—a game where players compete head-to-head with others around the globe in a contest where the winner is the one who does the best job of piercing, scarring, tattooing, or otherwise mutilating virtual Mildred. But wait, there's more. Players are limited by the cash they have on hand to buy modifications, and if an infection sets in…well, you better get some ointment, fast! A winner is determined weekly, and the current week's Parade of Freaks is always online for viewing. Think of the game as aggression therapy, or a beauty makeover. Whatever, Mildred doesn't care.

out the introduction to the Go Teaching Ladder, read the FAQ, and browse the archive of reviewed games.

How to Play Go on the Internet

http://www.well.com/user/mmcadams/
igs.howto.html

Play Go via Telnet. Mindy McAdams explains the step-by-step about getting an Internet account, getting the right Telnet client software, and getting on the Go server. Also find an introduction to the game and access to other Go pages on the Web.

JavaGO

http://vanbc.wimsey.com/~igors/java/
go.html

Play Go with anybody on the Internet (whose browser can support Java) via Igor's JavaGO applet. Players can play, but the server is still in development. Be sure to read the instructional information before jumping into the action.

Ken's Go Page

http://ltiwww.epfl.ch/~warkent/go/go_
intro.html

Ken Warkentyne's extensive Go resource page holds something for most everyone, whether a beginner or veteran. Enjoy a background narrative on the game with imbedded links to sources for additional information. Browse the Go Web Index, which boasts a comprehensive list of Go-related Web pages. Or, link to the home pages of other Go players. Information on learning how to play Go and to improve in skill and tactical thinking is only a link away.

The Web Go Page Index

http://ltiwww.epfl.ch/~warkent/go/
golinks.html

If Go resources are the goal, go here. This gigantic resource links to players' home pages, products, books, articles, tournament announcements, news, and general information including FAQs, rules, and game collections. Also find links to playing on the Internet via Telnet and Java applets, pointers to worldwide associations and clubs, and FTP sites. Compiled and hosted by Ken Warkentyne, the index is well organized and easy to use.

MAHJONG

Durian League of Mahjong Official Server

http://www.best.com/~hirokun/

This instructive site helps players learn mahjong. Find rules and a Java applet to play online. Durian League information and results are also featured along with downloadable mahjong software for Windows. A Java-enabled browser is required for play.

The Internet Mahjong Meta-Server

http://www.math.princeton.edu/~ztfeng/mj_
servers.html

Play mahjong online, in real time, against real opponents from around the world using this Java applet by

Thomas Zuwei Feng. Links to sites running the server are featured along with a list of players who frequent each site. Also find links to other mahjong pages and the mahjong mailing list. For those interested, the source code for this applet is available. A Java-enabled browser is required.

Jonathon's Mahjong Page
http://www.atdesk.com/jon/mahjong.html
Jonathan Butler posts illustrations of mahjong tiles organized by type. See The Dragons, The Four Winds, the suit tiles, and the optional tiles. A link to Nanette Pasquarello's explanation of how to play the game is also featured.

Mahjong: The Chinese Game of Four Winds
http://www.cs.utk.edu/~clay/mahjongg/
Clay Breshears hosts this tutorial explaining the tile game mahjong. Find a description of the tiles, instructions for starting, playing, and winning a hand. Scoring and playing a full game are also covered. A list of books on the game and links to other mahjong sites on the Web are also featured.

OTHELLO

International Internet Othello Association's Guide to the Game of Othello
http://web.cs.ualberta.ca/~brock/othello.html
Here's the official line on the game which shares the name of Shakespeare's ill-fated, Moorish prince. Find the Othello FAQ, tournament news, official player standings, and the Othello phone book. Other resources include the rules of the game, links to online play, and game databases. Also find pointers to newsgroups and mailing lists of specific and topical interest.

Othello Pages
http://www.maths.nott.ac.uk/othello/othello.html
A resource for all manner of Othello player, this page, hosted by the Department of Mathematics at the United Kingdom's University of Nottingham, features an official beginners section and articles of interest from the British Othello Federation. Players looking to jump into the fray will also find a Telnet link to the original Othello server at the University of Paderborn in Germany.

RISK

The Battle Zone: The Risk Page
http://www.macshack.com/johns/RISK/risk.html
Risk enthusiasts will find plenty to ponder at this gamer's devotional to the "take that you imperialist dog!" game of monumental risks and continental rewards. Enjoy "The Battlemaster," an onsite newsletter developed for players to share and become aware of winning strategies. Download a Windows version of the game. Browse the directory of players and search for other Risk enthusiasts with whom to play. Or look into playing variations of the standard game. Gaming

tips, an online rule book, and links to topical pages leave little room to wonder why this site is entitled the Battle Zone.

Risk FAQ—Version 5.2

http://www.bath.ac.uk/~mapodl/html/riskfaq.html

Visit this fact-filled question-and-answer file for a fast, clear reference covering some of the finer points of the Parker Brothers game Risk. Find a discussion of variations in the game's "official" rules, a look at basic probability in relation to the game, and gaming variants contributed by Risk enthusiasts. Pointers to download sites where the game and the FAQ are available are also featured.

The Risk Page

http://www.cif.rochester.edu/users/tacoman/RISK/risk.html

Parker Brother's classic board game of strategic imperialism comes under the spotlight at this site devoted to exploring the various facets of the game where players "conquer" the continents of the world. Opening with an FAQ covering the rules of play, the site then reviews gaming strategies. Players looking for electronic versions of the game will enjoy the download section offering versions for the Mac and PC. And though no Web-based Risk game is available as yet, a link does point to a similar game, Global Diplomacy.

SCRABBLE

NET-Scrabble

http://elf.udw.ac.za/~scrabble/

Gamers! Play Scrabble in public or in private on this server which requires nothing more than a Web browser to play. Though this is not a real-time game server, play can go quickly if opponents are so inclined. An automatic e-mail notice feature alerts players when it's their turn to play. Be sure to read the Hints and Tips section of the Rules and Information; knowledge

is the key to winning and having a good game. By the way, lurkers are welcome, too!

OSPD2+ Word List Generator

http://www.umcc.umich.edu/~jgm/scrabble/scrabmain.html

Jim Miller hosts this online, interactive search tool for generating lists of words which appear in Milton Bradley's "Official Scrabble Players Dictionary." This is not an anagram server (something that rearranges letters to make words); rather, this handy server searches the official Scrabble word list for letter combinations. Input a letter combination, tell the server how big of a word is needed (how many letters), and the generator returns a list of words with the specified length which contain the letter combination.

Scrabble FAQ

http://www.teleport.com/~stevena/scrabble/faq.html

More than simply an FAQ, this directory points to a host of Scrabble and crossword game-related resources on the Internet. Look into rules for Scrabble tournament play in North America and around the world, find out when and where tournaments are taking place, and check to see if a Scrabble club is close enough to join. New words accepted by the official Scrabble monitors, articles of interest, and player ratings are also featured. Those interested in play-by-mail games can find out how to become involved, while computer versions of the game are also covered, including shareware versions available via FTP.

SHOGI

JavaShogi

http://dora.olu.info.waseda.ac.jp:8080/shogi/index.html

Play Shogi in real time against real opponents at this Java-based server. Two versions are featured, standard and light. Links lead to helpful gaming resources which include the rules of play. Text is available in English and the native language where the server is located, Japan.

Pieter Stouten's Shogi Home Page
http://www.halcyon.com/stouten/shogi.html
A comprehensive Shogi-player's resource, this site points to pages of interest to novice players and masters alike. Opening with a brief overview of the Japanese chess-like game, links then point to a list of rules, a look at problem solving, and annotated games. SHO-GI-L, a discussion list devoted to the game, a players list, tournament information, and links to Shogi software and equipment sites are then featured. This site is an excellent place to begin for those just starting out.

The Shogi Page
http://stripe.colorado.edu/~leonarm/shogi/shogi.html
Hosted by Matt Leonard, this instructional page introduces players to Shogi, its components, rules, and strategies. Begin with a simple description of the game, look at the board, examine the pieces and how each maneuvers, then set up the board and review basic moves like capturing, promoting, and dropping. Leonard even includes sections on handicapping, etiquette, and standard gaming notation. For those who want to learn this venerable Japanese game, here's a site worth studying.

XIANGQI (CHINESE CHESS)

Xiangqi Home Page
http://www.io.org/~sung/xq/xq.html
Here's the motherlode site for anyone ready to move from Chinese checkers to Chinese chess. Site features include basic information, a link to the rules FAQ, a game archive, and maneuvers masters need to know. News of interest to players, pointers to organizations, and a link to the Usenet newsgroup are also included. Those inclined to play online will find links to Telnet sites and Java sites where play is the order of the day.

AUTHOR'S PICK

World Wide Web Ouija
http://www.math.unh.edu/~black/cgi-bin/ouija.cgi
Contact the ghosts in your machine using this online Ouija arrangement and seek answers to your most pressing questions. Forget psychic call-in services, this setup by Kelly Black offers the real deal, a direct line to the other side (of your computer screen). Great for solitaire play or group fun, the World Wide Web Ouija works just like the standard game, only players use their mouse as the pointer. Some would suggest this game is not a toy to be trifled with; others would say trifle away. Do spirits really exist? Perhaps you should consult the World Wide Web Ouija to find out.

Player rankings and software round out the many offerings available.

Xiang Qi Corner
http://tonka.bu.edu/~xianwang/
Play Chinese chess in real time against real folks via this Java-based site. Easy to follow instructions aid first-timers with the applet, but players should come to the game already knowledgeable about the rules and strategies of play. This site serves the game only.

Xiang Qi—Elephant Chess—Chinese Chess
http://www.xencom.com/java/ele/elephant.html
Hosted by Xencom Communications, Inc., this server offers players a chance to play Chinese chess against the computer. A brief discussion of the difference between "elephant" chess and international chess offers some help, but players should arrive ready to maneuver. Those needing instruction can link to a site where help is available. This is a Java application, so a Java-capable browser is needed.

YAHTZEE

Web Yahtzee
http://www.cs.fsu.edu/~kalter/yahtzee.html
Bill Kalter offers Yahtzee players their choice: play the Java version, the frames version, the graphics version, or the text-only version. So no matter what type browser a player has, they can play here. Better know a little something about the game upon arrival, however. There's little in the way of game instruction.

YahtzREE
http://uranium.chem.umn.edu/~evan/Yahtzee/
R. Evan Easton presents his Java applet for playing the dice game Yahtzee. Players play by themselves but compete with other players' high scores. A game primer, miscellaneous YahtzREE facts and a High Scores list are featured along with the game. A Java-enabled browser is required to play.

FAVORITE CARD GAMES

BLACKJACK

Blackjack Basic Strategy Engine
http://www2.netdoor.com/~kensmith/bjstrat.html
Card enthusiasts can help improve their blackjack game by consulting this online tool created to return the best playing strategy, given the game conditions entered. Tell the server how many decks will be used, if and when doubling is allowed, and whether the dealer hits or stands on a "soft" 17. The engine then brings back a set of charts detailing when to split pairs and when to take a hit on "soft" totals. Reports are available with or without tables.

Black Jack on the World Wide Web
http://www.web-source.com/blackjack/
Most anyone with a Web browser can belly up to this virtual gaming table and try their hand at blackjack. Care was given in the creation of this server so no "special technology" is needed to enjoy it. Folks fuzzy about the rules of play will find online help, and anyone eager to leave a comment for the dealer are encouraged to do so. Of course, play is for points, so no jackpots can be won. But the best players do appear on the Top 10 list.

Casino Blackjack
http://www.best.com/~mcintyre/sage/
Sage Software invites players to download its PC shareware version of the Sage Blackjack Simulator (a 311K self-extracting file), a program that teaches players basic blackjack strategies and counting methods. Those without a PC may still want to review the Sage page of Blackjack Myths, Facts, and Playing Suggestions, especially if the casinos are a favorite haunt. Some of this information might come as quite a surprise!

Universal Access Inc. Blackjack Server
http://blackjack1.ua.com/welcome.mhtml
Start with $1,000.00 "play-money" and see how much you have left at the end of play. Standard rules apply (and are available for review). Players can choose the

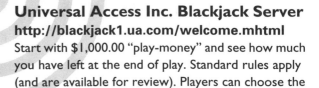

regular blackjack option, which shows play information as the game progresses, or professional blackjack, which only shows card images. Nothing fancy in the way of a Web browser is needed, just point, click, and play with most any model. Registration is requested, but not required.

Virtual Blackjack

**http://www.cyberdragon.com/cgi-bin/
php.cgi/bj/index.shtml**

This Java-based server deals blackjack to anyone who has a Java-enabled browser, though registration is requested. No money changes hands (play is for "points"), so a good time can be legally had by all. Check the FAQs for specifics about the server and the possibility of downloading the game to play without a network connection. If you need to review game rules, they're available, too. Other than that, good luck in becoming one of VB's Top Ten Money Makers!

Web Emporium's Blackjack Page

**http://www.webemporium.com/arcade/bj/
bjnhome.htm**

Most any standard Web browser which can support tables is all that's needed at this no-nonsense, come-on-let's-play blackjack server. Enter a bet (100, 250, 500, or 1,000 points, of course), enter a name (any name will do), and get to it! Play is easy and intuitive.

BRIDGE

Bob's Bridge Book Bonanza

http://www.spyglass.com/~bob/

Those who prefer to tackle their subject by reading books may want to consult this collection of titles and reviews if bridge is the topic of interest. Books are classified by type: Learning to Play, Comprehensive, Declarer Play, Bidding, Tactics, Defense, and Problem Solving. There are even sections on fiction and nonfiction, and pointers to sources for purchasing books. All are welcome to contribute their book knowledge to this collection.

AUTHOR'S PICK

Multiplayer Dot Com

http://www.multiplayer.com/

This simple, yet excellent resource points the way to multiplayer outlets on the Internet where those who so desire can seek out the company (and challenge) of fellow game-players in cyberspace. Categorized and alphabetized, each entry in the directory is annotated so players generally know what's available at the site before they go. Categories include: Multiplayer Sites; Multiplayer Information and Links; and General Gaming Links. From action adventures to virtual worlds, if the game allows multiplayer action, there's probably a way to get in on the fun from here.

Bridge Archives

ftp://rgb.anu.edu.au/pub/Bridge/FAQ/

Find answers to questions commonly asked about the game of bridge, how it is played, and who is playing it. This FTP archive holds a treasury of articles and other resources that cover everything from bidding to World Wide Web pages devoted to the game. Find clubs, computer aids, international player rankings, jargon, images, tournament news, and tons of other items of specific and topical interest.

Bridge Player Live

**http://www.bridgeplayer.com/~bridge/
bplive.html**

The International On-Line Bridge Club, Inc. hosts this subscriber service for online play. Stop by to check out the membership, look into competitions, browse the forum, read the club news, and generally get a feel for the place. Software is available for download, and visitors so inclined can arrange free tables.

Great Bridge Links

http://www.cbf.ca/query/GBL.html

The title tells it all! These are great bridge links and there are loads of them, too. No matter what anyone is after, they'll find direction here. Pointers link to organizations, magazines and newsletters, online play, software sites, players' bridge pages, archives, newsgroups, and mailing lists. There is even a bridge shopping mall. The page is well organized and maintained by Jude Goodwin-Hanson.

Internet Gaming Zone: Bridge
http://igz2.microsoft.com/bridge.html
Play bridge against others or practice against the computer at Microsoft's Internet Gaming Zone. Play is free, but users must download the necessary software (PC-based only) before connecting to "the Zone" for play. Visit this page for the details on playing bridge, or link to back to the Zone's home page for information on the other card and gaming options available.

OKbridge
http://www.okbridge.com/install.html
Another pay-to-play bridge service, OKbridge offers newcomers a 30-day free trial period before requiring payment. Options include playing via Web or Telnet connection, via a preferred OKbridge provider, or via another Internet provider. Stop by this page for an overview on getting started playing OKbridge.

For more information on bridge, see:

Bridge Today
http://www.ny-bridge.com/bt.html
Online version of magazine, strategy articles, columns, Q&A.

CANASTA

Canasta
http://www.cs.man.ac.uk/card-games/ rummy/canasta.html
Presented through the combined energies of two card-playing enthusiasts, this page offers an easy-to-understand tutorial on the four-player, two-deck card game. From dealing and playing, to going out and scoring

hands, everything players need to know to enjoy the game and win are here. Tips on game variations help veteran canasta players keep the deal fresh and lively.

For more information on canasta, see also:

Canasta Rules
http://www.uni.uiuc.edu/~ksutton/www/ Canasta.html

HEARTS

The Internet Gaming Zone: Hearts
http://igz2.microsoft.com/hearts.html
PC-users can play hearts and other games live, with real, live people, at the Internet Gaming Zone. Users must first download and install the IGZ software, but once done, they can launch the program through their standard Winsock application and enter the gaming room. Visit this page to learn more about the protocol at the tables where hearts is being played, or to find out how to download the needed software file.

POKER

Araneums Cyber Poker
http://www.araneum.dk/poker/indexuk.html
Anyone with a standard Web browser can play and enjoy this video 5-card draw poker simulation game. Players begin with a $5,000 credit in play money and try to build from there. Jacks or better are needed to win; nothing is wild. Registration is only required for those who want to be ranked among the other players.

Dan's Poker Dictionary
http://www.universe.digex.net/~kimberg/ pokerdict.html
Dan Kimberg presents this hyperlinked dictionary of terms used in poker play. If a definition uses a word or expression that also appears in the dictionary, the

word or expression is hyperlinked to its definition, so those who need it can get immediate clarification. An excellent resource for poker players at all levels.

The Inside Straight: A Guide to Poker Resources
http://www.panix.com/~ssf/poker.html
Looking to get into a poker game? Want to improve the caliber of your play? Curious about what the professional players are up to? Then this is the resource for you. Find information on odds, gaming theories, outlets for online play and discussion, computer products, and data on tournament and casino action.

IRC Poker Dealing Program
http://www.cs.cmu.edu/afs/cs/user/ mummert/public/www/ircbot.html
The home page of the IRCbot poker dealing program provides visitors a history of the program and useful instruction on how to connect. A command list along with IRC helps and hints offers additional player support.

IRC Poker Home Page
http://maelstrom.cc.mcgill.ca/poker/ poker.html
Here's the home page of the EFNet Poker Channels, where players can join games of poker and risk nothing but points. No money changes hands; it's all for bragging rights and nothing more. Find general information about the server, a help manual, and an FAQ. A players list and rankings indicate who's on top and who's definitely not.

Mike Naylor's Five by Five Poker
http://www.serve.com/games/5x5poker/ 5x5poker.cgi
Though not exactly a poker game, poker knowledge and skill are needed to win this game. The object is to build (in columns and rows) ten good poker hands. A game explanation and hints for play help first-timers find their way. Netscape Navigator Version 2.0 or higher required to play.

AUTHOR'S PICK

Virtual Vegas
http://www.virtualvegas.com/
Working to make this site as family-oriented as the city of Las Vegas is working to become, Virtual Vegas is constructing a variety of venues for different types of entertainment. That doesn't change the central focus of the site one bit, however. If you like to game but hate to lose real money, this site is nothing short of paradise. Enjoy all the major games—slots, craps, and cards—and don't fret over losses. Play is for points, even when playing against real-live opponents. Visitors need to check the software requirements to access the various games. Virtual Vegas promotes games using the latest technologies.

The Perfect Casino: Video Poker
http://link2.com/casino/gameroom.html-ssi
Play video poker and win pay-outs like the real machines—only here, pay-outs are in points. Demo action is available, but for credited play, registration is required.

Poker FAQ
http://www.conjelco.com/faq/poker.html
Here's the Frequently Asked Questions file from the Usenet newsgroup rec.gambling.poker. Find answers to basics such as the ranking of hands, as well as more advanced concerns like how tournament strategy differs from regular game strategy. Information about playing online, computer programs, and books worth reading is also featured. Anyone new to poker can learn a great deal; even veterans may pick up a tip or two.

The Poker Room
http://amusing.roc.servtech.com/poker.shtml
Here's another Java poker game dealing 5-card draw. Download the source code (takes about four minutes),

ante up, and play either humans or robots. Again, this game will only work with browsers that support Java.

Poker Variants

http://www.wolfenet.com/~peter/poker/

What's the difference between draw and stud poker? Peter Sarret posts this information resource that explains the deal. Along with the standard poker games, also find descriptions for variations on poker play, miscellaneous games, and non-poker games. Ever heard of Howdy Doody? The list of poker terms and hand rankings will be of great use to those who've never played.

POKERwwwORLD

http://pokerwwworld.com/

Self-described by its author, Darryl Phillips, a.k.a. RazzO, as an "InterNET Magazine," this site hosts a little bit of everything from the world of poker. Link to newsgroups, find out about poker events, and play poker on the Internet. Check out what's happening at casinos and gaming rooms, find tourism and show guides from Las Vegas, and read interviews with world class players. The archive is also open to review past postings. There's plenty to do and see, and well worth a look.

Undernet Poker

http://www.atlantic.net/~phod/

Which is the best IRC poker server on the Internet? That's up to individual players to decide, but this server's following is certain they're in the right place. Find out the who, what, when, and where to judge for yourself, or visit the Vault of Glittering Prizes to see why Undernet Poker players, and casual passers-by, think this server is something special.

Video Poker on the Web

http://www.inlink.com/~jmgberg/poker/poker.html

A Java-capable browser is required to play and jacks or better are required to win. Test Lady Luck and risk nothing but time; play is for points only.

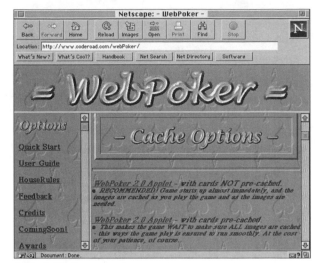

WebPoker

http://www.coderoad.com/webPoker

Play video-style 5-card draw, 7-card stud, or "high-low" 7-card stud via this Java applet. Netscape 2.0 with Java is required for play. An online user guide and house rules help the unfamiliar settle in for fun. Play is for points; no money changes hands.

For more information on poker, see also:

Card Player Magazine

http://www.cardplayer.com/

The magazine "for those who play to win."

ROOK

Rook—The Official Internet Page

http://www.naples.net/~nfn02644/rook.html

Visit this page to review the "Princeton rules" for playing the Parker Brothers card game Rook. This text-based tutorial takes players step-by-step through beginning, bidding, playing, and scoring. Those looking for a software version of the game can follow the pointer provided to the site of a company selling a variety of card game software including Rook.

For more information on Rook, see also:

Rook

http://www.cs.man.ac.uk/card-games/kt5/rook.html

SHEEPSHEAD

Sheepshead Page
http://www.uwm.edu/~oz/sheepshead/
sheepshead.html
Learn to play the card game where the kings get no re-spect—read the history of this Middle European game to find out why. Played with 32 cards, the point of the game is to take tricks which total in point value to at least 61. The basic rules, scoring, playing strategies, and tips are all covered. Illustrated examples help to make key points. Players who want to practice on their own will find PC shareware available for downloading.

See also:

How to Play Sheepshead
http://www.psy.cmu.edu/~sb6s/sheepers.html
Sheepshead according to Hoyle, Bushnell, and most of Milwaukee, WI.
http://www.mcw.edu/~etb/sheepshead.html

SPADES

Dan & Brad's Spades Tribute Page
http://www.unc.edu/~dano/spades.html
For those who can stand Dan and Brad's boasting about what great spades players they are, there's plen-ty of good game information up for grabs at this site. Find a game history, rules, and links to software. Those interested in online play (and perhaps a chance to beat this dynamic duo) will also appreciate the pointers to sites open for play.

Internet Gaming Zone: Spades
http://igz2.microsoft.com/spades.html
Play spades against others or take a seat in the gallery and watch a hand or two at Microsoft's Internet Gam-ing Zone. Play is free, but users must download the necessary software (PC-based only) before connect-ing. Visit this page for the details on playing spades, or

link to back to the Zone's home page for information on the other card and gaming options available.

Network Spades
http://www.cris.com/~Cdrom/dnload.shtml
Here's a pay-to-play outlet for those who enjoy the challenge of spades. Download the necessary Telnet client and find out how to join the group at CRIS.

WebSpades
http://okapi.dws.acs.cmu.edu/fred/
webspades.html#anchor224676
Play a rousing game of spades in real time against oth-ers around the globe. Online instructions for joining a game and rules for playing spades help make newcom-ers feel right at home. A Java-capable browser is re-quired for play.

PUZZLES AND MISCELLANEOUS GAMES

CONCENTRATION

Cindy Crawford Concentration
http://www.facade.com/Fun/concentration/
Jonathan Katz presents this model twist on the old "match the like images" game. Here a Cindy, there a Cindy, everywhere a Cindy. Fans of the supermodel need no luck with this game; they've won once they've loaded the page.

Concentration
http://www.i5.com/cgi-bin/concentration
Choose the card scheme (select from famous artwork, Jennifer Aniston, Sandra Bullock, and other "themes"),

 **AUTHOR'S PICK**

Play by Mail (PBM) Games Homepage
http://www.pbm.com/~lindahl/pbm.html
Greg Lindahl's browser-friendly directory isn't fancy at all, but it does offer a good resource for enthusiasts interested in play-by-mail games—either postal mail or e-mail. The page opens with links to the Usenet newsgroup rec.games.pbm and the FAQ which offers a quick overview of play-by-mail gaming. Then comes a link to the list of "all known" games which offer a play-by-mail option. Currently there are 94 games divided into 23 categories. Next find links to the Play-by-Email Fanzine and to two FTP sites offering a variety of topical information. Finally, pointers to pages of topical interest round out the offerings.

set the difficulty level (from absurdly easy to insane), and have a go at this Web version of the classic game. Written and presented by Joel Nordell, the game requires Netscape 2.0 or better.

CROSSWORD PUZZLES

A Crossword Applet In Java
http://www.clearlight.com/~vivi/xw/big.html
A rather friendly Java site, this one offers useful links so those without Java-enabled browsers won't have wasted their time if they wander by. Those with Java can work the crossword; those without can follow links to puzzles that don't require Java.

CrossWord for the Web!
http://virtumall.com/cgi-bin/crossword
Solve this crossword puzzle online without any special browser requirements. Hosted by Virtumall, the puzzle offers a click and play interface: click on a clue, type the answer, press Enter, and the grid gets filled in.

Crossword Puzzles
http://www.primate.wisc.edu/people/hamel/cp.html
Ray Hamel has compiled and hosts this extensive directory of crossword resources available online. Featured links lead to tournament information, organizations, puzzle generators, and sites offering puzzle play. There's plenty to do and see.

Crosswords Uncrossed: Solve Your Crosswords
http://www.eecg.toronto.edu/~bryn/HTML/Crosswords.html
Stuck on a particularly difficult puzzle clue? Need a little help to get started? Just like to cheat? Here's a site for anyone who answered yes to any or all of these questions. Find a word-puzzle solver, a crossword solver, and a jumble solver ready to figure out the answers. Instructions are included.

The Daily Crossword of the Chicago Tribune
http://www.unc.edu/dth/xword.gif
Suitable to print and work offline, the puzzle offers a real challenge to those who enjoy word games. The answer to the puzzle is also featured, turned upside down.

Java Crossword Puzzle
http://www.dareware.com/cross.htm
Download the Java applet and work the crossword puzzle online. Instructions offer easy how-to guidance. Must have Java-enabled browser to play.

Jumble & Crossword Solver
http://odin.chemistry.uakron.edu/cbower/jumble.html
Here's another online helper for those who sometimes need some assistance solving word jumbles and crossword puzzles. Read the directions, feed the clue into the computer, and *voilà!* Instant answers.

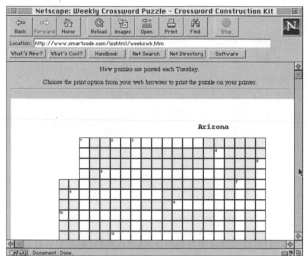

Puzzle Connection
Weekly Crossword Puzzle
http://www.smartcode.com/isshtml/
weekcwk.htm
A new puzzle is posted every Tuesday which is suitable to print and then work offline. The puzzles are theme-oriented and compatible with Puzzle Connection's Crossword Construction Kit. A link back to the Puzzle Connection leads to more gaming fun.

Puzzle of the Month
http://www.customcrosswords.com/
month.htm
Hosted by Custom Crossword, here's another site offering a printable crossword puzzle for offline fun. Links to related puzzle sites are also featured.

Usenet Crossword FAQs
http://www.cis.ohio-state.edu/hypertext/
faq/usenet/crossword-faq/top.html
Find answers to the Frequently Asked Questions (FAQ) posted in the Usenet newsgroup rec.puzzles.crosswords. The FAQ file is broken into three segments for easy access.

Web Feetures CrossWWWord
http://www.unc.edu/dth/xword.gif
A Shockwave-based puzzle, this online crossword offers scrolling clues, scoring, and other unique site features. Puzzles change weekly. A link to demos of Alpahbyte Soup, another Web Feetures word game, is also available.

The WWW Anagram Generator
http://csugrad.cs.vt.edu/~eburke/
anagrams.html
Eli Burke
Take a word (or words), mix it all up, and see what other words shake out. That's what anagrams are all about. Try this online server for fun and folly. Those interested in the source code can check that out, too.

X-Words at Misc. World HQ
http://www.speakeasy.org/misc/
XWordIndex.html
Clark Humphrey creates and sells his X-Words crossword puzzles to alternative weeklies around the country. Stop by this archive to sample the unique 11x13 puzzle. Puzzles suitable for printing and offline play are featured along with the answers.

For more crossword puzzles, see also:

iGuide's Multimedia Crosswords
http://www.iguide.com/games/xwords/index.htm
USA Today Crossword Puzzle Viewer
http://www.usatoday.com/life/puzzles/
puzzle.htm

HANGMAN

Hangman
http://www.cm.cf.ac.uk/htbin/RobH/
hangman?go
Robert Hartill hosts this bare bones version of the letter guessing game. The game features line art, a used letter display, and of course, letter blanks to fill in to form the word. Remember: R,S,T,L,N, and E are the most commonly used letters.

Alien Autopsy
http://www.theyknow.com/alien/
Here's a game for anyone desiring to turn the tables and probe a space alien for a change, or for those who just can't get enough of extra-terrestrials, dead or alive. In this graphically vivid simulation, players assume the role of the doctor in charge of examining an alien being that was taken from a downed UFO. With surgical precision, you disassemble the alien who is bound hand and foot, spread-eagle on a metal table. As might be expected, a warning is posted at the entrance of the examination room advising that children under the age of 13 are required to have adult supervision. This demonstration is not for the queasy or the humorless.

Hangman—Java
http://bigwave.ca/~mgsmith/smitty4.htm
Guess the target word letter by letter. Instructions state that a player's CapsLock should not be engaged. A Java-enabled browser is required to play.

Hangman—Java Games
http://weber.u.washington.edu/~jgurney/games/Hangman.html
Written by Patrick Chan of Sun Microsystems, this Java applet presents yet another Web version of the classic kids guessing game. A Java-enabled browser is required to play.

Letter R.I.P
http://www.dtd.com/rip/
Here's a graphically gruesome spin on an old favorite. It's Hangman all right, but rather than building a stick figure to twist from the gallows, missed letters mean Zeppie the Zombie loses a limb. The words are a cut above on the difficulty scale...all the worse for Zeppie!

Madlibs
http://www.mit.edu:8001/madlib
The original interactive fiction game comes to the Web via this Massachusetts Institute of Technology server. Simply enter the dozen or so words requested (players need to know the difference between nouns, verbs, adjectives, etc.) and let the computer do the rest. It will return a story using the words specified. Of course, the stories don't always make strict sense, but they generally generate a giggle or two. A selection of story themes is available to choose from, or players can let the computer randomly select the theme.

NetNoose
http://home.netscape.com/people/nathan/netnoose/index.html
Pick a level (beginner, intermediate, or advanced) and then pick a letter. A forms-capable browser is required. Simple art and a used-letter display are featured.

MASTERMIND

Genetic and Annealed Master Mind
http://kal-el.ugr.es/mastermind.html
More of a programmer's version of the game (offering code and the like), this edition of Mastermind does everything inside the "black box." Once players set the combination of colors, the computer takes over the game, plays, and returns the results. Links to other Mastermind sites are also available.

Mastermind
http://141.46.90.5/mastmind/emmstart.htm
Demo the game anonymously, or register and compete for a place on the High Score List. Those unfamiliar with the game are encouraged to read the rules,

and all should read the introductory material before beginning play. In English and German.

Mastermind—Java

http://www.tdb.uu.se/~karl/java/ mastermind.html

Karl Hörnell hosts this Mastermind Java applet. Players can set the difficulty level by choosing the number of colors to play with. Those curious about such things, can also access the game's source code. A Java-enabled browser is required to play.

MasterWeb

http://imagiware.com/masterweb.cgi

Guess the color code the computer has devised at this gaming site patterned after the classic Mastermind game. Easy-to-understand instructions explain the game, and customizable options allow players to control the difficulty level. The game was written by Brian Casey.

Switches

http://users.ox.ac.uk/cgi-bin/safeperl/ quee0275/switches.pl

Similar to Mastermind, Switches requires players to guess a pattern which has been generated by the computer. Online help acquaints newcomers to this British game.

WebMind

http://einstein.et.tudelft.nl/~mvdlaan/ WebMind/WM_intro.html

Players can set the difficulty level (beginner to expert) at this Web version of the classic "crack the code" game. Easy instructions explain how things work, and a Hall of Fame sets the target to shoot for. A link to an interactive games list points to other fun on the Web.

AUTHOR'S PICK

Games Kids Play

http://www.corpcomm.net/~gnieboer/ gamehome.htm

Here's a simple reminder that not all the best games require the use of a computer. In fact, some of the best games are actually played outside, in real time, with real live people. Geof Nieboer maintains this archive posting the rules to various backyard delights including hand-me-down games like Kick the Can, Dodgeball, and Tag. Games aimed at an even younger crowd include Duck Duck Goose, Mother May I, and Red Light/Green Light. Though the site itself is quite simple, its purpose is quite compelling: to transcribe the oral tradition that passes these games from generation to generation in the hope that neither they, nor the enjoyment they bring, becomes lost in an overly electronic world. Contributions to the collection of game rules are kindly appreciated.

MR. POTATO HEAD

Mr. Edible Starchy Tuber Head

http://winnie.acsu.buffalo.edu/potatoe/

Sure it's a game, but it's also a bit of a Web wonder. Apart from the game, there's a truckload of starchy things to do and see. The site is a must for "potatoe" lovers and lovelorn alike. International versions include Pig Latin and Canadian.

Tater Man!

http://lark.cc.ukans.edu/~asumner/shock/ potato/

Who would have thought putting facial features on a spud would catch on? Now everyone can "virtually" do it. Aaron Sumner presents his version of the kid's game where the potato really does have eyes. Requires Shockwave.

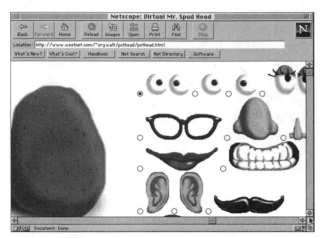

Virtual Mr. Spud Head (Regular or Java)
http://www.westnet.com/~crywalt/pothead/pothead.html

Chris Rywalt makes a good thing even better. Players can stick body parts anywhere on Mr. Spud Head they want, rather than being limited to the holes provided in the real-life game model. Those needing instructions will find they're only a click away. And anyone seeking a Java version to play can follow the link provided.

NIM

The Fruit Game
http://www.2020tech.com/fruit/

This version of the classic game Nim replaces matchsticks with fruit. The player who takes the last piece of fruit off the table loses. Challengers go first; the computer plays second. Those unfamiliar with the game may want to check the rules; those who lose may want to find out why.

The Game of Nim
http://ourworld.compuserve.com/homepages/FransG/nim.htm

Frans Gustafson hosts this extensive Nim resource. Offering a background and history of the game, the page also points to sites offering online play. Links to downloadable programs for offline play are also included. A look at available literature rounds out the page's offerings.

AUTHOR'S PICK

Virtual Nashville
http://virtualnashville.com/index.html

Is it a game, is it a promotion for the city of Nashville, or is it both? Take a virtual tour of Music City while participating in a cross-town scavenger hunt. Players are required to collect the items listed before they can go to Music Row, get a recording contract, and make it big in the virtual country music industry. Registration is required to play (aliases are okay), but the game is free, entertaining, and worth a wander through. Where else can a body tour a famous Tennessee town, see the sights, hear the sounds, pick up interesting items like goo goo clusters, and make a run for the Virtual Nashville Hall of Fame? And all from the comfort of home.

The Game of Nim
http://mars.superlink.net/user/abogom/nim_st.html

Visit this informative gaming site to review the rules and the theory behind Nim. Or, just enjoy the online play! The page is hosted by Alexander Bogomolny, a software specialist with a Ph.D. in numerical analysis. The talk can get fairly heady, but the game remains the same test of wits.

Match 23
http://www.gold.net/users/fj17/index.htm

Twenty-three matches are arranged in three rows; players take turns with the computer removing one, two, or three matches. The one who removes the last match loses. Presented by David Andrews, this versions allows players to decide if they or the computer goes first.

Nim!
http://www.robtex.com/robban/nim1.htm

Those who don't know how to play can review the rules online; others can proceed straight to the play area. Simple instructions detail how to manipulate the matches. Good luck!

Safety Matches Game
http://www.sanet.sk/~milan/JAVA/ matches.html
This Java applet of the Nim game allows players to decide how many matches to begin with. Once done, play begins and the one to take the last match loses. Requires a Java-enabled browser.

Strawberry Macaw's Chomp Puzzle
http://www.serve.com/games/chomp/ chomp.htm
Polly want a cracker? Here's a variation on Nim, or 23 Matches, using crackers. The player left with the poison cracker loses. Easy-to-follow instructions lead to immediate play.

Strawberry Macaw's 23 Matches Puzzle
http://www.serve.com/games/23match/ 23match.htm
Play the Strawberry Macaw game of Nim. Let the bird go first or take the initiative yourself and remove one, two, or three matches. The one left taking the last match loses. The game's set-up allows for intuitive play. Beat that bird!

PUZZLE COLLECTIONS

Fun Game!
http://asylum.cid.com/~eveander/game/ fungame.html
Eve Andersson posts this small collection of puzzles offering challenge and fun. Players will currently find an anagram, two logic puzzles, and one cryptogram. Game puzzles may change from time to time.

AUTHOR'S PICK

Puzzle Depot
http://www.puzzledepot.com/
Pinnacle Solutions posts this paradise for puzzle-playing enthusiasts. Offering all manner of brain teaser and mind bender from crosswords to trivia, the site even presents information on puzzle challenges offering prizes that collectively total over $10,000 a month. Stop by the games gallery to review board game options; the shareware shelf offers puzzle software that can be downloaded; and the book stacks catalog publications of interest to those who enjoy solving puzzles. Links connect with over a dozen other sites of topical interest.

The Grey Labyrinth
http://www.cybercom.net/~kevinlin/ labyrinth/
Exercise the old gray cells with this collection of teasers and benders hosted by Kevin J. Lin. Find puzzles that range in difficulty from the easy to the complex, but are all designed to inspire thought, paint new perspectives, and generally amuse. Topical links and a bibliography add to the resources available for those with questioning minds.

Juanune Online Puzzles
http://weber.u.washington.edu/~juanune/ game.html
Join the elite who solve the logic puzzlers posted and toasted here. Like something out of a Mensa quiz, these mind benders can hurt the addled and those with low self-esteem. Take care and good luck! Hosted by John Green.

Mind Games
http://weber.u.washington.edu/~jlks/ mindgame.html
Jordan Schwartz hosts these games sprung from his interest in the study of psychology. Choose from: The

Pick-A-Number Game, Mind Control, The Math Game, Three Men and a Hotel, or 2=1. If none of those strike a chord, try: The Grammar Game, The Grammar Game II, or the Pattern Game.

Period.Com Puzzles
http://www.period.com/puzzles/puzzles.shtml

Those looking for a break can try their hand at solving this week's puzzle postings. Puzzles are rated to give an idea of their charms, and all players are asked the Goldilocks question: Were the puzzles too hard, too easy, or just right?

The rec.puzzles Archive
http://einstein.et.tudelft.nl/~arlet/puzzles/index.html

This should be the first stop and could be the last for anyone looking for puzzles. Compiled from the Usenet newsgroup rec.puzzles, this archive organizes puzzles (and their solutions!) by subject category and points the way. Find things like language equations and probability puzzles, as well as trivia, riddles, and games. A link to the rec.puzzles FAQ is also featured.

The Sphinx
http://stud1.tuwien.ac.at/~e9226344/Themes/Puzzles/sphinx.html

Enjoy puzzles sorted by category and level of difficulty. Categories include logic, math, and physical puzzles. Playing levels run from the very easy to the very hard. The page is hosted by Marcus-Christopher Ludl.

Zoma's Land O' Logic
http://lc.gulfnet.com/user_pages/dstern/logic.htm

Match wits with Zoma and see who's the smarter. Puzzle out the answer to the featured logic problem. Zoma knows the answer…anyone else?

ROCK, PAPER, SCISSORS

Rock, Paper, and Hedge Trimmer?
http://www.pinncomp.com/cgi-bin/game/game.pl

It's the classic game, only the name has been changed to protect the person who was supposed to bring the scissors to scan when this site was developed. Oh well. Those who seek a modicum of fame can play for a place among the elite on the Top Scores page.

Rock, Paper, Scissors
http://www.shadow.net/~proub/rps.html

Idle away the hours trying to beat Paul Roub's Web version of the old school yard game where rock breaks scissors, scissors cut paper, and paper covers rock. Choose a weapon and go for it.

Rock, Scissors, Paper!
http://jgsullivan.com/demo/rsp/

Using graphics of human hands imitating rock, scissors, and paper (just like in the school yard!), this server keeps tabs of the round and who's winning—the computer or the challenger. Feeling lucky?

Twilight Games Page
http://www.twilightgames.com/
Java applet players, stay abreast of the latest and best Java powered games on the Web. Twilight Games scours the Internet and provides annotated listings of the games available for online play. Review all the games alphabetically, or sort and review them by game genre, including: shoot-em-ups, board games, arcade games, puzzles, card games, and solitaire games. Each applet listed is followed by a brief description and hyperlinked to take players directly to the game. As an added features to its site, Twilight Games also spotlights what it considers the Top 5 games and offers tips for enjoying Java play.

Roshambot
http://chappie.stanford.edu/cgi-bin/
roshambot
Is this a Rock, Paper, Scissors game or a religious experience? That's up to every player to decide. Perry Friedman, the site's developer and resident philosopher, can help shed light for the true seeker. Others are welcome just to enjoy the play. A registered version of the game which keeps score is available for interested players.

For more Rock, Paper, Scissors, see also:

Rock, Paper Scissors
http://trash.com/game/

Rock, Paper, Scissors
http://ampere.scale.uiuc.edu/~bart/cgi/C/rps/

Rock, Paper, Scissors!
http://www.virtumall.com/fast/rockpaper.html

RUBIK'S CUBE

Rubik's Cube
http://wwwserv.caiw.nl/~pbrijs/cube.html
Created by Song Li, this site offers a three-dimensional version of the classic Rubik's Cube puzzle. Instructions are included to manipulate the object, but generally speaking, players rotate the cube by using their mouse to drag it. This is an applet, so a Java-enabled browser is required.

Rubik's Cube Java Applet
http://www.best.com/~schubart/rc/
Michael Schubart presents his Java applet simulation of the Rubik's Cube. Twist the colored squares until all the colors are together. Playing instructions are online for those who need them; the source code is also available for those curious enough to want to know how the cube works. Play requires a Java-enabled browser.

Rubik's Cube Resource List
http://www.best.com/~schubart/rc/
resources.html
Compiled and presented by Michael Schubart, this excellent gamer's resource points toward almost all the Rubik's Cube sites on the Internet. Find interactive cubes of most every description including VRML, Shockwave, and Java. Access sites offer manmade and automated puzzle solutions, topical publication lists, and mailing lists. Or link to the pages of other folks fascinated by the puzzle.

WebCube
http://info.gte.com/gtel/fun/cube/cube.html
Here's a Web version of the Rubik's Cube almost any browser can handle. Created by Steve Belczyk, WebCube is composed of 27 colored cubes; players manipulate the cube to get the colors to line up. Easy to follow instructions help the newcomer get acquainted with the game.

World Wide Web Rubik's Cube
http://www.proximity.com.au/~brian/rubik/
rubik.cgi

SLIDING TILE PUZZLES

Arlet's Puzzle Page

http://einstein.et.tudelft.nl/~arlet/slide.cgi

The page may be titled A Simple Puzzle, but the game is a challenge nonetheless. Slide the numbers around until they're in order. For those who are interested, information on how the puzzle was created is available.

McGrew Puzzles

http://www.colorgraphics.com/puzzle.htm

Play with sound or without at this puzzle page hosted by McGrew Color Graphics. Puzzles are created randomly from a bank of six pictures. Read the instructions (multiple tiles can be moved in a single play) and let the game begin!

Mike Curtis' Slider Puzzle

http://www2.smart.net/mcurtis-cgi-bin/slider.html

An elegant version of the standard "move the numbered tiles until they're sequential" game. This version highlights the tiles which can be played during any given move. Give this one a try; it's very easy on the eyes and play proceeds rather smoothly.

Mosaic: The Game

http://virtumall.com/cgi-bin/mosaic

Virtumall hosts this puzzle challenge. There are 15 numbered tiles and 16 slots; arrange the tiles sequentially from top left to bottom right. Sounds easy until you try.

Picture Puzzles by Colin

http://www.rahul.net/runaway/puzzles/puzzles.html

Colin Andrews invites players to select a photo and then unscramble the tiles to recreate it. Works with almost any browser, plus a Lynx option is also featured. Choose from a mountain scene, a spider, or a clock.

Puzzlers' Sliders

http://www.accessus.net/~drasys/Puzzlers/Slider/index.html

Choose from four different sliding tile puzzles demanding a slightly higher caliber of play. Easy-to-follow instructions explain the point of each puzzle. A frames- and Java-enabled browser is required to enjoy the challenge.

Sliding Puzzle

http://genesis.tiac.net/puzzle.html

Yet another game by Steve Belczyk, this sliding puzzle is an HTML version of the kid's game but using letter tiles instead of numbers. Click the tile to move it to the adjacent blank space. Those interested in how this game works can take a look at the technical details.

SLOT MACHINES

CyberSlots

http://www.cyberact.com/cyberslots/

Pick a theme and go for the glory. Current slot themes include art, fish, hot sauce, and roses. Any frames-enabled browser will work on this game.

Hunter's Slot Machine

http://www.bznet.com/me/hunter/

Here's another Shockwave slot machine, this one hosted by Chris Hunter.

Jackpot

http://www.cs.umu.se/cgi-bin/scripts/jackpot

Another basic slot machine interface. Play for points, for laughs, or for want of anything better to do. A basic Web browser is all that's required to play.

The Jackpot

http://www.initiative.com/

Classic Media hosts this live slot machine where players can win payouts of real U.S. cash. From all indications, play is free and prizes come from the site sponsors. Check for restrictions that may apply.

The Perfect Casino: Slots

http://link2.com/casino/gameroom.html-ssi

Play slots and win payouts like the real machines—only here, payouts are in points. Demo action is available, but for credited play, registration is required.

Slot Machine

http://www.cni-inc.com/slot.html

Hosted by cni.inc, this slot machine sports the latest bells and whistles; it's a Shockwave site! Appropriate browser required.

Slot Machine Java

http://www.itivity.com/Java/Slot/ slotMachine.html

Hosted by InetNetivity, Inc. of Canada, the site is meant as a presentation on the benefits of Java for product demonstration. Who cares. Let's play!

SlotMania

http://slots.inetwave.com/

Offering a simulated Las Vegas-type experience, this server features a variety of slots and uses Java, HTML, and VRML enhancements for better display and action. Credited play requires registration, but registered players are eligible to win prizes.

The Virtual Slot Machine

http://www.pacificnet.net/~sonic/vslot.html

Begin with five virtual coins and try to build a bank from there. Pull the handle and spin to win. This site offers a basic interface that requires only a forms-enabled browser.

WebSlots

http://pandarus.usc.edu/ken-bin/ slot2.pl?instruct=start

Sporting a "new improved" design, this server starts players with $500.00 in play money. Bet $1.00 to $5.00

AUTHOR'S PICK

UK National Lottery: All Lottery Links

http://www.connect.org.uk/lottery/Links/ All.html

From the official United Kingdom National Lottery site, this page offers links to the world's lotteries. Find pointers to official and unofficial lottery pages from North America, Europe, and Australia. Find everything from official results to random number generators and strategy software. Offering (literally) a world of links, this page is a must for players who queue each week for a ticket to ride.

per spin. Before leaving, players can deposit their winnings in the DigitalVegas Bank.

TIC TAC TOE

Quic Tac Toe

http://hero.com/~eric/ttt/ttt.html

Eric Cole boasts his Java applet offers the "quickest game of Tic Tac Toe on the Web." Players get to decide if they or the computer goes first and can change between two skill levels. A Java- and frames-enabled browser is required.

Steve's Tic Tac Toe

http://www-personal.engin.umich.edu/ ~stevomek/tttind.html

The computer begins with an X in the center square. Players then pick where to place their O, and so on and so forth until a winner or tie is determined. A forms-capable browser is required.

Strawberry Macaw's Tic Tac Toe
http://www.serve.com/games/tictac/ tictac.htm

The graphics make it look just like a game at school, only visitors play the Strawberry Macaw instead of school chums. Challengers play first; the macaw plays second. Takes about a minute to preload the images but play, once begun, moves right along.

Stubbed Toe
http://www.stardot.com/~lukeseem/ stubbed.html

Pay attention to this Tic Tac Toe server! After the computer plays, it tries to trick its opponents into making bad moves. Or are they bad moves? Stay alert!

Tic Tac Toe
http://fjwsys.lanl.gov/cgi-bin/ttt

The computer opens with an *X* in the center square and challenges "*O*"pponents to beat it. The easy point and click interface is very browser-friendly. The game is the work of Daniel Whiteson.

Tic Tac Toe
http://linex.com/~donham/ttt.html

Set the skill level (very easy, easy, or hard) and chose *X*s or *O*s, then press Play to get the game underway.

The challenger starts; the computer plays second. Those wondering how Jake Donham did it, can review the game's source code for answers.

Tic-Tac-Toe
http://netpressence.com/npcgi/ttt

Jeff Boulter hosts still another browser-friendly server prepared to take on all challengers. Set the playing options desired (up to a 7x7 grid) and let the Tic Tac Toe begin! Go first if you like.

Toe
http://student-www.uchicago.edu/users/ gmturner/

Described by its developer, Gregory M. Turner, as a "(supposedly) multiplayer game," this Java applet lets players from across the Internet square off on a 5x5 grid to play a version of Tic Tac Toe where four in a row wins. Easy-to-follow instructions help to orient new players. A Java-enabled browser is required.

For more Tic Tac Toe, see also:

Tic Tac Toe
http://www.bu.edu/Games/tictactoe

Tic Tac Toe (Java)
http://dmawww.epfl.ch/~kuonen/Java/ttt.html

Tic Tac Toe to the DEATH!!!
http://www.xnet.com/~warinner/startxox.html

TOWERS OF HANOI

Towers of Hanoi
http://www.dcs.napier.ac.uk/a.cumming/ hanoi/index.html#__1_234

Move all of the rings to the right-most peg. You may only move one ring at a time, and you must never allow a larger ring to rest on a smaller ring. Browser-friendly.

For more Towers of Hanoi, see also:

Multi-Threaded Towers of Hanoi
http://www.best.com/~jcon/towers/index.shtml

VIRTUAL ANIMAL RACING

Ferret Frenzy
http://www.delphi.co.uk/delphi/interactive/ferrets/intro.html
Everyone starts with an even stake but only those with an eye keen enough to pick the winners get ahead. Place bets and watch the field of ferrets race down the track. Races begin with regularity and a new race is probably starting right now. But be warned: For ferret races, these are kind of slow!

The Track: Home of Server-Push Horseracing
http://www.boston.com/sports/thetrack/cgi-bin/horse_race.cgi
Racing sports fans begin with a $500.00 virtual stake from which they can place bets on server-push horse races. The server tracks a player's wins and losses, and players can watch the virtual race. Compete for a spot among the Top Ten winners. Registration is required for "accounting" purposes.

WORD SEARCH PUZZLES

John's Word Search Puzzles
http://www.NeoSoft.com/~jrpotter/puzzles.html
John Potter treats word search enthusiasts to a huge collection of puzzles he has created. Organized by theme, topics range from cities and states to Greek gods and goddesses with most everything in between. New puzzles are added each month.

Puzzle Connection Weekly Word Search Puzzle
http://www.smartcode.com/isshtml/weekwsk.htm
A new puzzle is posted every Tuesday suitable to print and work offline. The puzzles are theme-oriented and compatible with Puzzle Connection's Word Search

Zarf's Ex-List of Interactive Games on the Web
http://www.leftfoot.com/realgames.html
Here's a last hurrah and last huzza to a venerable old Web directory that has seen its day come and go. Its purpose was to catalog the best HTML games available on the Web, but with the advent of Java, HTML games may soon become a memory. At any rate, the site's maintainer, Andrew Plotkin, won't be doing anymore site maintenance. But the links are still good and point to a bounty of virtual toys, gadgets, and games. Build-a-monster anyone? How about a game of Ghost or Dread? Connect Four, Dots, Fake Out? Find dozens of games and do-dads—some original, some not so original. But hurry. There's no telling when all this fun will just go away.

Construction Kit. A link back to the Puzzle Connection leads to more gaming fun.

The Web Word Search Plus!
http://www.geocities.com/WestHollywood/2555/puzzle.html
Enjoy working this collection of puzzles and mazes presented by Kerry Shatzer. Suitable to print and work offline, the word search puzzles hold an added bonus: Letters which remain unused combine to form a quote about a puzzle's theme. The puzzles and mazes are updated at irregular intervals.

Wordsearches on AngliaNet
http://www.anglianet.co.uk/home/lighter/wordsearch/index.html
Ten puzzles by Gareth Glaccum await the seek-a-word enthusiast. Play online using the interactive form or print the puzzles for offline play. Puzzles are theme-oriented.

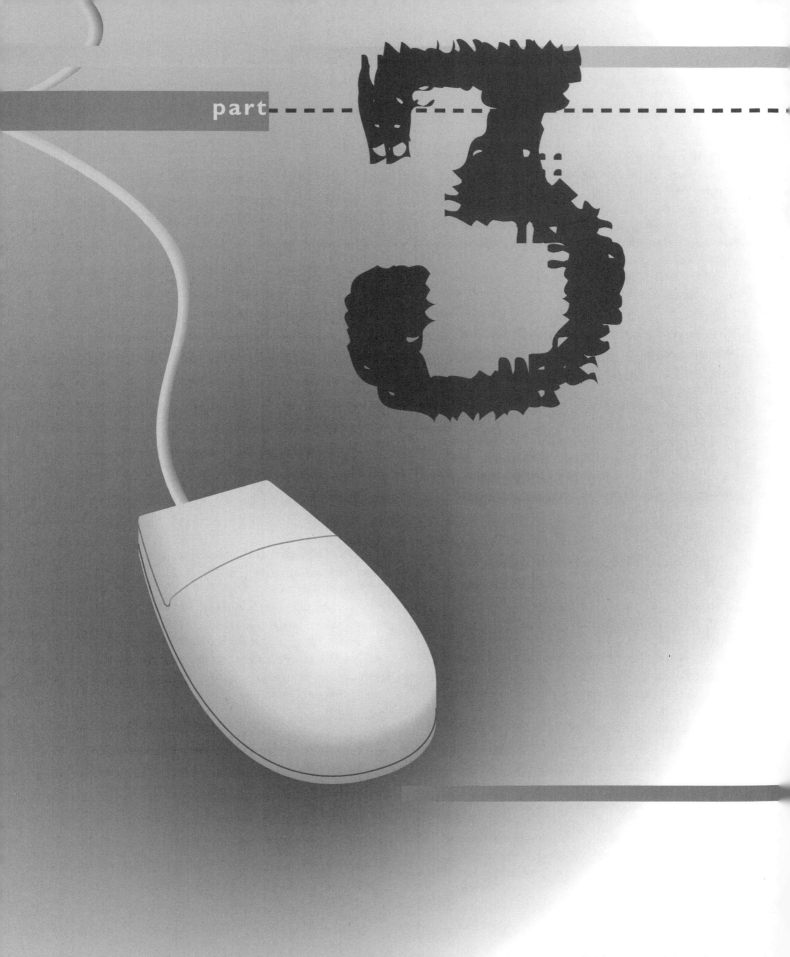

part 3

OTHER INTERNET GAMES RESOURCES

FTP SITES

A QUICK GUIDE TO GAME-RELATED USER NEWSGROUPS

TELNET GUIDE

GAME NETWORKS

GAMING E-ZINE SITES OR MAGAZINE'S ONLINE EDITIONS

ARCHIVED OR MEGA SITES

COMPUTER GAME COMPANY SITES

10

FTP SITES

FILE Transfer Protocol (FTP) is considered one of the forefathers of the Internet—it has been around for many years and has been a reliable standard protocol for transferring files between remote computers. UNIX workstations and mainframes used FTP sites exclusively until individual PC users gained access to the Net and used FTPs as a substitute to bulletin boards. Graphical, more user-friendly browsers were developed out of demand as the Internet grew in popularity. Archie and Gopher programs (popular file-finding server software) were replaced by the World Wide Web as a more successful method of simplifying and locating information over the Net. Although most *surfers* these days access FTP sites through a Web front door, many still prefer direct FTP connection for its simple, powerful, and fast file exchange. In other words, the Net has gone "mainstream" and is now a household word because of the birth of the World Wide Web. The Web's colorful, graphical, and easy to navigate system has revolutionized the online world. But the meat and potatoes of most Web sites lie in the area most people don't see—the FTP server—and here is where all the cool files are for you to download. I am going to show you how to tap into these vast (albeit bland) storage areas and extract great games and gaming accessories.

HOW WE LOOK AT FTP SITES

Many of us Internet users can access FTP sites with our current WWW browser, such as Netscape Navigator or Microsoft Internet Explorer. You may also choose to use FTP software such as the popular CuteFTP, Windows Sockets FTP (WS_FTP), or WinFTP (based on WS_FTP). These shareware FTP programs offer Windows-like environments to view and trade files on FTP sites. Although they may be faster and have a few more specific features, most of us will use our Web browser, since it is easier to navigate through and doesn't require us to switch programs while online. Figures 10.1 through 10.4 show how the look of the same FTP site (Maxis Software at ftp://ftp.maxis.com/) can differ depending on what software you are using.

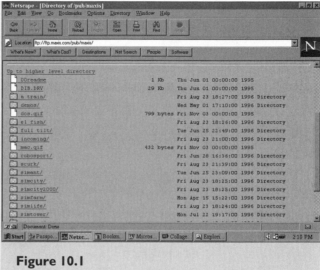

Figure 10.1

Netscape Navigator's view of the Maxis FTP server

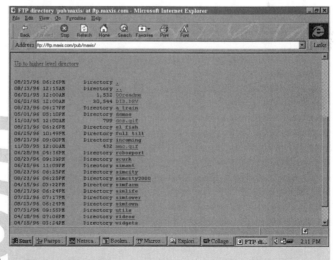

Figure 10.2

Microsoft Internet Explorer's view of the Maxis FTP server

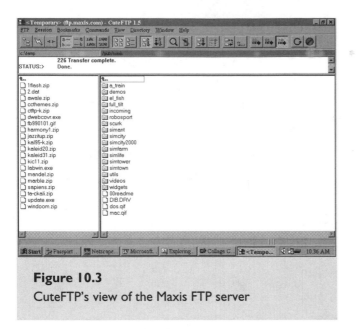

Figure 10.3
CuteFTP's view of the Maxis FTP server

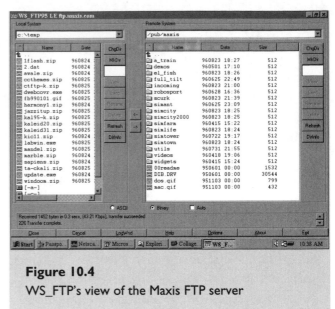

Figure 10.4
WS_FTP's view of the Maxis FTP server

WHAT CAN I GET ON FTP SITES? WHAT *CAN'T* I GET THERE?

There is an abundance of terrific gaming FTP pages that house many free computer game demos, shareware, and freeware. Other free files such as hints, tips, patches (bug fixes), add-on levels, FAQs, and cheat codes can also be accessed on various FTP sites. File Transfer Protocol pages sound like exactly what they are—an often huge list of software that can be downloaded or added to (you can also *upload* files from your computer to their server). Unlike the WWW, there are no online games, chat/discussion groups, or game reviews on FTP sites. Nor are there real-time head-to-head or multiplayer games. FTPs also do not contain graphics, music, animation, or video to experience while perusing through their pages. These FTP sites are only raw lists of files and these games must be transferred to your hard drive first in order to play them (once on your own system they can be either single- or multiplayer games).

BEFORE WE GET STARTED

I would like to make two suggestions before we continue. First, it is handy to make a directory on your hard drive exclusively for downloaded files. I have one called *temp* (for "temporary"), and I save all files I retrieve off the Net here first, before I decide where they should go. For example, if I download four files into my temp directory (see Figure 10.5), once offline I can look at the contents of that directory and move these files as follows: I would drag-and-drop the custom-built Duke Nukem 3D level LeRock.zip into my c:\games\duke3D directory, the doom.bmp wallpaper into my c:\windows directory, the quake.zip shareware game onto floppy disks for a friend, and expand the Shockwave plug-in driver (called n32z0006.exe) into my Netscape directory. As you can see, it is much easier for organizational purposes to have a temp or hold directory.

Second, the majority of files that you will be downloading from the Internet will be *zipped*, or compressed, for faster, simpler file transfer. In

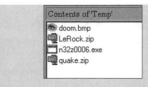

Figure 10.5

A temporary directory in Windows Explorer

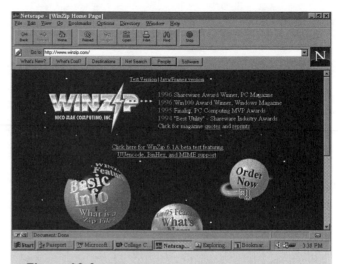

Figure 10.6

The WinZip home page

other words, a freeware computer game such as a Tetris clone may, in fact, be 12 files (executable, help, data, or icon files) totaling 830K. However, when compressed, tetris.zip is only one file with a size of only 510K. For this reason, you will need a utilities program on your computer to *unzip* these files back into their original larger sizes. The DOS standard is pkunzip/pkzip, which is still widely used, but if Windows (3.1 or higher) is your current operating system I suggest you pick up WinZip (http://www.winzip.com/). (See Figure 10.6 for the WinZip home page.) WinZip is shareware itself and can handle ZIP, TAR, gzip, and UNIX compress format files on its own, however, external programs are required for the less frequently used ARJ, ARC, and LZH formats.

FINALLY...

There are three main kinds of FTP gaming sites: commercial game companies, university servers, and large archive file centers (often independently run). Note there are thousands upon thousands of FTP sites located worldwide, and many of them are mirrors of one another. Therefore, if one site is *busy* (too many users at that time), you can get the same games or game files from their mirrored site. Although commercial gaming companies have their product demos on their own FTP server, they can most often be downloaded elsewhere as well. Also remember , most of the game companies and

mega-archive sites are using the World Wide Web now as a graphical front door to their FTP sites. In our case, we are cutting straight to the source and using raw FTPs directly, so don't look for colorful attractive pages to peruse through.

For our purposes, when logging onto an FTP site you will access the system as user *anonymous*. This should be automatic, so don't even pay attention to it. If it says "Use Anonymous access denied," this just means the FTP connection has reached the maximum capacity at that time. Most gaming files will be located under the main *parent directory* under *games* or *pub* (or *public*) directory. File names may come with a very similar name above or below it but with a *txt* as a suffix (text document). Mouse-clicking on this will describe the contents of the game file so you can decide if you want to download it or not (see Figure 10.7). Other FTP sites may have an *index* or *readme* file to click on that will explain what the files on that particular page are. The game file you wish to download may also have a *byte* size count to let you know how big the file is, and a date when the file was first available or last modified. Simply click on the desired game file and you will be prompted by your browser to choose where on your hard drive you wish to save it (e.g. C:\temp). That's it! Don't be discouraged if you can't get into an FTP site right away—try again later, see if they give a mirrored site, or visit another archive that may have the same files you are looking for. Enjoy!

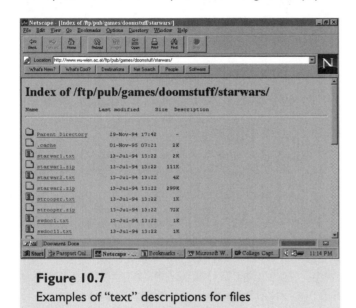

Figure 10.7

Examples of "text" descriptions for files

TOP 25 MAJOR GAME-RICH FTP SITES

America Online Mirrored Site
ftp://mirrors.aol.com

Under the pub directory is a whole slew of PC and Mac game demos and shareware hits. A separate section for Doom (codes, add-ons) is highlighted and cheats, cracks, and game hints are located in the romulus sub-directory. The games and gamehead sub-directory contains an extensive list of many action, strategy, ed-ucational, and sports games either by company name or game title. Game developers will also find numerous files in the programming section.

Best Internet Communications, Inc.
ftp://ftp.best.com/

Self-proclaimed as "the BEST Anonymous FTP server," this site does have quite a large collection of free and shareware titles to download. Since the pub directory contains over 10,000 files, it is arranged alphabetically and will allow you to zap right to the game or file name of choice.

Center for Innovative Computer Applications
ftp://ftp.cica.indiana.edu

A large but often tough site to get into. CICA contains many computer games and video game files such as Sega and 3DO screen shots and strategy tips. A huge PC, Mac, and UNIX section are provided, but you must first log into *pub,* then click on your desired platform. This site is also available at www.cica.indiana.edu or gopher.cica.indiana.edu.

Finnish University and Research network FUNET
ftp://ftp.funet.fi/

A very large FTP site with a hearty gaming section. Read Index00 for file descriptions in the pub/msdos/ games/ area. Click on the solution sub-directory for a walkthrough of the tougher games; the strategy section for hints and tips; and the demos area for shareware hits, both old and new. Bonus section: many Tetris variations!

FlexNet
ftp://ftp.dungeon.com

A multi-directory American FTP site that is hot on Quake levels and Windows 95 games. Not as large as some of the other mega-FTP sites, but useful PC action files are offered. Patches and other game utilities are available.

Games Domain FTP
ftp://ftp.gamesdomain.com

ftp://ftp.gamesdomain.co.uk

ftp://ftp.gamesdomain.ru

A huge listing of game demos, shareware, freeware, and all the additions you'll need for a lifetime. Add-ons such as cheats, codes, patches, levels, FAQs, and hints are obtainable for numerous games across many platforms. Once in the pub directory you can decide where you want to go from there into sub-directories called demos, companies, walkthroughs, faqs, kidstuff, etc. A well-organized and content-rich gaming site.

Gate, The
ftp://ftp.gamers.org/

A very large FTP site dedicated exclusively to the world of gaming. A 3D game section, mailing lists, and a WTF production area (Doom WADs) are notable areas to visit here. Custom Doom and Doom 2 levels should be uploaded to the mirrored ftp://ftp.cdrom.com and will be copied nightly back here for download. An all-around useful site with an emphasis on the 3D action game genre.

Halcyon
ftp://ftp.halcyon.com/pub/go/games/

Quite a large list of "amateur" and "professional" games, as they put it. MS-DOS and Mac Net games and puzzle games make up the bulk of these titles. Halcyon's files are mirrored on ftp.pasteur.fr and on rzserv3.rz.tu-bs.de. This is a good place to find unconventional, hard-to-find game gems.

Multi-Players Game Network
ftp://ftp.mpgn.com/

Just as the name suggests, this FTP archive site holds many head-to-head and multiplayer games, demos, and add-ons. Their gaming sub-directory contains many downloadable goodies separated in various game names. Make sure you browse each sub-section's readme files.

Oakland University Software Repository
http://oak.oakland.edu/

This is another mirror to the giant Walnut Creek archive. Oakland U also shares the world's largest collection of OS/2 software and information files. Rogue-like games are featured here.

Pacific Hi Tech (PHT)
ftp://ftp.pht.com/
A mirrored site with WinSite at ftp://ftp.winsite.com/

PHT is a huge gaming repository holding many game demos and utilities for your existing games. Go directly to the public section, then click on your gaming interests: MUDs, Mac, MS-DOS, Gamehead, or Demos sections. Much to see and download here.

Soft Choice File Archive
ftp://ftp.softchoice.com/

A clean and well-organized gaming FTP site. In the *pub* and *games* sub-directories you can view and download various games and gaming files. Listed into company names as clickable folders makes it easy to navigate, but you must know the gaming manufacturer's products. Only the newest and most popular titles are given. Also try the "Command & Conquer" theme to spice up your Windows 95 desktop.

SunSITE Northern Europe
http://src.doc.ic.ac.uk/computing/systems/ibmpc/

With over 60GB of publicly available files, this large archive center houses many games and various game files. This collection at SunSITE in London, England weighs more toward PC MS-DOS and Windows 3.xx or 95 games. Check out their vast 3D action game section, game editors, and cool flight simulator scenery add-ons.

Swedish University Network SUNET
ftp://ftp.sunet.se/

Clicking on pub will bring you to the games section of this large FTP site. Choose your operating system and the file name to download. SUNET is chock-full of older classic shareware games as well as newer popular titles. One of Europe's best.

UCNET ("Blitzen") FTP Site, Australia
ftp://blitzen.canberra.edu.au

The pub/games sub-directory contains many games, patches, and bonus game scenarios. Individual folders such as chess, msdos, Descent levels, id software, and strategic are listed, plus others. An ARJ uncompression utility may be needed to extract these games on your hard drive—pick it up at http://www.dunkel.de/ARJ/.

Universität Heidelberg, Germany
ftp://ftp.urz.uni-heidelberg.de/

A very large gaming archive collection here. Game hints, solutions, demos, editors, cheats, codes, cracks, hints, walkthroughs, and add-ons are available for all computer platforms. Once in public access files, there are three main sub-directories that contain all the gaming files you need: games, game demos, and game solutions. Many more gaming files can be reached at their Web site

(http://ftp.uni-heidelberg.de/). Other areas of this FTP site are mirrored with Walnut Creek (ftp://ftp.cdrom.com/) and WinSite (ftp://ftp.winsite.com/).

University of Lulea, Sweden
ftp.luth.se

The ground-breaking game Doom is highlighted here at one of Europe's biggest FTP sites. Various add-on levels, patches, upgrades, hints, FAQs, secrets/codes, and walkthroughs are accessible here. This Doom sub-section is mirrored around the world in many other FTP sites listed below.

University of Nevada, Reno
ftp://ftp.honors.unr.edu/

Jump right to the pub, then games sub-directories for a long list of game-related demos and additional files for your favorite computer games. Choose your platform and shareware game to download, but you may have to know what you are looking for—there are no descriptions or helpful index files. There are many more MS-DOS games than Windows titles here.

University of Paderborn
ftp://ftp.uni-paderborn.de

Open 24 hours a day, 7 days a week, this FTP site has many demos, mainly in the msdos/pcgames sub-directory. From there each gaming genre is broken up (3D games, puzzles, adventure, sims, etc.), and the romulus section has all the cheats, cracks, and hints files. Mirrored with the AOL site mentioned above.

University of Queensland, Brisbane, Australia
ftp://ftp.dstc.edu.au/

An Australian center for many PC games, including a "Games Domain" mirror and two id software sections (Doom, Quake). To keep up with what's available read the readme, changes, last.24hours, and last.7days files first. Download the free Kali95 software while here so you can play favorite strategy and action games head-to-head over the Internet.

University of Stellenbosch, South Africa
ftp://ftp.sun.ac.za/

All game files are located in the pub and msdos directories. As a mirror to the Walnut Creek FTP site, many game files are available, from downloading games to enhancing your collection with add-ons and cheats. Choose your demos by the year released or alphabetically. Heavy on action and 3D titles.

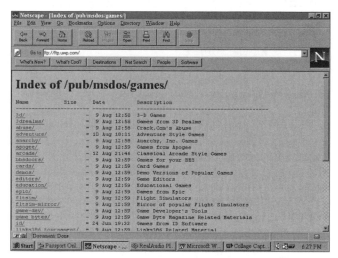

University of Wisconsin-Parkside
ftp://ftp.uwp.edu/

One of the largest gaming sites on the Internet is here at the University of Wisconsin-Parkside FTP archive. If you would like to make a contribution you can send your files to the directory /pub/incoming/games. Most of us, however, will want to fill up our hard drives with the UWP's many computer games and game additions. Many of these gaming folders will seem familiar to you, as this site is mirrored on various other FTPs in this chapter. Nevertheless, if you can get into this site (I always seem to have a *busy* message), make sure you visit the demo, 3D, puzzle, and arcade folders.

Walnut Creek Archive
ftp://ftp.cdrom.com/

WU_Archive is one of the most popular U.S. FTP sites and can hold 1,200 users at any one time. This FTP site contains over 72GB of information on its server. Most of these gaming files are also on a Walnut Creek CD-ROM available for purchase through the site. Don't bother reading the *readme* file first—it is the same as the intro page. Simply go right to the *pub* sub-directory. Here you'll have a choice to read the contents of the games, game patches, quake, doom, doom2, id-games (id software), Mac, or Windows 95 sections.

Washington University in St. Louis, Missouri USA.
http://wuarchive.wustl.edu/ or ftp://ftp.wustl.edu/

One of the best all-around sites, with many games and game files. Shareware, cheats, editors, and walk-throughs are all available in the /MSDOS_UPLOADS/ games/ and /WINDOWS_UPLOADS/games directories. Separate folders house different types of games, such as RPGs and action/adventure.

WinSite
ftp://ftp.winsite.com/

An archive FTP site containing many Windows-based games and other utilities. Windows 3.1(1), Windows NT, and Windows 95 files are available. Each sub-directory has a games area. Read the index file in each group for a brief description of the games.

MAJOR GAME COMPANIES

If you know what you are after or if you know who makes it—here is an alphabetical list of some of the main gaming manufacturer FTP sites.

3D Realms
ftp://3drealms.best.com/

Accolade
ftp://ftp.netcom.com/pub/ac/accolade/

Apogee
ftp://apogee.best.com/

Blizzard
ftp://ftp.blizzard.com/

Electronic Arts
ftp://ftp.ea.com/

Epic MegaGames
ftp://ftp.epicgames.com

GT Interactive
ftp://ftp.gtinteractive.com/

id Software
ftp://ftp.idsoftware.com/

Interplay
ftp://ftp.interplay.com/ or
ftp://ftp1.interplay.com/

Lucas Arts
ftp://ftp.lucasarts.com/pub/

Maxis
ftp://ftp.maxis.com/pub/maxis/

Microprose
ftp://ftp.microprose.com/

Microsoft
ftp://ftp.microsoft.com/

Origin
ftp://ftp.ea.com

Papyrus
ftp://ftp.std.com/vendors/papyrus/

Sierra
ftp://ftp.sierra.com/

Silver Lightning
ftp://ftp2.iap.net.au/

SIR-TECH
ftp://ftp.sir-tech.com/

Spectrum-Holobyte
ftp://ftp.microprose.com/

Virgin
ftp://ftp.vie.com/

Westwood
ftp://ftp.westwood.com/

Other Important Gaming FTP Archives (in no particular order)

ftp://ftp.zdnet.com/

ftp://ftp.hawaii.edu/

ftp://ftp.cc.monash.edu.au/

flinux.tu-graz.ac.at

ftp://ftp.netcom.com/

ftp://ftp.dstc.edu.au

ftp://ftp.nectec.or.th

ftp://ftp.calvacom.fr

ftp://ftp.fu-berlin.de

ftp://ftp.sun.ac.za

ftp://ftp.orst.edu/

ftp://ftp.ulowell.edu/

ftp://ftp.linkline.be

ftp://ftp.ais.net

lesvos.med.auth.gr

ftp://blitzen.canberra.edu.au/

ftp://ftp.dstc.edu.au

ftp://ftp.cnit.nsk.su/

ftp://ftp.powerup.com.au

ftp://ftp.primenet.com/

ftp://ftp.tp.jussieu.fr

ftp://ftp.io.com/

ftp://ftp.aist-nara.ac.jp/pub/games/

ftp://ftp.tu-bs.de/

ftp://ftp.ee.pdx.edu/

ftp://ftp.man.szczecin.pl/

ftp://ftp.x.org/contrib/

ftp://ftp.inria.fr/X/contrib-R5/games/

ftp://ftp.gmd.de/if-archive/

ftp://ftp.bga.com/vendors/moraff/

ftp://ftp.mei.co.jp/free/news/answers/games/
   video-games/

gopher://risc.ua.edu:70/11/games/solutions

ftp://ftp.gmd.de/if-archive/solutions/

ftp://ftp.iup.edu/flight-sim/

ftp://ftp.std.com/vendors/COMPUTER_EXPRESS/
   Index

ftp://ftp.aimnet.com/

ftp://ftp.inf.tu-dresden.de/pub/ms-dos/

ftp://ftp.amug.org

http://www.tamu.edu/~ftp/pub/games/

http://www.wu-wien.ac.at/ftp/pub/games/

http://augustus.csscr.washington.edu/

ftp://ftp.next.com.au/

ftp://netslave.midnight.com.au/pub/demos/

ftp://ftp.usa.net/

ftp://ftp.procyon.com/pub/game_archive/

gopher://spinaltap.micro.umn.edu:70/11/fun/
   Games

AROUND THE WORLD IN A CLICK

Feeling ambitious? Check out some more of these international FTP servers that have tons of games and game-related files:

azabu.tkl.iis.u-tokyo.ac.jp

b65103.student.cwru.edu

caisr2.caisr.cwru.edu

csun1.cc.ncu.edu.tw

chopin.forest.dnj.ynu.ac.jp

elvis.msk.su

epona.physics.ucg.ie

ftp://ftp.admu.edu.ph

ftp://ftp.bme.hu

ftp://ftp.chemietechnik.uni-dortmund.de

ftp://ftp.chey.com

ftp://ftp.cis.nctu.edu.tw

ftp://ftp.cis.ufl.edu

ftp://ftp.cityscape.co.uk

ftp://ftp.cnit.nsk.su

ftp://ftp.cs.pdx.edu

ftp://ftp.cs.titech.ac.jp

ftp://ftp.cs.tu-berlin.de

ftp://ftp.cuslm.ca

ftp://ftp.cwru.edu

ftp://ftp.demon.co.uk

ftp://ftp.di.fc.ul.pt

ftp://ftp.ee.auth.gr

ftp://ftp.elvis.msk.su

ftp://ftp.enst.fr

ftp://ftp.fct.unl.pt

ftp://ftp.fh-wolfenbuettel.de

ftp://ftp.firstnet.net

ftp://ftp.foretune.co.jp

ftp://ftp.hmc.edu

ftp://ftp.iclnet.org

ftp://ftp.iesd.auc.dk

ftp://ftp.ims.uni-stuttgart.de

ftp://ftp.inria.fr

ftp://ftp.irisa.fr

ftp://ftp.island.net

ftp://ftp.iunet.it

ftp://ftp.kcl.ac.uk

ftp://ftp.kuis.kyoto-u.ac.jp

ftp://ftp.lasermoon.co.uk

ftp://ftp.lysator.liu.se

ftp://ftp.mathematik.uni-ulm.de

ftp://ftp.ms.uky.edu

ftp://ftp.nc.nihon-u.ac.jp

ftp://ftp.orland.su

ftp://ftp.pacific.net

ftp://ftp.pasteur.fr

ftp://ftp.phys.keio.ac.jp

ftp://ftp.pu-toyama.ac.jp

ftp://ftp.reed.edu

ftp://ftp.risc.uni-linz.ac.at

ftp://ftp.tu-chemnitz.de

ftp://ftp.uni-erlangen.de

ftp://ftp.uni-muenster.de

ftp://ftp.uoknor.edu

ftp://ftp.uu.net

ftp://ftp.linkline.be/mirror/

ftp://ftp.warwick.ac.uk

ftp://ftp.win.tue.nl

ftp://ftp.xenitec.on.ca

gaitlab1.uwaterloo.ca

gatekeeper.dec.com

geocub.greco-prog.fr

gogol.cenatls.cena.dgac.fr

hagar.arts.kuleuven.ac.be

iamftp.unibe.ch

jupiter.sun.csd.unb.ca

kids.kotel.co.kr

larry.mcrcim.mcgill.edu

ls6-www.informatik.uni-dortmund.de

ocf.berkeley.edu

pomona.claremont.edu

qiclab.scn.rain.com

splicer2.cba.hawaii.edu

ssc.nsu.nsk.su

suned.zoo.cs.yale.edu

sunsite.dcc.uchile.cl

uiarchive.cso.uiuc.edu

uspif.if.usp.br

ccphys.nsu.nsk.su

sunsite.doc.ic.ac.uk

ftp://wiretap.spies.com/game_archive/

A QUICK GUIDE TO GAME-RELATED USENET NEWSGROUPS

THINK of newsgroups as being similar to a collection of electronic bulletin boards. Organized by broad categories which are then subdivided into smaller, topic-oriented subcategories, these bulletin boards provide space for people to post observations, ask questions, and generally communicate with one another. An easy Internet protocol to master, Usenet newsgroups offer game-players a noncompetitive venue to share their enthusiasm with like-minded folks, join in discussions about the finer points of play, and search for resources that have otherwise proven elusive.

There is a vast number of Usenet newsgroups currently active, but not everyone has access to every newsgroup. Which newsgroups a person can access is determined by the news-administrator at that person's Internet Service Provider (ISP). The news-admin decides which newsgroups will be allowed through the ISP's newsfeed, and consequently which newsgroups their customers can read. Selectivity generally boils down to a question of the ISP's storage space and picking those newsgroups with the widest appeal. Let's make it personal to them: If there is newsgroup you would like to subscribe to but can't locate, ask your system adminstrator …But most ISPs are nothing if not accommodating. If there is a newsgroup you'd like to access but can't, just ask your system administrator to add it.

Like the rest of the Internet, Usenet is a dynamic environment where new newsgroups are being added constantly. For those new to Usenet then, learning a few key facts and following a few suggestions could prove beneficial down the road.

UNDERSTANDING NEWSGROUP NAMES

As mentioned earlier, newsgroups are organized by category. These categories have grown over the past several years through the addition of local newsgroups, but there is a recognized group of categories which generally serve as the core category list, and another group which acts as an alternate list.

The seven traditional newsgroup categories include: *comp*, which is used to discuss computer hardware, software, and programming languages; *misc*, which is a catch-all category for topics that don't fit into the other six core categories; *news*, which offers guidance and discussion about the Usenet; *rec*, which covers games, hobbies, sports, and all manner of leisure activities; *sci*, which focuses on the sciences, offering forums for both simple and complex discussion of related matters; *soc*, which turns attention to social issues and cultures around the world; and *talk*, which is, as it suggests, talk, talk, and more talk about topics that generally spark heated debate.

The alternate list of categories includes but is not limited to: *alt*, which is used as another catchall area where topics run the gamut; *biz*, which provides the business community an area for discussions of general trends and specific companies; and *gnu*, which hosts discussions concerning the Free Software Foundation, an organization dedicated to promoting the free distribution, copying, and modifying of all software. Other alternate categories cater to the biology community, K-12 educators and students, and VMS operating system users; also included are a few newswire service feeds and international newsgroups.

Under each category, a plethora of topics can be discussed. For example, the rec category offers a wide range of newsgroups devoted to games, but also has groups devoted to movies. Similarly the comp category has tons on computer programming and languages, but also offers a selection of newsgroups discussing games. It's necessary then for each person to look through the list of newsgroups available through their ISP to find the ones which most appeal to their particular tastes.

A good place to start for anyone who is new to the Usenet is in the news category—not because it holds information on games, but because it holds the answers to the questions most frequently asked by folks beginning their exploration of the Usenet. Try the following newsgroups: *news.announce.newusers,* which is a moderated forum that caters to helping new users become familiar with newsgroups; and *news.newuser.questions,* which provides a question-and-answer explanation of the Usenet.

Notice how the newsgroups mentioned above are named. The category comes first, followed by a period and a topic, followed by a period and a topic descriptive. Newsgroups are generally named so that browsers can readily figure out what is being discussed by the participants of that group. Names can be as short as two words separated by periods, or they can be made of many words, with each successive word defining the topic more narrowly.

USENET "NETIQUETTE:" SIMPLE COURTESY AND COMMON SENSE

Always remember that the postings on the Usenet are available to a wide, often worldwide, audience. What some may consider loose talk, others will find downright offensive. In other words, when posting, try to exercise a vocabulary that does not depend upon profanity for passionate expression. Too, remember that personal responses to postings aren't necessarily of interest or benefit to the entire newsgroup. In this case, a private e-mail rather than a newsgroup posting might be the best course of action.

Opinions are welcome, but argument for argument's sake is pointless. If a disagreement arises, do not let the situation spiral out of control into what is called a "flame war," where insults and accusations rule the discourse. Always be civil and courteous. If someone attempts to start a flame war, ignore the ignorance and move along. Rude behavior is neither cute nor funny, nor appreciated.

For a more detailed look at Netiquette on the Usenet, refer to the *newsgroups news.announce .newusers.*

A BEGINNER'S DIRECTORY OF GAMING NEWSGROUPS

The following is only a representative sampling of currently active newsgroups devoted to one or another aspect of gaming. The list has been divided into broad topics for easy access and quick reference.

General Gaming

alt.games.upcoming-3d
Preview what's on the 3D horizon and critically review the progress in the 3D gaming arena.

bit.listserv.games-l
Find out what's out there with this list of computer games.

rec.games.abstract
Stop in here for heady talk about gaming theory and strategy.

rec.games.misc
Join in general discussions about games of most every design.

relcom.games
Talk about electronic games.

Card Games, Collectible Card Games, and Trading Cards

Those looking for newsgroups with general discussion concerning card collecting and games may try:

rec.collecting.cards.discuss
Add to general discussions about trading cards.

rec.collecting.cards.non-sports
Same as above, only no sports talk, please.

rec.games.playing-cards
Talk about standard deck card games that don't involve gambling.

rec.games.trading-cards.announce
Visit this moderated forum for news of interest to collectible card game fans.

rec.games.trading-cards.marketplace.misc
Strike deals or simply talk of buying, selling, and trading collectible cards.

rec.games.trading-cards.misc
Examine collectible card games with other fans in this unmoderated forum.

Those looking for newsgroups covering specific card games might try:

alt.games.whitewolf.rage
Discuss White Wolf's fantasy CCG called Rage.

rec.games.bridge
Chat about the classic card game with fellow enthusiasts.

rec.games.trading-cards.jyhad
Discuss the Jyhad CCG (a.k.a. Vampire: The Eternal Struggle).

rec.games.trading-cards.magic.misc

rec.games.trading-cards.magic.rules

rec.games.trading-cards.magic.strategy

rec.games.trading-cards.marketplace.magic. auctions

rec.games.trading-cards.marketplace.magic.sales

rec.games.trading-cards.marketplace.magic.trades
Discuss the various aspects of the Magic: The Gathering CCG.

rec.games.trading-cards.startrek
Discuss the Star Trek: The Next Generation CCG.

Games Programming

alt.mud.programming
Talk with MUDers about building text-based environments.

comp.ai.games
Explore the idea of artificial intelligence in electronic games.

comp.infosystems.www.authoring.cgi
Seek and find discussion about writing CGI scripts.

comp.infosystems.www.authoring.html
Seek and find discussion about writing HTML.

comp.lang.java.programmer
Seek and find discussion about using Java.

comp.lang.perl.misc
Seek and find discussion about the Perl language.

rec.games.design
Answer the question: What constitutes a good game design?

rec.games.programmer
Discuss adventure game programming with programmers.

Role-Playing Games

Those looking for newsgroups with general discussion concerning role-playing games may try:

rec.games.frp.advocacy
Fight for the honor of a favorite role-playing system.

rec.games.frp.announce
Visit this moderated forum for news of general interest to the role-playing community.

rec.games.frp.archives
Browse this moderated archive for fantasy stories and ideas.

rec.games.frp.live-action
Find out why they call it live-action role-playing.

rec.games.frp.marketplace
Buy, sell, or trade objects of interest to role-playing enthusiasts.

rec.games.frp.misc
Discuss fantasy role-playing games with those who share the interest.

rec.games.mud.admin
Take up the issues involved in administering multiple-user dungeons (MUDs).

rec.games.mud.announce
Keep abreast of the lasted MUD news via this moderated forum.

rec.games.mud.diku
Find out all about and discuss Diku MUDs.

rec.games.mud.lp
Find out all about and discuss LP MUDs.

rec.games.mud.misc
Explore the various facets of multiple-user dungeons (MUDs).

rec.games.mud.tiny
Find out all about and discuss Tiny MUDs.

rec.games.roguelike.announce
Stop in for the latest moderated news on rogue-style computer-based role-playing.

rec.games.roguelike.misc
Discuss the rogue style of role-play gaming.

Those looking for newsgroups covering specific role-playing games might try:

alt.games.atr.rpg
Visit with characters experiencing Alternate Trek Reality.

alt.games.final-fantasy
Plug into the Final Fantasy universe.

alt.games.frp.dnd-util
Talk Dungeons and Dragons utilities with other D&D fans.

alt.games.illuminati
Explore the Illuminati world of conspiracy and intrigue.

alt.games.vampire.the.masquerade
Enter a World of Darkness where the undead roam free.

alt.games.vampire.tremere
Join the Clan Tremere for biting talk and bloody tales.

alt.games.whitewolf
Talk about the horror and gothic RPGs from White Wolf.

alt.starfleet.rpg
Find out what it takes to join Starfleet.

alt.startrek.tos.trekmuse
Discuss the MUSE sprung from the original "Star Trek" series.

rec.games.frp.cyber
Relate to the world of cyberpunks and discuss the fantasy.

rec.games.frp.dnd
Revel in the original role-playing fantasy, Dungeons and Dragons.

rec.games.roguelike.angband
Get rough and rowdy with fellow Angband rogues.

rec.games.roguelike.moria
Talk the talk with fellow Moria rogues.

rec.games.roguelike.nethack
Not everyone can hack it. Get the what's up on Nethack.

rec.games.roguelike.rogue
Visit this Rogue gallery for insight into the game.

Title-Specific Computer Games

alt.games.air-warrior
Find aid and comfort from fellow Air Warrior combatants.

alt.games.civnet
Discover how civilized CivNet's networked civilians can be.

alt.games.command-n-conq
Help and be helped; that's how to Command &
Conquer.

alt.games.dark-forces
Discuss Dark Forces with fellow Star Wars gaming fans.

alt.games.descent
Talk up the game Descent.

alt.games.doom
Cut to the chase with veteran players of DOOM.

alt.games.doom.announce
Visit this moderated forum for news of interest to
DOOM fans.

alt.games.doom.newplayers.
Be smart and visit this DOOM newsgroup before the
others.

alt.games.doom.ii
Yes! DOOM II has its own newsgroup, too.

alt.games.duke3d
Stop in for bits and pieces about Duke Nukem 3D.

alt.games.gb
Explore the thrills and spills of Galactic Bloodshed.

alt.games.marathon
Discuss the Mac attack sci-fi game Marathon.

alt.games.mechwarrior2
Exchange combat tales with other MechWarriors.

alt.games.mk
Engage in talk of Mortal Kombat.

alt.games.mk.mk3
Engage in talk of Mortal Kombat III.

alt.games.mtrek
Meet the multiusers who play among the Multi-Trek
stars.

alt.games.sf2
They're all fighting words in the Street Fighter 2
newsgroup.

alt.games.warcraft
Discuss the fine art of Warcraft—the skill and thrill,
too.

alt.games.wing-commander
Brief and be briefed about the Wing Commander
flight sim.

alt.games.xpilot
Join the Xpilots and explore the thrills of the game.

alt.games.xtrek
Discuss the networked game with fellow Xtrek
enthusiasts.

rec.games.computer.doom.announce

rec.games.computer.doom.editing

rec.games.computer.doom.help

rec.games.computer.doom.misc

rec.games.computer.doom.playing
For those who like their DOOM as doomed as
DOOM can be.

rec.games.computer.quake.announce

rec.games.computer.quake.editing

rec.games.computer.quake.misc

rec.games.computer.quake.playing

rec.games.computer.quake.
For those looking to shake up their Quake.

rec.games.computer.stars
Explore the strategies for conquering Stars!

rec.games.computer.ultima-dragons
Read what fans of the Ultima games have to say.

rec.games.computer.xpilot
Talk about Xpilot missions.

rec.games.empire
Discover what it takes to build and defend an Empire.

rec.games.mecha
Find out about playing games with enormous robots.

rec.games.netrek
Call it Netrek or Xtrek II, just talk about it here.

rec.games.xtank.play
Plot strategy and talk Xtank tactics.

rec.games.xtank.programmer
Discuss programming for the Xtank game.

Title-Specific Miscellaneous Games

rec.games.backgammon
Talk of rolling dice and moving backgammon discs.

rec.games.chess.analysis
Discuss and dissect the chess moves that win.

rec.games.chess.misc
Find news and general chat of interest to chess players.

rec.games.chinese-chess
Talk about Chinese chess in search of a player's advantage.

rec.games.diplomacy
Discuss ruling the world with Diplomacy.

rec.games.go
Go here for discussion on the Asian board game Go.

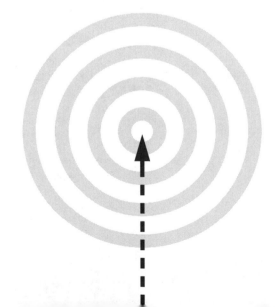

12

TELNET GUIDE

AT its most basic, Telnet is an Internet application through which people can log their personal computers onto a remote host computer and then issue commands to that host through a simple interface. In other words, through Telnet, users can turn their personal computers into an extension of other—usually more powerful and memory rich—computers. For those who enjoy games, this ability to log on to host computers allows for real-time interaction with other game-players, and thus creates the opportunity for competitive and cooperative play.

Originally, Telnet only supported text-based games such as card games and multiple-user dungeons (MUDs). However, the introduction of graphically-enabled application software has spawned an evolution in Telnet gaming. Now many of the games which are available via Telnet rival other computer games in their appealing visual presentations.

Since most of the games offering "enhanced" visuals require the use of specific application software, they are often "fronted" by a Web page which explains the game environment that is available via Telnet and points players to the site where the graphical interface can be downloaded. Many of these games can be found in the other sections of this book and will not receive further coverage here. Instead, let's turn our attention the quintessential Telnet games, the MUDs.

A QUICK GUIDE TO MUDS

Multiple-user dungeons offer players an imagination-rich environment in which to explore, role-play, build, and/or do battle. These environments are as diverse as the hundreds of games currently running, but generally fall within the realms of the science fiction, gothic horror, and fantasy genres; or they take a more social approach, offering players an arena in which to chat and joke around.

Often referred to collectively as "M*s," the specific type of game—MUD, MUSH, MUCK, or any of the other "M*" variations—is determined by the type of programming code, or server, used to create the game. Many of these servers are variations or complete rewrites of earlier codes. They vary in nuance, flexibility, and other attributes of importance to game programmers; however, to players, the major distinction seems to be whether the game offers combat options and whether players are allowed to build onto the environment.

For those unfamiliar with MUDs, a good place to begin learning about these text-based games is to read the three-part FAQ prepared by Jennifer Smith (a.k.a. Moira). It offers a general introduction to MUDding and explores the kinds of MUDs which are available. The FAQ also examines the Telnet interfaces, or clients, which work best with various computer platforms and where they can be downloaded. The FAQ can be found on the World Wide Web at http://math.okstate.edu/~jds/mudfaqs.html. An alternate version can also be found at http://www.lysator.liu.se/mud/faq/faq1.html.

Another good source for general information about MUDding is The MUD Resource Collection posted by Lydia Leong (a.k.a. Amberyl). This collection of information can be found on the Web at http://www.cis.upenn.edu/~lwl/mudinfo.html.

Beyond learning the basics, it is left to each individual player to search out and find the MUD environments that prove most enjoyable. To assist in that task, the following list points out hundreds of MUDs organized by type. Known as Doran's Mudlist, this popular roster is the work of Adam Wozniak (a.k.a. Doran) and Kristin Amundsen (a.k.a. Indium) and is posted to the Usenet newsgroups rec.games.mud.diku, rec.games.mud.lp, rec.games.mud.misc, rec.games.mud.tiny, and rec.games.mud.admin. The list is also available on the World Wide Web at http://www.cm.cf.ac.uk/User/Andrew.Wilson/MUDlist/ and http://shsibm.shh.fi/mud/Mudlist.html. Or, for the most recent issue, players can send e-mail with the word ISSUE in the subject line to: mudlist@satellite.eorbit.net.

The list organizes all the MUDs presented by the type of programming code used to author the game. The name of the code heads the grouping and, where available, a brief description of the code follows. Many are referred to as "hack and slash type" MUDs, an indication that combat is a key element of those games. Each MUD entry includes the game's name and the two forms of its Internet address. The first address is comprised of the remote host's name and the port where the game is found. The second address is the numeric conversion of the first address—what is known as the IP. For most players, the first address will work fine.

Key codes are used to advise players of the features found in many of the individual games. These are the two-letter codes found underneath a game's name. Not all entries have these codes, however. Only those games whose authors have provided the codes will have this detail in their entry. Another set of codes advises players when the Doran's Mudlist maintainers last attempted or succeeded in connecting to a game. These are the symbols which precede the games' names. Again, not all game entries carry these codes, but the extra information is made available where possible.

Doran's Mudlist

Date: Sun Aug 25 13:53:50 1996—Total muds: 559

Key

?—no successful connect on record—may be removed from future lists

*—last successful connect more than 7 days ago

#—last successful connect more than 3 days ago

@—last successful connect more than 1 day ago

MO—More than the four standard classes (mage, thief, warrior, cleric)

MR—Multiple Races

PK—Player Killing

RE—Rent: some MUDs charge rent for you to keep equipment when you quit

MC—Multiclassing

QU—Quests

AC—Automated Character creation: you do not need a wiz to do it for you

RH—Restricted Hours: the MUD is not open 24 hours

CO—Color

$$—Pay MUD: you have to pay money to play on this MUD

NB—Non-Restricted Building: anyone can build on this MUD

OA—MUD contains at least 75% Original Areas (areas not on ANY other MUD)

Theme

SF (sci-fi), FA (fantasy), HO (horror), TO (toon), FU (furry), MI (mixed)

Copyright 1995-1996 Adam Wozniak (Doran) and Kristin Amundsen (Indium)

TYPE ?unknown? (12)

No information available.

MUD Key Codes (if available)	Hostname IP Address	Port
4th Space [Chinese]	ccca1.CCCA.nctu.edu.tw	7777
	140.113.5.151	7777
Casamia	ds5240.as.ntu.edu.tw	8888
	140.112.66.19	8888

MUD Key Codes (if available)	Hostname IP Address	Port
Cheeseworld	swindon.city.ac.uk	4000
	138.40.1.3	4000
Cobalt	mud.hiper.net	9000
MO MR PK AC CO FA	206.5.38.201	9000
Doom Star	phys10.phys.nchu.edu.tw	9999
	140.120.11.10	9999
*Dreams of Anarchy	tiger.vut.edu.au	3454
	140.159.28.7	3454
*Five Star Stories	eesun2.ee.nchu.edu.tw	5000
	140.120.31.202	5000
*Lothlorien	sac.uky.edu	6679
	128.163.1.163	6679
MUD++	phoenix.mercer.peachnet.edu	5000
	131.144.194.184	5000
Rhostshyl MR AC CO NB FA	rhostshyl.nu.edu	4201
	198.17.145.1	4201
Storm Riders	storm.pcix.com	1234
	206.113.11.202	1234
SvenskMUD [Swedish]	bodil.lysator.liu.se	2043
	130.236.254.152	2043

TYPE aber (18)

An old hack-and-slash style MUD.

MUD Key Codes (if available)	Hostname IP Address	Port
Atlantis	amp2.flashnet.it	6715
	194.21.12.232	6715
Dark Moon QU CO	pegasus.unm.edu	6715
	129.24.8.16	6715
DragonMUD	dragon.fmi.uni-passau.de	6715
	132.231.10.4	6715
Eclipse MUD	path.upmc.edu	6715
	128.147.183.75	6715
Eradicated Worlds	odie.et.fnt.hvu.nl	6715

MUD Key Codes (if available)	Hostname IP Address	Port
	145.89.82.30	6715
Infinity	sirius.nmt.edu	6715
	129.138.4.119	6715
*Kender's Kove QU AC CO FA	bitsy.hollyfeld.org	6715
	38.240.235.1	6715
Mirage III	puma.cyberport.com	6715
	204.134.75.6	6715
Northern Lights	harlie.ludd.luth.se	6715
	130.240.16.29	6715
Orion II	teaching4.physics.ox.ac.uk	6715
	163.1.245.204	6715
SilverMUD QU AC CO OA	Mud.MVP.Net	6715
	205.139.224.135	6715
Sleepless Nights	sleepless.cheese.org	6789
	194.217.167.167	6789
Stargate	mud.erols.com	5000
	205.252.116.63	5000
TerraFirmA QU AC CO OA	buster.lboro.ac.uk	8888
	158.125.130.107	8888
Terradome QU CO AC OA	terradome.ds-data.dk	8888
	130.227.74.4	8888
Virtual Sun	lord.technomancer.com	6715
	198.82.204.17	6715
Vortex	juliet.pacsense.com	6716
	204.182.45.225	6716
XTC	xtc.tsa.net	6969
	208.129.19.6	6969

TYPE circle (53)

A diku-spinoff hack-and-slash style MUD.

MUD Key Codes (if available)	Hostname IP Address	Port
A Moment in Tyme	tyme.op.net	6969
	204.153.195.113	6969
Alvoria	conan.ids.net	4000
	155.212.1.12	4000
AnotherWorld	aw.pp.se	4000

MUD Key Codes (if available)	Hostname IP Address	Port
MO MR QU AC CO NB FA	206.129.66.10	4000
ArchaicMUD	xanadu.rsabbs.com	6969
	204.180.235.4	6969
Archipelago	island.essex.ac.uk	24
	155.245.180.15	24
Artemis	artemis.earth.monash.edu.au	8000
	130.194.168.3	8000
AugMUD	marcello.augustana.ab.ca	4000
	199.185.3.120	4000
Bio-Hazard	triton.cs.csufresno.edu	6666
	123.8.1.9	6666
BlueMage	spock.cse.hks.se	4000
	193.10.221.52	4000
CheesyMUD	cheese.kosone.com	4001
	199.246.3.134	4001
Cities of Glory	bucket.ualr.edu	4000
	144.167.10.237	4000
ColimaMUD MO RE CO MI	orion.qro.itesm.mx	4000
	132.254.90.24	4000
ConanMUD	mail.bcpl.lib.md.us	4001
	204.255.212.10	4001
Darkover	darkover.revnet.com	6000
	198.51.35.19	6000
Death Zone	ahcbsd1.ovnet.com	2000
	198.77.6.50	2000
Dominion, The	persephone.cs.umsl.edu	8400
	134.124.30.27	8400
DoomMUD MO MR MC QU AC CO OA FA	falkor.hacks.arizona.edu	4000
	128.196.230.15	4000
Dragons' Land	victim.earthlink.net	4000
	206.85.99.36	4000
Elite	xbyse.nada.kth.se	4000
	130.237.222.237	4000
Eternal	smith.syr.edu	4000
	128.230.31.20	4000
Europa	europa.rjl-consulting.com	4000
	206.230.63.6	4000

MUD Key Codes (if available)	Hostname IP Address	Port
Fantasy Realm	athena.asms.state.k12.al.us	4001
MO PK AC FA	199.20.31.3	4001
GODMUD	cam037103.student.utwente.nl	4000
	130.89.226.53	4000
Gathering, The AC CO OA SF	saturn.netusa1.net	4000
	205.139.170.11	4000
ImagicaMUD	ftp.rijnhaave.nl	4000
MR RE QU AC OA FA	194.151.56.23	4000
IndyMUD	nova.nuc.umr.edu	4444
	131.151.10.126	4444
*Keep, The	ravenloft.iue.indiana.edu	6666
	149.165.1.120	6666
LordMUD	eagle.dmv.com	4000
	206.30.64.2	4000
MULTI MUD	uhura.biologie.uni-freiburg.de	4242
MR RE QU AC CO	132.230.36.55	4242
Malicious Bliss	linux.newwareclub.com	4000
	206.0.142.36	4000
Mists of Annwyn, The	awake.gstand.com	3970
	204.183.202.75	3970
Moon Mud MO MR AC	mud.bluemoon.net	4000
	206.42.160.105	4000
Mordor	sauron.neurotech.net	4000
	206.54.163.4	4000
New Eden PK RE QU CO MI	jason-main.dcs.qmw.ac.uk	7000
	138.37.88.214	7000
Phantazm	fpa.com	4000
	198.242.217.1	4000
Prime Evil	ozramp.net.au	4000
	203.17.73.1	4000
Quarantine MO MR AC	exit1.i-55.com	4000
	204.27.97.1	4000
Quickening, The	prometheus.digital-rain.com	4000
MO MR PK AC CO FA	206.87.85.1	4000

MUD

Key Codes (if available)	Hostname IP Address	Port
RavenMUD	pantera.openix.com	8000
	206.64.16.200	8000
*Razor's Edge	spodbox.linux.org.uk	4000
	193.62.1.250	4000
*Realms of Aurealis	roa.cs.sunyit.edu	4000
MO PK QU AC CO OA FA	192.52.220.100	4000
Realms of Magic	b11.informatik.uni-bremen.de	4000
MR RE MC QU AC CO OA FA	134.102.201.111	4000
Realms_of_Mit'uen	mordor.os2bbs.com	4000
MO MR PK QU AC CO OA FA	204.194.180.112	4000
Rifts, The	rifts.tcimet.net	6666
MO MR PK RE MC QU AC CO NB OA FA	198.109.160.155	6666
Ruin! Mud	wired.uvm.edu	4000
	132.198.104.40	4000
TDome II	tdome.montana.com	5555
	199.2.139.13	5555
Tap chat AC CO	bird.taponline.com	4000
	204.32.153.202	4000
Tempus	styx.ph.msstate.edu	2020
	130.18.152.61	2020
Ultraviolence	mars.galstar.com	3000
	204.251.80.4	3000
Void, The	rosebud.umiacs.umd.edu	4000
MO MC QU AC CO MI NB	128.8.120.103	4000
Winds of Chaos	chaos.nlm.nih.gov	4000
	130.14.60.202	4000
Wisney MUD	levant.cs.ohiou.edu	5000
	132.235.1.100	5000
aGe oF iNsaNitY MR PK CO FA	newton.whit.org	4000
	205.238.84.11	4000

TYPE custom (23)

No information available.

MUD

Key Codes (if available)	Hostname IP Address	Port
AnonyMUD	anon.corenet.net	7137
	156.46.50.17	7137
Arctic	arctic.csua.berkeley.edu	2700
	128.32.43.55	2700
Avalon	avalon-rpg.com	23
	206.67.154.62	23
Avalon	avalon.co.uk	23
	193.132.124.130	23
Chatting Zone, The AC CO NB	tcz.galaxsw.co.uk	8342
	194.72.92.3	8342
DragonSpires	boris.eden.com	7734
	204.177.170.33	7734
Dreamscape - MUD	drscape.com	23
	192.197.215.2	23
Forbidden Lands	centcon.com	5000
	207.113.128.18	5000
Ground Zero	mud.inc.net	6666
	204.95.194.4	6666
LegendMUD	mud.aus.sig.net	9999
MO PK MC QU CO AC MI	199.1.78.16	9999
Medievia Cyberspace	medievia.netaxs.com	4000
	198.69.186.36	4000
Moongate	alpha.pulsar.net	4000
MO MR PK MC QU AC CO OA FA	206.161.93.30	4000
Paradigm	paradigm.microwave.com	5000
	206.48.64.10	5000
Realm of Legends MUD	diversion.com	23
	204.189.48.1	23
RetroActive MUD	shell.id.net	3000
	199.125.1.12	3000
Scimitar of Goth	drscape.com	23
	192.197.215.2	23
Shades of Evil	soe.nuc.net	6666

MUD

Key Codes (if available)	Hostname IP Address	Port
MO MR PK MC QU AC CO OA FA	204.49.61.4	6666
Spa, The	the-spa.com	23
	204.97.227.2	23
Synergy	synergy.sigmasoft.com	2000
MR PK QU OA MI	204.94.181.12	2000
Tera	tera.teralink.com	4000
	199.199.122.9	4000
*Tron USA PKMUD	paris.servint.com	4000
	205.177.90.11	4000
Web of Destiny	rabbit.cudenver.edu	9000
	132.194.10.14	9000
YAMud	beldin.it.com.au	6789
	203.8.116.4	6789

TYPE dgd (7)

A hack-and-slash style MUD very similar to lp.

MUD

Key Codes (if available)	Hostname IP Address	Port
Albion Mud	mud.veda.is	4000
	193.4.230.1	4000
DemonWorld	lwsun3.lanware.de	3000
	194.45.175.1	3000
IgorMUD	igor.algonet.se	1701
	193.12.207.11	1701
Might, Magic and Mushrooms	mmm.megabaud.fi	6047
	192.89.182.3	6047
*Tene Mud	nic.follonett.no	3000
	194.198.33.70	3000
University of MOO	janus.lamf.uwindsor.ca	7777
NB	137.207.192.76	7777
Xyllomer	mud.uni-paderborn.de	3000
	131.234.10.45	3000

TYPE diku (83)

A hack-and-slash style MUD.

MUD

Key Codes (if available)	Hostname IP Address	Port
Abyss IV	aux.lrc.uwm.edu	4000
	129.89.68.89	4000
AlexMUD	alexmud.stacken.kth.se	4000
QU RE	130.237.50.102	4000
Allandria	directcheck.aries.net	7777
MO MR MC	204.229.202.7	7777
Alter Aeon	sl9vg.dorms.usu.edu	4000
	129.123.230.80	4000
AnotherMUD	mud.compart.fi	4000
	193.64.198.202	4000
Apocalypse IV	sapphire.geo.wvu.edu	4000
	157.182.168.20	4000
Arctic	mud.arctic.org	2700
MO MR PK RE QU AC CO FA	204.62.130.76	2700
AustinMud	ragnarok.imv.aau.dk	4000
	130.225.2.6	4000
Banished Lands	power.uafadm.alaska.edu	4000
	137.229.22.121	4000
Black Gamma II	imagery.kosone.com	4001
	199.246.2.5	4001
Burning MUD	burning.stacken.kth.se	4000
	130.237.50.103	4000
Carrion Fields	maple.can.net	9999
	199.246.170.4	9999
ChaosMUD	chaos.entech.com	4000
MO MR RE QU AC CO FA	198.65.158.23	4000
Creator's Shadow, The	botsrus.crystalball.com	4000
	198.49.119.106	4000
Crystal Shard	newsun.mhv.net	9000
MO MR PK RE MC QU AC CO FA	199.0.0.6	9000
Cygnus	cygnus.et.put.poznan.pl	4000
	150.254.29.97	4000
Cythera	isis.usi.utah.edu	4000
	128.110.138.155	4000

MUD Key Codes (if available)	Hostname IP Address	Port
Dark Castle MUD	jitter.rahul.net	6666
	192.160.13.8	6666
Dark Chronicles	mud.iglou.com	4000
	192.107.41.6	4000
Dark Realms	ftoomsh.progsoc.uts.edu.au	5000
	138.25.6.1	5000
Dead of Night	barracuda.fishnet.net	3443
	205.216.133.15	3443
Death's Domain	cybernet.cse.fau.edu	9000
	131.91.80.79	9000
Deathwish	dwmud.sj-coop.net	4000
	207.104.147.250	4000
Delta Mud	playground.tky.hut.fi	4444
	130.233.33.219	4444
*DizzyMud	webserver.fone.com	9000
	205.159.146.120	9000
Dragon MUD	conan.ids.net	5000
	155.212.1.12	5000
Dragon Realm	drake.ntu.edu.tw	3000
	140.112.2.33	3000
Duris: Bloodlust	duris.mi.org	6666
	199.177.127.66	6666
Dutch Mountains	asterix.icce.rug.nl	4000
	129.125.14.130	4000
Edge of Darkness, The	edge.uccs.edu	2001
	128.198.65.19	2001
Empire	einstein.physics.drexel.edu	4000
	144.118.44.120	4000
FID-MUD	uhunix2.its.Hawaii.Edu	9999
	128.171.44.7	9999
FieryMud	fiery.eushc.org	4000
	163.246.96.103	4000
Final Frontier [German]	csmd50.cs.uni-magdeburg.de	7600
	141.44.22.50	7600
Fires of Heaven	cheshire.cwrl.utexas.edu	4000

MUD Key Codes (if available)	Hostname IP Address	Port
MO MR CO AC QU PK FA	146.6.97.163	4000
*Forbidden Tundra	lionx1.rdsnet.com	4000
	199.234.116.210	4000
FormosaMUD	db84.csie.ncu.edu.tw	4000
	140.115.50.84	4000
FuskerMud	dorothy.ibmpcug.co.uk	4000
	192.68.174.69	4000
Gizmo	Gizmo.BCHS.UH.EDU	6969
	129.7.40.44	6969
GrimneMUD	grimne.pvv.unit.no	4000
	129.241.210.220	4000
GrungeMUD	malasada.lava.net	4000
	199.222.42.2	4000
Harshlands Mud	photobooks.atdc.gatech.edu	1234
	130.207.133.27	1234
Harz-Site-Diku	bingo.in.tu-clausthal.de	4000
	139.174.100.14	4000
Hercules MUD	sunshine.eushc.org	3000
	163.246.96.102	3000
Holomud	sprawl.fc.net	7777
	204.157.153.6	7777
Holy Mission 2	wildsau.idv.uni-linz.ac.at	2001
	140.78.40.25	2001
Imperial	mandrake.cs.hut.fi	6969
	130.233.40.66	6969
*Impmud	spodbox.linux.org.uk	2150
	193.62.1.250	2150
KAOS HQ MO MR MC RE QU AC CO	flower.aud.temple.edu	4000
	155.247.42.7	4000
KIDmud	server1.powernet.net	5120
	199.172.142.2	5120
*Land, The MR RE CO OA FA	eva.next.hig.no	4000
	128.39.140.153	4000
Last Outpost, The	lo.millcomm.com	4000
	199.170.133.6	4000
Legend of the Winds	ccsun44.csie.nctu.edu.tw	4040
	140.113.17.168	4040

MUD Key Codes (if available)	Hostname IP Address	Port
Lost Atlantis, The	eespcc.ncku.edu.tw	1234
	140.116.32.56	1234
Lost Realms MUD	phoenix.mercer.peachnet.edu	4000
	131.144.194.184	4000
Lost World of Stonia, The	stonia.ut.ee	4000
	193.40.5.125	4000
MUME	medusa.sparta.lu.se	4242
	130.235.248.4	4242
MUME	mxsg1.epfl.ch	4242
	128.178.108.11	4242
MUME	shire.ncsa.uiuc.edu	4242
	141.142.103.6	4242
MooseHead SLED	sled.moosehead.com	4000
MR PK MC QU AC FA	204.122.16.31	4000
Mystical Mud	mystical.netwalk.com	4000
	205.156.197.12	4000
NetherWorld	ruby.telmaron.com	3666
	204.180.173.11	3666
Nilgiri, The Forgotten World	rivendel.com	8888
	205.197.159.2	8888
Northern CrossRoads	ncmud.io.org	9000
MO MR PK RE MC QU AC CO MI	198.133.36.164	9000
Pkeurope	beyond.malmo.lth.se	5000
MO PK AC	130.235.4.20	5000
*Perilous Realms(PR MUD)	www.com	23
	155.229.2.6	23
Phidar	cdsgw.CrystalData.COM	9000
	198.49.103.129	9000
Realms of Ambiguity	mville.edu	9009
MO MR	199.97.98.3	9009
RoninMUD	arjun.hudsonet.com	5000
MO RE MC QU AC CO OA	206.25.166.3	5000

MUD Key Codes (if available)	Hostname IP Address	Port
Shadow of Terror	zeus.initco.net	4000
	205.162.172.3	4000
Shadowdale	dale.community.net	7777
	140.174.119.12	7777
Silicon Realms	sampan.ee.fit.edu	4000
	163.118.30.9	4000
SillyMUD	phoenix.piedmont.net	4000
MO MR RE AC CO FA	205.245.76.2	4000
SlothMUD II	ai.eecs.ukans.edu	6101
	129.237.80.113	6101
Snebo-Land	odesha.isca.uiowa.edu	2477
	128.255.200.28	2477
Spam MUD	atlantis.igc.net	5000
MO MR PK QU AC OA MI	207.89.0.40	5000
Strange MUD	grumpy.cc.utexas.edu	9332
	128.83.42.61	9332
Thieves World	tw.imaxx.net	5000
MO MR PK MC QU AC CO OA SF	208.195.84.40	5000
Tietgen MUD	dec51.tietgen.dk	4711
	130.226.136.4	4711
Valhalla MUD	valhalla.wtm.tudelft.nl	4242
	130.161.249.7	4242
Ways, The	-	4000
	198.65.216.254	4000
Worlds of Carnage	dionysis.cu-online.com	4000
	205.198.248.13	4000
ZeeMUD	pcnet3.pcnet.com	4000
PK AC CO FA	204.213.232.7	4000

TYPE dum (4)

No information available.

MUD Key Codes (if available)	Hostname IP Address	Port
Arcania	arcania.ing.umu.se	2001
	130.239.116.238	2001
CanDUM II	tanstaafl.ts.umu.se	2001

MUD

Key Codes (if available)	Hostname IP Address	Port
QU AC CO FA	130.239.18.134	2001
DUM II	dum.ts.umu.se	2001
	130.239.18.7	2001
FranDUM II	mousson.enst.fr	2001
QU FA	137.194.160.48	2001

TYPE dyrt (1)

No information available.

MUD

Key Codes (if available)	Hostname IP Address	Port
Asylum	asylum.rsc.co.uk	6715
QU AC CO FA	194.73.130.30	6715

TYPE envy (8)

No information available.

MUD

Key Codes (if available)	Hostname IP Address	Port
AsylumX	asylumx.aros.net	4500
MO MR	205.164.111.40	4500
Commonwealth	cwealth.traveller.com	8500
MC PK AC QU CO MI	198.49.103.129	8500
Dragon Realms	dominions.ozramp.net.au	4444
MO MR PK CO OA FA	203.17.73.20	4444
Land of Legends	jubjub.wizard.com	1234
MO MR AC	199.171.28.9	1234
Monster Mud	ids1.idsweb.com	1210
MO PK QU AC CO FA	206.85.136.102	1210
Our Place	the.express-news.net	6543
MO MR QU AC CO NB MI	204.57.68.3	6543
TNT	inferno.cs.bris.ac.uk	4000
	137.222.102.176	4000
Underworld Dreams	dot.cs.wmich.edu	3000
	141.218.40.80	3000

TYPE lp (111)

A hack-and-slash style MUD.

MUD

Key Codes (if available)	Hostname IP Address	Port
3-Kingdoms	marble.confusion.net	5000
	162.114.196.140	5000
Adamant	rm600.rbg.informatik.th-darmstadt.de	4711
	130.83.9.19	4711
After Hours	ra2.randomc.com	2000
	205.160.16.21	2000
Alatia	alatia.org	3000
QU AC OA MI	205.177.90.11	3000
Aldebaran	mud.tap.de	2000
QU AC OA FA	194.162.200.11	2000
Ancient Anguish	ancient.anguish.org	2222
	205.226.195.7	2222
Astaria	astaria.phl.pond.com	5555
MO MR QU AC CO OA FA	198.69.82.29	5555
Aurora	trono.etsiig.uniovi.es	3000
	156.35.41.20	3000
BatMUD	bat.cs.hut.fi	23
	130.233.40.180	23
Callandor	orion.tyler.net	5317
	205.218.118.5	5317
Chaos II	chaos.lpmud.edu	3456
MO MR QU AC CO OA FA	207.104.147.246	3456
Chatter	hawking.u.washington.edu	6000
	140.142.58.99	6000
Conservatorium	crs.cl.msu.edu	6000
	35.8.1.10	6000
Crossed Swords	shsibm.shh.fi	3000
	128.214.106.5	3000
Dark Side	rsls5.sprachlit.uni-regensburg.de	6666
	132.199.136.35	6666
DarkPowers	cam037103.student.utwente.nl	6666
	130.89.226.53	6666
*DarkeMUD	darke.shadowlands.com	5559

MUD Key Codes (if available)	Hostname IP Address	Port
MO MR PK FA	199.1.96.66	5559
Darker Realms	Darker-Realms.nostrum.com	2000
	206.28.8.8	2000
DartMUD	dartmud.rose-hulman.edu	2525
MO MR PK RE MC QU AC CO FA	137.112.1.116	2525
Dawn of Immortals	immortal.ncsa.uiuc.edu	2000
	141.142.214.8	2000
*Deeper Trouble	alk.iesd.auc.dk	4242
	130.225.48.46	4242
Defiance	ra2.randomc.com	3011
	205.160.16.21	3011
Discworld	discworld.imaginary.com	4242
MO PK QU AC CO OA	204.73.178.25	4242
Dragon Realm	mud.inna.net	4000
MR PK QU CO QA FA	206.151.66.11	4000
Dragon's Den	hellfire.dusers.drexel.edu	2222
PK QU AC MI	129.25.56.246	2222
DragonFire	typo.umsl.edu	3000
	134.124.42.197	3000
DragonHeart	atomic.com	8888
PK MR AC CO OA	206.109.6.67	8888
Dranath	dranath.educom.com.au	9999
	203.11.217.1	9999
Dream Shadow	telmaron.com	3333
	204.180.173.2	3333
Dune	paris.servint.com	8888
	205.177.90.11	8888
Elements of Paradox	elof.acc.iit.edu	6996
	198.87.165.30	6996
Elephant MUD	elephant.org	4444
	194.70.126.10	4444
Eloria	brunel.herts.ac.uk	1995
	147.197.206.250	1995
Elveszett Vilag	mud.westel.hu	6666
	193.224.154.77	6666

MUD Key Codes (if available)	Hostname IP Address	Port
Enulal	enulal.u-aizu.ac.jp	2222
	163.143.125.117	2222
Eodon	rood.sci.kun.nl	5555
	131.174.124.32	5555
*Etheria	csgi60.leeds.ac.uk	7777
	129.11.144.190	7777
Final Realms	fr.hiof.no	2001
	158.36.33.52	2001
Frandel	kjw.kw.net	3000
	204.187.87.226	3000
Frontiers	seahorse.acs.brockport.edu	5555
	137.21.166.20	5555
Fury of the Dragon	ts1.cdsnet.net	3000
MR PK QU AC CO OA FA	204.118.244.4	3000
Genesis	spica3.cs.chalmers.se	3011
	129.16.227.203	3011
Genocide	genocide.shsu.edu	2222
	192.92.115.145	2222
Hall of Fame	hof.df.lth.se	2000
	194.47.252.38	2000
Hyperborea	eclipse.sundial.net	2000
	204.181.150.114	2000
Icewind	icewind.hifm.no	2021
	158.39.14.40	2021
Idea Exchange	ie.imaginary.com	7890
	204.73.178.25	7890
*Infinity	infinity.firstcomm.com	4242
	204.179.248.42	4242
Insomnia	cal006014.student.utwente.nl	4000
	130.89.227.74	4000
Ithacas' Mud	light.lightlink.com	6969
	205.232.34.1	6969
Ivory Tower	marvin.macc.wisc.edu	2000
	205.243.195.7	2000
Kingdoms	luthien.dd.chalmers.se	1812
	129.16.117.12	1812
KoBra	kobra.et.tudelft.nl	23

MUD Key Codes (if available)	Hostname IP Address	Port
	130.161.38.161	23
Laurasia	minerva.psc.edu	3000
	128.182.61.122	3000
Legacy	legacy.org	5000
MO MR RE MC QU AC CO FA	204.96.52.188	5000
Loch Ness	lochness.imp.ch	2222
	157.161.1.2	2222
LooneyMud	looney.lpmud.org	8888
MO MR QU AC CI OA TO	204.77.159.11	8888
*Lost Kingdom, The	cisppc1.cis.nctu.edu.tw	4000
	140.113.207.7	4000
Lost Mud	goofy.cc.utexas.edu	6668
	128.83.42.61	6668
Lost Souls	lostsouls.org	3000
MO MR MC QU AC CO FA	129.7.40.49	3000
Lost Wishes	link.xs4all.nl	5555
	194.109.12.41	5555
Lost in Time	gama.fsv.cvut.cz	7680
	147.32.131.52	7680
LustyMud	mckusick.brcf.med.umich.edu	2000
	141.214.32.35	2000
Midnight Sun	holly.ludd.luth.se	3000
	130.240.16.23	3000
Moonstar	pulsar.hsc.edu	4321
	192.135.84.5	4321
Moral Decay	zuul.cmd.usf.edu	2002
	131.247.1.58	2002
MorgenGrauen [German]	mud.uni-muenster.de	4711
	128.176.182.70	4711
Muddy Waters	mw.cs.washington.edu	3000
MR PK MC QU AC OA FA	128.95.4.92	3000
NewMoon	eclipse.cs.pdx.edu	7680
	204.203.64.89	7680

MUD Key Codes (if available)	Hostname IP Address	Port
NightFall	quest.tat.physik.uni-tuebingen.de	4242
	134.2.170.99	4242
NightMare	nightmare.imaginary.com	1701
	204.73.178.25	1701
Nirvana	elof.acc.iit.edu	3500
	198.87.165.30	3500
Onyx III	onyx.me.iastate.edu	3456
MR QU AC CO OA FA	129.186.2.245	3456
Outer Space	mud.stack.urc.tue.nl	3333
	131.155.141.166	3333
Overdrive	overdrive.concentric.net	5195
	199.3.123.51	5195
Paradox	adl.uncc.edu	10478
MO MR PK QU AC CO OA MI	152.15.15.18	10478
Paradox II	shimoda.cis.temple.edu	1691
	155.247.207.120	1691
Patterns of Time	shell.dialnet.net	6100
	206.65.248.2	6100
Phoenix	ALBERT.BU.EDU	3500
	128.197.74.10	3500
Prime Time	prime.mdata.fi	3000
	192.98.43.2	3000
Reality's Edge	suitcase.neurospeed.com	4000
	206.43.104.241	4000
Realms of the Dragon	rod.umd.umich.edu	3000
	141.215.69.7	3000
Realmsmud	realms.dorsai.org	1501
	206.127.32.200	1501
Red Dragon	RedDragon.Empire.Net	3000
	205.164.80.15	3000
Relative Absurdity	mirror.nol.net	8000
	206.126.32.200	8000
Revenge of the End of the Line	aus.Stanford.EDU	2010
	36.21.0.99	2010
RiftMUD	rift.cc.emory.edu	5000

MUD Key Codes (if available)	Hostname IP Address	Port
	170.140.38.71	5000
Ritual Sacrifice	vulture.ois.net.au	5555
	203.59.29.1	5555
Riverhold	mama.indstate.edu	3000
	139.102.70.201	3000
Rogue	rogue.coe.ohio-state.edu	2222
	128.146.144.12	2222
Swmud	Kitten.mcs.com	6666
	192.160.127.90	6666
Sanity's Edge	mathconnect.cc.colorado.edu	2020
MO PK MC QU AC OA MI	198.59.4.175	2020
Shadow Gate LpMud	mud.oregon.com	2000
	205.238.1.170	2000
StickMUD	pellinor.cc.jyu.fi	7680
MO MR PK RE QU AC RH CO FA	130.234.40.11	7680
Sushi	cvrayleigh.swan.ac.uk	5500
	137.44.102.200	5500
TAPPMud	surprise.pro.ufz.de	6510
MO MR QU MC AC FA	141.65.40.11	6510
Titan	vulture.king.ac.uk	2020
MO MR MK QU AC RH CO OA FA	141.241.196.1	2020
Tron	polaris.king.ac.uk	3000
	141.241.84.65	3000
Tsunami IV	tsunami.netusa.net	2777
	204.141.0.40	2777
TubMUD	morgen.cs.tu-berlin.de	7680
	130.149.19.20	7680
Twilight	sparrow.crc.nus.sg	5000
MO MR PK QU AC CO FA	137.132.111.80	5000
UNItopia [German]	unitopia.uni-stuttgart.de	3333
	129.69.221.130	3333
Underworld	cal012031.student.utwente.nl	5445
PK QU AC OA FA	130.89.227.165	5445

MUD Key Codes (if available)	Hostname IP Address	Port
Valhalla	hal-alt.hal.com	2444
	192.88.244.34	2444
ViKaR	spaghetti.unix-ag.uni-kl.de	9999
	131.246.89.7	9999
VikingMUD	viking.pvv.unit.no	2001
	129.241.210.232	2001
Virrel [German]	rzij.rz.uni-karlsruhe.de 20001	
	129.13.97.10 20001	
Wunderland Arachna	wilma.rz.uni-leipzig.de	4711
MR QU AC FA	139.18.11.78	4711
Xanadu	scooby.cs.sunyit.edu	4242
	192.52.220.60	4242
ZombieMUD	poro.oulu.fi	3000
	130.231.96.144	3000
angalon	angalon.tamu.edu	3011
	128.194.47.139	3011

TYPE mare (1)

An adventure role-playing MUD.

MUD Key Codes (if available)	Hostname IP Address	Port
WindsMare	CYBERION.BBN.COM	7348
	192.1.100.41	7348

TYPE merc (29)

A diku-spinoff hack-and-slash MUD.

MUD Key Codes (if available)	Hostname IP Address	Port
Avatar	walrus.com	3000
	206.24.16.2	3000
Barren Realms	barren.coredcs.com	8000
	198.150.193.1	8000
Brigadoon	sacam.oren.ortn.edu	9000
	160.91.128.2	9000

MUD Key Codes (if available)	Hostname IP Address	Port
Dark Chambers	cal011102.student.utwente.nl	4000
MO PK QU AC FA NB	130.89.222.72	4000
Dragon Swords	karma.physics.iastate.edu	1234
	129.186.117.106	1234
Eyeball MERC	phobos.cimtek.com	4444
	198.69.137.50	4444
Farside	farside.corenet.net	3000
	156.46.50.17	3000
Final Challenge, The	irc1.primenet.com	4000
MO MR PK MC QU AC CO FA	206.165.5.60	4000
FunkyMUD	Funky.monks.galstar.com	3000
	204.251.80.4	3000
Glass Dragon, The	dragon.ods.com	4000
	160.86.50.108	4000
Gmud	mercury.cnct.com	9999
	165.254.118.47	9999
Haunted Pass, The	lionx1.rdsnet.com	4000
	199.234.116.210	4000
Hidden Worlds	earth.usa.net	4000
	192.156.196.1	4000
Isles, The	sauron.hacks.arizona.edu	2000
	128.196.230.7	2000
Killer Instincts	trolls31.ccm.itesm.mx	4444
MR QU AC CO	148.241.155.86	4444
Mirkwood	haystack.ncsa.uiuc.edu	4000
	141.142.222.42	4000
Mortal Realms	-	4321
	204.162.115.56	4321
Mystic Adventure	miniac.etu.gel.ulaval.ca	4000
	132.203.14.100	4000
Off the Deep End	lancelot.hits.net	4000
	204.188.88.5	4000
Patterns of an Age	dunkin.donet.com	4000
	205.133.113.191	4000
Realms of Despair	realms.game.org	4000

MUD Key Codes (if available)	Hostname IP Address	Port
MO MR PK QU AC CO (FA, HO)	207.136.80.35	4000
Rivers of Mud	rom.efn.org	9000
	198.68.17.122	9000
Sanctuary	pauli.sos.clarkson.edu	9000
MO MR PK QU AC CO	128.153.8.6	9000
Shacra Mud [Spanish]	cipres.cec.uchile.cl	9000
	146.83.3.129	9000
Shadows of the Mind	infobahn.icubed.com	4000
MR PK MC CO FA	199.234.114.2	4000
Studnia Dusz [Polish]	akson.sgh.waw.pl	4000
	148.81.202.9	4000
Troll MUD	carbon.cudenver.edu	9000
	132.194.10.4	9000
Turf U.K.	teaching6.physics.ox.ac.uk	4000
MR MC QU AC RH OA MI	163.1.245.206	4000
Turf U.S.A.	imeid.com	4000
MR MC QU AC OA MI	204.27.210.179	4000

TYPE moo (24)

A tiny-spinoff chat mud with an object-oriented internal programming language.

MUD Key Codes (if available)	Hostname IP Address	Port
BayMOO	baymoo.sfsu.edu	8888
	130.212.41.251	8888
CyberSphere	altair.vv.com	7777
	206.27.96.11	7777
Digital Wasteland	wasteland.calbbs.com	8888
PK AC CO SF NB	207.71.213.2	8888
Diversity University	moo.du.org	8888
	128.18.101.106	8888
Dragonsfire	isumataq.eskimo.com	7777

MUD

Key Codes (if available)	Hostname IP Address	Port
	204.122.16.31	7777
EdenMOO	avatar.phys-plant.utoledo.edu	4444
	131.183.124.59	4444
Eon	mcmuse.mc.maricopa.edu	8888
	140.198.66.28	8888
FireSong	-	-
	-	-
Ice-nine	The-B.org	1138
	208.194.120.66	1138
JHM	jhm.ccs.neu.edu	1709
	129.10.118.111	1709
LambdaMOO	lambda.moo.mud.org	8888
NB	192.216.54.2	8888
Little Italy [Italian]	kame.usr.dsi.unimi.it	4444
	149.132.130.48	4444
MOOsaico [Portugese/English]	alfa.di.uminho.pt	7777
	193.136.20.3	7777
Mammoth	antimony.kdps.com	7778
	206.101.250.66	7778
Mundo Hispano [Spanish]	io.syr.edu	8888
	128.230.33.138	8888
NecroMOO	maverick.mcc.ac.uk	7777
AC NB	130.88.202.49	7777
NetwerkMOO	espresso.netwerk.com	8889
	207.2.82.17	8889
PMC	hero.village.Virginia.EDU	7777
	128.143.200.59	7777
PSCS VEE	speakeasy.org	7777
	199.238.226.1	7777
ParkMOO	sun1.gwent.ac.uk	7777
	193.63.82.129	7777
RiverMOO	kelp.honors.indiana.edu	8888
	129.79.171.42	8888
Sprawl, The	ginger.sensemedia.net	7777
	204.188.85.3	7777
Tory	tory.adsnet.com	7777
	206.158.2.2	7777

MUD

Key Codes (if available)	Hostname IP Address	Port
Weyrmount	dragon.lei.net	9020
AC FA NB	204.188.85.3	9020

TYPE mordor (1)

No information available.

MUD

Key Codes (if available)	Hostname IP Address	Port
ChaosMUD	mordor.bio.uci.edu	5150
MO MR PK QU AC CO FA	128.200.21.105	5150

TYPE muck (19)

A tiny-spinoff chat MUD with an internal programming language like FORTH.

MUD

Key Codes (if available)	Hostname IP Address	Port
Animal Nation	an.velox.com	7777
	204.157.47.1	7777
Brazilian Dreams	red_panda.tbyte.com	8888
	198.211.131.13	8888
CaveMUCK	tcp.com	2283
	206.40.34.130	2283
Delusions	mud.iglou.com	4999
CO NB FA	192.107.41.6	4999
DruidMuck	moink.nmsu.edu	4201
	128.123.70.22	4201
FluffMUCK	brain.acmelabs.com	8888
	207.100.79.46	8888
FurToonia	red_panda.tbyte.com	9999
	198.211.131.13	9999
FurryMUCK	furry.org	8888
MO MR FU	199.201.68.101	8888
Ghostwheel	casper.realtime.com	6969
	205.238.128.161	6969
Heaven's Door	peacedove.org	2212
	137.159.177.113	2212

MUD Key Codes (if available)	Hostname IP Address	Port
HoloMUCK	Holo.Rodents.Montreal.QC.CA	5757
	132.206.78.1	5757
Lion King	ritchiesawyer.com	7675
	198.182.207.40	7675
Pathways	bonkers.neosoft.com	8888
	206.109.2.48	8888
QuasiMuck	gumby.npcts.edu	8000
	192.217.204.1	8000
TerraFrore	redwall.otterspace.com	8765
	198.182.207.37	8765
Tiger	tigerden.com	8888
	198.30.162.1	8888
Unbridled Desires	epona.magibox.net	8888
	206.26.142.3	8888
Virtual Surreality NB OA FU	jaguar.velox.com	8888
	204.157.47.2	8888
Wacko	red-branch.mit.edu	6003
	18.70.0.203	6003

TYPE mug (1)

No information available.

MUD Key Codes (if available)	Hostname IP Address	Port
UglyMUG PK AC MI	wyrm.compsoc.man.ac.uk	6239
	192.84.78.147	6239

TYPE murpe (2)

No information available.

MUD Key Codes (if available)	Hostname IP Address	Port
Aldara MURPE	ragweed.cs.engr.uky.edu	4001
	128.163.146.25	4001
MirtosMURPE	jitter.rahul.net	4001
	192.160.13.8	4001

TYPE muse (12)

A tiny-mush spinoff chat MUD.

MUD Key Codes (if available)	Hostname IP Address	Port
Cowmuse	mcmuse.mc.maricopa.edu	4208
	140.198.66.28	4208
Cyburbia (MUSE)	micro.ee.usm.maine.edu	4201
	130.111.148.46	4201
Deep Space AC CO SF	arther.castle.net	1701
	204.97.214.3	1701
FantasyMUSE MR PK MC CO MI NB	educ0015.RuLimburg.NL	4201
	137.120.81.15	4201
MicroMUSE	chezmoto.ai.mit.edu	4201
	18.43.0.102	4201
Oceana CO NB	oceana.sdsc.edu	4201
	132.249.40.200	4201
Q&P-MUSE	puck.rosaparks.cambridge.k12.ma.us	4201
	192.233.10.12	4201
*TCUmuse	edunix1.sed.tcu.edu	4201
	138.237.128.138	4201
N# TimeMuse	<host name not available>	4201
	205.233.219.1205.233.219.1	4201
TrekMUSE	laurel.cnidr.org	1701
	128.109.179.14	1701
VirtualChicago MC AC CO MI NB	vchicago.org	4201
	198.4.164.68	4201
WELLmuse	well.com	4201
	206.15.64.10	4201

TYPE mush (59)

A tiny-spinoff chat MUD.

MUD Key Codes (if available)	Hostname IP Address	Port
AcademICK!	auden.fac.utexas.edu	7777
	146.6.97.133	7777
Amtgard I MUSH	horus.anth.utep.edu	1995

MUD Key Codes (if available)	Hostname IP Address	Port
	129.108.63.11	1995
Angst	crystal.palace.net	5150
	205.231.120.1	5150
AnimeMUSH	anime.mush.com	6260
AC SF MI	199.245.105.102	6260
ApexMUSH	apex.ccs.yorku.ca	4201
	130.63.237.12	4201
Aurora	aurora.org.au	4201
MO QU AC MI NB	206.103.114.13	4201
BattleStar MUSH	consider.ferris.edu	4201
	161.57.201.5	4201
Belior Rising	BRAZIL-NUT.ENMU.EDU	4301
	198.59.108.172	4301
Bloodletting	piaget.psych.mun.ca	4991
	134.153.20.10	4991
*Castle D'Image (CDI)	gs67.sp.cs.cmu.edu	5555
CO NB OA FA	128.2.203.147	5555
ChromeMUSH	colossus.acusd.edu	4444
	192.195.155.200	4444
Concrete Dreams	jaguar.velox.com	6250
	204.157.47.2	6250
CrystalMUSH	moink.NMSU.Edu	6886
	128.123.70.22	6886
Darkweb	telmaron.com	6251
	204.180.173.2	6251
Deep Seas	muds.okstate.edu	6250
	139.78.113.1	6250
DeltaMUSH	premier1.net	1701
	204.157.151.3	1701
DinerMUSH	cow.net	1812
	204.96.52.4	1812
Double Cross	coyotes.snni.com	6250
	165.113.174.4	6250
DragonLance	harker.dnaco.net	6666
	206.150.232.50	6666
*Elendor	elendor.sbs.nau.edu	1892
	134.114.66.33	1892

MUD Key Codes (if available)	Hostname IP Address	Port
Enchanted Path	agora.ualr.edu	1212
	144.167.9.253	1212
Garou	cesium.clock.org	7000
	17.255.4.43	7000
GateWorld	harker.dnaco.net	6250
	206.150.232.50	6250
Global MUSH	lancelot.cif.rochester.edu	4201
	128.151.220.22	4201
Idyll Mountain	ayla.idyllmtn.com	4201
	206.16.238.1	4201
Ierne Island	MSERV1.WIZVAX.NET	6000
	199.181.141.2	6000
Imbris [German]	sun1.lrz-muenchen.de	6250
MO MR FA	129.187.10.86	6250
Invocations	chaos.k2nesoft.com	7777
	205.164.147.30	7777
Jurassic Weyr	adamwest.INS.CWRU.Edu	6250
	129.22.8.52	6250
Kingdom Come	aurasun2.aura-philips.com	3231
	204.162.236.21	3231
LA by Night	peacedove.org	1995
	137.159.177.113	1995
Legacies	nile.wizvax.net	4201
	199.181.141.2	4201
Living Fiction	purple.cow.net	8888
	204.96.52.10	8888
Lost Tribes	gargoyle.duadmin.du.edu	1066
	130.253.208.80	1066
Magic MUSH	heaven.hamline.edu	4201
	138.192.2.89	4201
MystHaven	madant.med.wayne.edu	4201
	146.9.3.251	4201
NeverEnding Story	snowhite.ee.pdx.edu	9999
	204.203.65.60	9999
NexusWars	nexuswars.nexusprime.org	3050
	206.30.174.7	3050
Other	Other.org	4201

MUD Key Codes (if available)	Hostname IP Address	Port
	204.151.79.125	4201
Patternfall	misc.acf.nyu.edu	4444
	128.122.207.19	4444
Pax Magica	mellers1.psych.berkeley.edu	7911
	128.32.243.78	7911
PernWorld	ritchiesawyer.com	2222
AC FA	198.182.207.40	2222
PrairieMUSH	bluestem.prairienet.org	4201
	192.17.3.4	4201
Realtime	sati.pci.on.ca	6125
	207.0.177.103	6125
*Robotech	marvin.df.lth.se	2142
	194.47.252.42	2142
SacMUSH	sacmush.swac.edu	4201
	205.165.192.254	4201
Sanguinis Nobilis	master.tardis.ed.ac.uk	4444
	193.62.81.6	4444
Star Wars: Battle for Freedom	polkaroo.tor.hookup.net	4201
	165.154.46.2	4201
Strange New Worlds TrekMUSH	tsb.weschke.com	4201
MR PK QU CO OA SF	204.91.224.2	4201
Tales of Ta'veren	fly.ccs.yorku.ca	4201
	130.63.237.11	4201
TinyTIM	myelin.uchc.edu	5440
MO MR PK MC QU AC MI NB	155.37.1.251	5440
Trails MUCK	trails.velox.com	8888
	204.157.47.1	8888
Transformers 2005	aptlabta.wpi.edu	5555
	130.215.48.117	5555
Two Moons MUSH	twomoons.lupine.org	4201
	205.186.156.3	4201
Whispers and Dark Secrets	madant.med.wayne.edu	6250
	146.9.3.251	6250
WoD MUSH	sanctuary.isisnet.com	902
	199.126.216.70	902

MUD Key Codes (if available)	Hostname IP Address	Port
World of Pain	wop.atnet.it	6669
	194.184.37.3	6669
Xmush	oneworld.owt.com	3000
	204.118.6.2	3000
YakMUSH	ayla.idyllmtn.com	1800
	206.16.238.1	1800

TYPE mux (12)

No information available.

MUD Key Codes (if available)	Hostname IP Address	Port
Bhelliom	jpd.ch.man.ac.uk	4242
	130.88.12.119	4242
Chivalry	cadman.cit.buffalo.edu	7301
	128.205.10.15	7301
En Pace Requiescat	ruby.telmaron.com	9000
AC CO HO	204.180.173.11	9000
Gateway MUX	mserv1.wizvax.net	5600
	199.181.141.2	5600
Guardians	jitter.rahul.net	4205
	192.160.13.8	4205
Mayhem	thoth.anth.utep.edu	4201
	129.108.26.29	4201
Nightfall	telmaron.com	5250
	204.180.173.2	5250
Scotland	L4.eorbit.net	6250
	206.190.75.69	6250
Solar Realms	solrelms.netnet.net	7221
	198.70.64.3	7221
Verboden	adb.no.neosoft.com	6666
	206.27.187.132	6666
*Waterdeep MUX	risky.wcslc.edu	6666
	146.86.1.2	6666
Zone	fantasy.yab.com	4444
	204.94.255.9	4444

TYPE oxmud (1)

Unique, written from scratch, for those who liked MYST.

MUD Key Codes (if available)	Hostname IP Address	Port
Island	teaching4.physics.ox.ac.uk	2092
OA PK QU AC RH MI	163.1.245.204	2092

TYPE rom (34)

No information available.

MUD Key Codes (if available)	Hostname IP Address	Port
Aesir	asgard.ncsa.uiuc.edu	7000
MR AC	141.142.103.48	7000
Arcadia	arcadia.ior.com	4000
MO MR PK MC QU AC CO FA	199.79.239.13	4000
Beyond Reality	neworder.cc.uky.edu	1234
QU AC CO FA	128.163.18.198	1234
Bloodgeon MUD	irc.aohell.org	9000
MR PK QU AC CO FA	205.229.48.20	9000
Cage, The	wakko.gil.net	9000
MO MR PK AC CO MI	207.100.79.10	9000
Chicken's Den	snack.p.lodz.pl	7000
	194.92.218.66	7000
*Children of Jyhad	rds.nbn.net	5000
	199.234.116.210	5000
Creeping Death	hub.eden.com	6969
	199.171.21.21	6969
Dragon's Haven	puck.nether.net	9000
MR AC CO FA	198.108.59.10	9000
Electric Dreams	Dreams.Iceworld.Org	4000
	199.199.16.75	4000
Endless Nameless	mserv1.wizvax.net	4301
MO MR QU AC CO MI	199.181.141.2	4301
Eternal Twilight	dodo.crown.net	9000
	204.179.112.1	9000

MUD Key Codes (if available)	Hostname IP Address	Port
*Evil Intentions	evil.linex.com	9000
AC CO	206.54.38.12	9000
Great Hunt, The	wheel.imaginary.com	4000
	152.11.5.110	4000
Helliconia	mother.biolan.uni-koeln.de	9000
	134.95.209.4	9000
Imperium Gothique	pitek7.pitek.fi	4000
	194.137.40.7	4000
KindergardenMUD	oden.hjampis.kiruna.se	1234
	193.45.226.10	1234
Kingdom of Apracia	mud.hattiesburg.com	4000
	204.238.121.150	4000
Kundalimun	tarod.dataex.com	9000
MO MR PK QU AC CO	199.201.114.5	9000
Landsend	landsend.dfwmm.net	4000
	207.16.54.195	4000
Last Aerie, The	apache.wildstar.net	1212
	206.103.114.11	1212
MadRom	hector.turing.toronto.edu	1536
	128.100.5.10	1536
Maximum Adren	issi.com	4000
	204.157.167.1	4000
Oblivion	harker.dnaco.net	1234
	206.150.232.50	1234
Prophecy	alastor.pt.lu	9000
	194.154.198.2	9000
Puddle -o- MUD	amber.greenwing.edu	9000
	204.107.81.193	9000
Shadow	dark.nrg.dtu.dk	4000
MO MR CO AC OA	130.225.92.246	4000
Shadow Realms, The	realms.mat.net	9000
MO MR PK QU AC CO NB FA	205.252.122.1	9000
Stick in the MUD	mud.stick.org	9000
	205.147.201.200	9000
Tesseract	cie-2.uoregon.edu	9000
MO MR PK AC FA	128.223.36.161	9000

MUD Key Codes (if available)	Hostname IP Address	Port
TunFaire	wwic.wwic.com	7000
	206.81.50.10	7000
Wicked Winds	gameserver.digitaledge.com	6969
	206.129.64.102	6969
Worlds End	hub.eden.com	9000
MI NB CO AC QU	199.171.21.21	9000
Xania	tsunami.lgu.ac.uk	9000
	140.97.12.3	9000

TYPE silly (6)

No information available.

MUD Key Codes (if available)	Hostname IP Address	Port
Dimension Beucheft [Span/Eng]	dichato.dcc.uchile.cl	4000
	192.80.24.65	4000
*Formosa	db82.csie.ncu.edu.tw	4000
	140.115.50.82	4000
NexusMud	charon.cohprog.com	4000
	193.247.238.5	4000
Plague Mud, The	plague.gsini.net	4000
	206.20.43.1	4000
Renegade Outpost	outpost.cnct.com	9999
	165.254.118.47	9999
*Wintermute	env01.env.duke.edu	6666
	152.3.58.197	6666

TYPE talker (34)

A little closer to IRC than a MUD. Definitely a place to hang out and chat.

MUD Key Codes (if available)	Hostname IP Address	Port
*Addicted	spodbox.linux.org.uk	4444
	193.62.1.250	4444
Argoed	zippy.spods.dcs.kcl.ac.uk	3000

MUD Key Codes (if available)	Hostname IP Address	Port
	137.73.8.13	3000
Asylum	shore3.intercom.net	4242
	204.183.208.13	4242
Batcave	interline.com.au	4545
	203.20.62.1	4545
Brecktown	alisa.brecknet.com	5000
	205.218.11.134	5000
Cirrus Nebula	asterix.helix.net	4040
	205.233.118.2	4040
City, The	toybox.infomagic.com	4567
	165.113.211.4	4567
Crypt, The	fermi.bangor.ac.uk	3000
	147.143.16.221	3000
CyberCiist	alfa.ist.utl.pt	5555
	193.136.132.2	5555
DotUK	bungle.spods.dcs.kcl.ac.uk	6543
	137.73.8.17	6543
Dreamscape	honey.bernstein.com	4040
	206.20.83.33	4040
FantasyLand	cachenet.com	5050
	206.61.202.2	5050
Foothills	toybox.infomagic.com	2010
	165.113.211.4	2010
Forest	ftoomsh.progsoc.uts.edu.au	3000
	138.25.6.1	3000
Gathering, The	zippy.spods.dcs.kcl.ac.uk	5000
	137.73.8.13	5000
Grange, The	orangey-beard.csc.stu.mmu.ac.uk	3232
	149.170.191.10	3232
MBA4	jumper.mcc.ac.uk	3214
	130.88.202.26	3214
Mustang	mustang.us.dell.com	9173
	143.166.3.49	9173
Necropolis	phred.org	6660
	199.245.105.227	6660
Neo Chat	unix.neont.com	3456
	199.190.100.3	3456

MUD

Key Codes (if available)	Hostname IP Address	Port
*Olympus	bungle.spods.dcs.kcl.ac.uk	2123
	137.73.8.17	2123
Portugal Virtual	ciunix.uc.pt	6969
	192.84.13.103	6969
*Reality Bytes	servint.com	8686
	205.177.90.11	8686
Resort, The	evans.cudenver.edu	2323
	132.194.10.19	2323
Snowcrash	syrinx.rsabbs.com	2112
	204.180.235.10	2112
SomeWhere Else	wibble.merlin.net	2010
	208.128.75.10	2010
Spaghetti House	mangusta.unimo.it	5050
	155.185.2.42	5050
Surfers	surfers.itf.org.uk	4242
	194.128.66.29	4242
Tainted Love	escargot.com	4000
	204.157.220.233	4000
Tower	vivid.net	8008
	206.65.48.2	8008
TwiLIGHT One	sand.it.bond.edu.au	7777
	131.244.8.21	7777
Underworld	underworld.demon.co.uk	2010
	158.152.1.76	2010
Vineyard	vineyard.igc.net	4242
	207.89.0.40	4242
Void, The	benland.muc.edu	5555
	199.18.40.53	5555

TYPE teeny (1)

A tiny-lookalike chat MUD.

MUD

Key Codes (if available)	Hostname IP Address	Port
(EVIL!)Mud	nile.intac.com	4201
PK AC MI NB	198.6.114.2	4201

TYPE tiny (3)

The original chat MUD.

MUD

Key Codes (if available)	Hostname IP Address	Port
DragonMUD	tinylondon.ucsd.edu	4201
QU AC FA	132.239.1.7	4201
MetropolisMUD	psicorps.org	4201
	152.52.52.40	4201
Necropolis	cesium.clock.org	6250
	17.255.4.43	6250

13

GAME
NETWORKS

MANY computer games these days support head-to-head or multiplayer connectivity. This adds a whole new element to gameplay, since single-player or stand-alone games (involving AI, or artificial intelligence) are often predictable and redundant. There is little else to compare to the thrill of competing against other real, live human opponents whose actions are as unexpected and spontaneous as your own. The majority of us computer gamers do not have the luxury of network connectivity, and computer-to-computer modem play is fine; unfortunately, you have to find someone in your area to play against, or the long-distance costs would be astronomical. So, we turn to the online world to satisfy our multiplayer and head-to-head gaming desires. With online commercial services and the Internet, we can now play against someone else (or a group of people) anywhere in the world as if they were in the same room. But you have to decide what type of service you want—that is, what games do these networks offer, do you need Internet access too, and how much are you prepared to pay?

Commercial pay networks sprouted in the late 80s, when online gaming meant a slow modem connection to bulletin boards or a no-frills Internet FTP site to read up on how to beat Infocom's Planetfall or Sierra's Leisure Suit Larry. Today, some services are still dedicated to gaming alone (ImagiNation Network, MPG-Net, DWANGO),

while others offer exclusive games along with a milieu of other services such as news, e-mail, sports, chat groups, etc. (America Online, Compu-Serve, Genie, Prodigy). As the online population continues to increase, and as modem speeds climb, these commercial services can offer better games across many gaming genres. But the growth of the Internet, and especially the World Wide Web, has recently cast a shadow on some of these online pay networks. Most of these commercial companies will give you access to the Internet through their service, but it is becoming more common, and much cheaper, to simply pay a local Internet Service Provider for direct hook-up to the Net (which, generally speaking, have much better games). These fast-growing Internet game networks allow the gamer to play games through a standard TCP/IP connection and they support the hottest 3D action and real-time strategy titles on the market today. With better sound and graphics (since the majority of the work is stored, and executed, on your computer), these networks allow you to play your CD-ROM games against others: The Entertainment Network (TEN), Kali, DWANGO, XBAND PC, and Mplayer GameWay.

Now that you know how they differ, read on for the specifics for each network. Both commercial services and Internet game networks vary in price, service, and games; and both are battling tooth-and-nail for your attention. So which will it be?

America Online

Phone: 800-827-6364

Price: 15 hours free upon registration. Then $9.95 U.S. for five hours a month, $2.95 U.S. for each additional hour.

On the Web: http://www.aol.com/

America Online (AOL) supports 15 or so titles ranging from the popular graphical Advanced Dungeons & Dragons NeverWinter Nights to other text-based RPGs such as Gemstones III, Federation, and Modus Operandi. Although text-based, these games look good, with sleek colorful screens and clickable icons. In the adult space fantasy game Federation you have the opportunity to be whoever—or whatever—you want in this imaginary universe full of exciting and ever-changing worlds. If trivia's your thing, then leave the beer and chicken wings at the bar today and play NTN Trivia from home. Other trivia and game shows available include Strike-a-Match and ABC News Quiz.

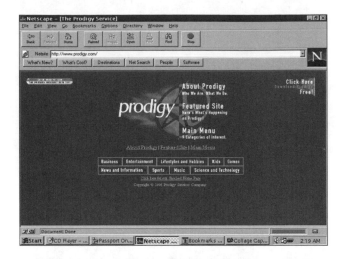

Prodigy

Phone: 800-776-3449

Price: $9.95 U.S. a month for five hours; $2.95 for each additional hour. Cheaper packages are also available.

On the Web: http://www.prodigy.com/

Unfortunately, Prodigy doesn't have much to offer real-time head-to-head enthusiasts other than the game of Checkers (no joke!). Single-player games, such as AJ Dakota & The Orb of Kings (a grid maze game reminiscent of Minesweeper for Windows), Match-it (Concentration-like game), MadMaze (a dungeon-crawler game), and Frantic Guts (a trivia game that costs you extra to play) seem extremely out-of-date . The best game, I suppose, is Prodigy's Baseball Manager (an MLBPA-licensed fantasy baseball league that will cost you $60.00 to $125.00 depending on your package and only runs from May to October). It is sad to say, but Java and Shockwave variations of most of these games are available on the Net for free.

The ImagiNation Network

Phone: 800-462-4461

Price: $9.95 U.S. for five hours, $1.95 to $2.95 U.S. per additional hour (depending on your membership package).

On the Web: http://www.inngames.com/

The ImagiNation Network (INN) is the oldest games-only online commercial service. Game software giants Sierra Online debuted INN in 1990 and now house over 30 multiplayer games, including Red Baron II (Dynamix's WWI air combat sim), Front Page Sports: Baseball Pro, the Incredible Machine 3, The Fate of Twinion (RPG), The Ruins of Cawdor (RPG), Trophy Bass 2, 3D Golf, MissionForce: CyberStorm, and a host of interactive card and board games (Backgammon, Bridge, Checkers, Chess, Cribbage, Euchre, Gin Rummy, Hearts, Poker, Reversi, and Spades). Through INN's 3D online community, CyberPark, you choose an avatar (virtual representation of yourself) and "walk" around in and visit the entire gaming virtual community and try out the wide selection of games. One of the best of the commercial online services, since games have always been their main focus.

GEnie

Phone: 800-638-9636

Price: $8.95 U.S. a month for four hours, $2.95 for each additional hour.

On the Web: http://www.genie.com/

GEnie has many text-based games available on other online networks such as Gemstones III, Federation, Modus Operandi, NTN Trivia, and the Island of Kesmai, but the majority of GEnie players indulge in head-to-head combat with the popular SVGA Warrior, CyberStrike, Multiplayer BattleTech (an older EGA Mech game), and Harpoon. Other games include the strategic Stellar Emperor and Hundred Years War; a text-based RPG game, Dragon's Gate; and a football coaching "call the next play" game called QBI. Overall, a fairly good selection of games (25 or so multiplayer titles), with rumors of Parallax/Interplay's Descent, Dragon's Tale, and Armored Assault also on the horizon.

CompuServe

Phone: 800-433-0389

Price: $9.95 U.S. for five hours per month, $2.95 U.S. for each additional hour, cheaper packages also offered.

On the Web: http://www.compuserve.com/

As with Prodigy, you wonder if games were a priority at all in the design of this commercial online network. CompuServe has a few games to select from, but they are much older games (some are even seven or eight years old—in other words, *ancient* in computer game years) such as Air Traffic Controller, MegaWars (strategic space sim), Sniper! (multiplayer WWII combat sim), Island of Kesmai, You Guessed It (more trivia!), British Legends, Classic Adventure, Black Dragon, and CastleQuest (text-based adventure games). Only a few mentioned have graphical front ends, and most are single-player as well. Not a strong contender as a gaming network against its online competitors.

Delphi

Phone: 800-695-4005

Price: 10 hours free upon registration.

10/4 Plan—$10.00 U.S. per month includes the first four hours of use each month. Additional use is $4.00 U.S. per hour. 20/20 Advantage Plan—$20.00 U.S. per month includes the first 20 hours of use each month. Additional use is $1.80 U.S. per hour.

On the Web: http://www.delphi.com/

A few different gaming genres to choose from, including the multiplayer Air Warrior and Flight Simulator, or the Fantasy Sports leagues (baseball, hockey, football, and basketball). Single-player games include chess, poker, and trivia. As with AOL, CompuServe, and Prodigy, this network, or online club, is designed to give the surfer more than just games: news, file libraries, business and finance happenings, and more. However, it is not a good representation of a solid gaming network by any stretch.

Interactive Creations, Inc.

Price: Five hours free upon sign-up, then $10.00 U.S. a month plus $1.75 U.S. or $2.00 U.S. per hour (depending on provider).

On the Web: http://www.icigames.com/

Interactive Creations Inc. (ICI) has developed one of the most popular multiplayer WWII flight combat sims online to date—Warbirds. Rivaling GEnie's SVGA Air Warrior and INN's Red Baron, Warbirds can be played (on DOS or Windows) with up to 100 opponents, with little or no visible frame-rate depreciation. On a Pentium, you can run the game at 1024x768 and still achieve more than 20 frames per second. Log onto your Internet Service Provider first, then Telnet to their page (if you choose CRIS, or Concentric Research Corp., it'll be cheaper). The new Planetary Riders is also available now at ICI—a Windows 95 and Macintosh PPC space battle sim with 3D sound, 256-color graphics at 1024x768, and free tech support. For more on Warbirds, see Chapter 6 on Simulation Games.

DWANGO

Phone: 713-467-8865

Price: $7.95 U.S. for five hours a month, plus $19.00 U.S. for an extra 10 hour block, $34.00 U.S. for 20 hours and $59.00 U.S. for 40 hours (any unused hours will carry over from month to month).

On the Web: http://www.dwango.com/ enter.html

DWANGO stands for Dial-up Wide-Area Network Gaming Operation. To log onto a DWANGO server, you simply download the client software found on their Web page; make sure you have at least a 14.4 baud modem and one of the supported CD-ROM games. They have set up 25+ servers in most of the larger North American cities, so the gamer logs on and finds opponents on the same server to play against (although near-future plans include linking all servers across the nation together). DWANGO also supports the BIG commercial releases, but you may have to

download the free patch available on their Web page. The game line-up is as follows (big breath here): Doom, Doom II, Ultimate Doom, Final Doom, Heretic, Hexen, Descent, Big R ed Racing, Warcraft II, Terminal Velocity, and NetMech, with card and sports games to come in the near future. DWANGO has a fast response time, and rates are even less than what you'd pay for a commercial online service. The only drawback is that you have to live in one of the major metropolitan centers of North America (and now in Tokyo, Japan!) if you don't want to spend long-distance charges. Current servers are listed below:

Table 13.1: DWANGO Servers to Date

Austin, TX	Oakland
Boston	Philadelphia
Chicago (2)	Phoenix
Dallas	San Diego
Denver	San Francisco
Detroit	San Jose
Houston	Seattle
Los Angeles	Shreveport, LA
Miami	St. Louis
Minneapolis	Tokyo, Japan (new!)
Montreal, Canada	Washington, DC
New York	Western Massachusetts

MPlayer GameWay

Price: TBA
On the Web: http://www.mplayer.com/
Enter the big bad World Wide Web. Mplayer Game-Way is the fastest Web-based online gaming service with real-time voice conferencing and contains the hottest titles: Command and Conquer, Quake, Mech-warrior 2, Terminal Velocity, Warcraft, Chaos Over-lords, Big Red Racing, Deadlock, Havoc, and SimCity 2000. To run Mplayer you must first download the free client software (or get their free CD-ROM sent to you), own a game from the list above, and have the following system requirements: Windows 95, Pentium processor, 8MB of RAM (16MB highly recommend-ed), a 16-bit sound card supported by Windows 95, a 14.4Kbps or faster modem (or a direct Internet con-nection through a LAN), and an Internet service pro-vider account. Go on a virtual tour to see how things work at Mplayer and point your browser to http://www.mplayer.com/about/about-virtual-tour.html.

By the time you read this, MPlayer may have already merged with another big Internet gaming network XBAND PC—go to http://www.xband.com for details.

TEN—The Entertainment Network

Price: TBA
On the Web: http://www.ten.net/
One of the best Internet gaming networks designed specifically for fast and fierce multiplayer action. Game fanatics hang out and play for free against each other with the TEN software bundled with most gaming magazines and many game CD-ROMs these days. You may also download it here for immediate connectivity. TEN supports such popular titles as CivNet, Panzer General, Warcraft, Deadlock, Terminal Velocity, Dark Sun, and Duke Nukem 3D (exclusive rights!). Like many other gaming networks, most of the games will be included for free on the disc. TEN can be reached through any ISP (Internet Service Provider) which provides a TCP/IP (PPP or SLIP account). If need be, TEN will also assist members in finding a fast enough service provider for high-speed play. Read the TEN FAQ for more information at www.ten.net/Pub-licTENFAQ.html. A hip and well-designed service with a strong future.

XBAND PC

Price: Free, for now, but other options (tournaments, contests, voice chat, league play, and celebrity opponents) will cost from $.50 U.S. to $5.00 U.S. to participate.
On the Web: http://www.xband.com/

Catapult's XBAND is no stranger to TV console multiplayer gaming, and they recently have dived into the PC and Internet market. Look for the "Play It on XBAND" logo on the packaging of your newer CD-ROMs, which means set-up should be a snap (right now XBAND PC is available on copies of the Windows 95 versions of Doom 2, Ultimate Doom, and Final Doom). Similar to how TEN works, you will need Windows 95, a 486 or Pentium processor, 9600 baud modem or higher, at least 8MB RAM, and an Internet Service Provider (ISP). Catapult has developed RAPID (Reduced-latency And Predictable Internet Delivery)—technology that significantly minimizes latency while improving overall gaming performance over a TCP/IP network. Games supported are Doom II, Final Doom, Ultimate Doom, Mechwarrior 2, Hexen, and Warcraft. Their exclusive rights line-up is equally as impressive: Locus, Marathon 2: Durandal (awesome game), Hardball 5 , Star Control 3, and Super Street Fighter II.

AUTHOR'S PICK

Kali

Price: $20.00 U.S.(one-time fee after free 15 minutes is up).
On the Web: http://www.axxis.com/kali/

Kali is the largest multiplayer gaming network, supporting over 25 games, 40,000+ users, and 100 servers in 23 countries. By downloading Kali's server software for either DOS, OS/2, Windows 95, or the Mac, you can partake in deadly head-to-head games against anyone, anywhere in the world on the Net (with a TCP/IP network connection). Kali is shareware and is free for a limited time, then a nominal fee is required for continued use (only $20.00 U.S. and you are registered for life). Whether your specialty is Action, Strategy, or Sports games, get this software and take advantage of what Kali has to offer the modern gamer. Speed will depend on your modem's capabilities, but I suggest having at least a 28.8Kpbs or higher. See the following list of current games available on Kali.

List of Kali-Supported Games

Apache	Mortal Kombat 3
Big Red Racing	NetMech (Win95 & DOS)
Command & Conquer	Quake
Descent	Rise of the Triad
Descent 2	Super Karts
Doom	Terminal Velocity
Doom II	Top Gun
Duke Nukem 3D	VR Pool
EF2000	Warcraft
Heretic	Warcraft 2
Hexen	

MPG-Net
Phone: 305-296-6665
Price: $9.95 U.S. a month (first month $4.95 U.S.).
On the Web: http://www.mpgn.com/
The Florida-based Multi-Player Games Network (MPG-Net) is another good, but underrated, Internet-based network with cool, addictive games. Titles such as The Kingdom of Drakkar (graphical Tolkien-like fantasy RPG), Empire Builder (award-winning single-player or multiplayer strategy board game), and Operation Market Garden (gorgeous top-down war game) are available here along with many more. MPG-Net works through your regular PPP or SLIP account connection from your Internet Service Provider. Download the Windows 95 system-access software with all the games first to your hard drive (25.8MB), read reviews, indulge on an online game tour, or visit their Resource Center—all from their Web page. They also house forums, e-mail, a library, links, and a virtual conference room.

14

GAMING E-ZINE SITES OR MAGAZINE'S ONLINE EDITIONS

ENJOY perusing through these magazine and e-zine pages—there are quite a few to choose from. E-zines (or electronic magazines) are those published exclusively on the Net. Magazine Web sites are a paper magazine's online counterpart to supplement, or replicate, its print version. Both have lots to offer the avid gamer, but we visit these pages for the style and vibe of the particular group of writers. Fresh articles and a subjective analysis of hot games by us gamers are often more trustworthy than the company press hype. Free games, cheats, FAQs, and chat groups are also usually provided here.

Amiga Power
http://www.futurenet.co.uk/

Part of FutureNet, the UK magazine empire, Amiga Power, "a magazine with an attitude," is a fresh look at an often shunned gaming system (well, in North America, anyway). Mostly reviews, news, and features are provided for Amiga games and other utilities. Articles are also taken from FutureNet's Amiga Format, Amiga Power, and Amiga Shopper magazines also found at http://www.futurenet.co.uk/. Subscription orders and past issues are also available with a valid credit card.

Burn Out
http://www.america.com/~mrfritz/BurnOut/

A refreshing angle towards news, reviews, previews, and downloads. All are available at this dynamic online electronic magazine; you can also visit the Top 10 PC and video games section, vote for your faves, or spend some time at "Gumshoe" (don't ask...just go there). The on-line gaming article is informative (August 1996), and I certainly enjoyed the nostalgic 8-bit console system "blast from the past" write-up as well. Creatively done.

Coming Soon Magazine
http://www.megatoon.com/~t15/

The online counterpart to the paper magazine *Coming Soon,* specializing in 3DO, PSX, PC, and Sega Saturn games. This popular Web site is best known, and used,

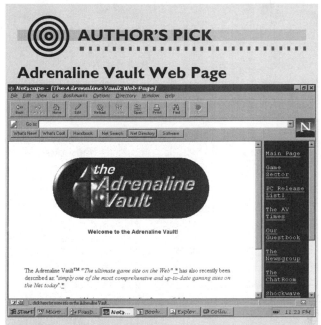

AUTHOR'S PICK

Adrenaline Vault Web Page

http://www.avault.com/

A beautiful award-winning page such as this only comes along once in a while. Plenty of time and labor went into designing Adrenaline Vault, and only the newest and hottest games are featured here. Plunge into the various side-bar columns here such as The Game Sector, The AV Times, Shockwave and Java-based real-time gaming, chat arenas, Newsgroups, links, and a new releases list. Each demo or shareware game outlined for download is color-coded to signify if it has a cheat code, FAQ, spotlight, or reviewed counterpart. This is one of only a small handful of sites I would recommend to hard-core gamers to have as their start-up page on the Net, so it goes here when signing on.

for its game reviews and previews. It's good to know there's somewhere to go to find out if it's worth spending $50.00 on the newest game. Coming Soon has added quite a few PC games to their site, including industry news and a Top 100 chart. Interviews with developers and a live chat room are also regular features here. Visit their Company Web site page to hot link to all your fave gaming manufacturers.

Competitive Edge Magazine
http://www.quiknet.com/oss/index1.html

Publishers One Small Step have brought board, card, and box game fans Fox One, Rebel Yell and Battlechrome. Competitive Edge (CE) magazine offline packages these complete games, and others, and provides strategy tips, interviews, and new scenarios for older CE games. This Web site serves as a background to their games and includes pictures, bonus missions, scenarios, and an online store.

Computer Game Review
http://www.nuke.com/cgr/cgr.htm

A nicely arranged and informative page for computer game review, previews, and game demos. Computer Game Review (CGW) always seems to get the low-down in their exclusive interviews, and they also shine in their valuable Strategy section. CGW also houses the CyberCents server which uses Kali—the head-to-head software to play your favorite arcade games against anyone on the Internet. Also check out their Radioactive Links (other related sites) and Ground Zero (downloads). Small fonts and detailed screen shots give this page a modern feel.

Edge
http://www.futurenet.co.uk/

This UK magazine's Web site is dedicated to any electronic gaming fan whether your preference is computer, console, or arcade systems. The Edge (self-pronounced "the future of interactive entertainment") has a colorful and effective design and brings fresh gaming content to its visitors. Each page offers reviews, behind-the-scenes scoops and previews, contests, hints n' tips, charts, and other eye-catching headlines. One such article dives into the world of game music and another is on computer art. What else would you expect from FutureNet's award-winning paper publication?

AUTHOR'S PICK

Computer Games Strategy Plus Online

http://www.cdmag.com/

A well-designed and content-rich site that complements its paper counterpart. Much effort and talent has gone into this Web page, which offers surfers a plethora of game genre previews, reviews, and hot downloads. SP Online is updated often with current industry news, contests, chat groups, and an online store. If this isn't enough, check out SP's vast archive section and download hundreds of past playable demo favorites broken down by gaming genre. Keep in mind, strategy tips are this magazine's forte, so make sure you take advantage of the many free downloadable hints on all sorts of computer games. This handsome site is definitely worthy of a permanent bookmark on your browser.

AUTHOR'S PICK

Computer Gaming World

http://www.zdnet.com/gaming/

Computer Gaming World (CGW) is an outstanding online counterpart to an ever-more outstanding paper publication, truly one of the most respected authorities on computer games from both the maker's and purchaser's side of this booming industry. The layout of the front page is very simple and text-oriented, but content is this Web site's biggest attribute: covering the latest scoops on PC games, reviews, previews, screen shots, FAQs, add-ons, secrets, surveys, strategy sections, patches, demos, and hot links. Peruse the current paper issue and exclusive articles for the CGW Web site alone, or browse through the archived collection of past issues. Bonus: Their well-organized Shareware section allows you to read the CGW review of the game prior to download.

Electric Shorts
http://www.win.net/~tybeelytes/chipnet/s7toc.html

A plain game and utility site that has some interesting Doom info and game reviews by John Di Saia. Although Electric Shorts has a cool "Doom Wad of the Month" section, you cannot download it here—the appropriate file name and FTP site is given only. Not much here peaked my interest, even though a Pamela Anderson WAD file for Doom II was retrieved on my visit!

Electronic Gaming Monthly
http://www.nuke.com/egm/egm.htm

This site possesses the identical graphical and content layout as the Computer Game Review site (also housed by the spiffy Nuke InterNetwork), but this time for console games. The latest and greatest for the PlayStation, Saturn, Nintendo 64, 3DO, and Jaguar is presented in print, but also in Real Audio and various video formats. The online version of the paper magazine contains a wealth of information: reviews, previews, interviews, and best of all—cool strategy tips and secrets to get through even the toughest games.

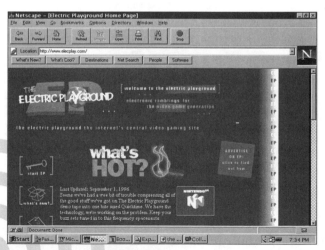

Electronic Playground
http://www.elecplay.com/

"Electronic Ramblings for the Video Game Generation." Slick Canadian e-zine with news, reviews, and previews of all TV gaming console systems, PC, Mac, arcade games, and hand-held units. Excellent graphics and animation (not just on their intro page, either) make this site entertaining to navigate though. When you cut through the glam you find some very informative features here (check out their non-gaming Sights, Sounds, and Syllables area too). You may have heard of the Electronic Playground from their U.S. and Canada television show of the same name.

Enemy Lock On!—The Military Flight Sim Magazine
http://www.webcom.com/elomag/

The Enemy Lock On (ELO!) UK print publication is read by flight sim fanatics in over 30 countries, and this Web site previews the material to be found in those pages. While at ELO! Online, download game patches, read many articles from past issues, hot-link through related links, or subscribe online. ELO! is delivered six times a year anywhere in the world.

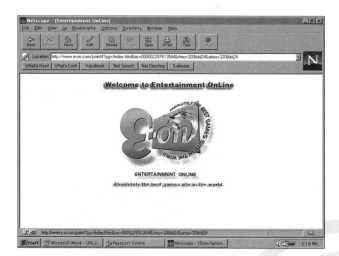

Entertainment Online
http://www.e-on.com/

Well, I may not agree that this Web site is "absolutely the best games site in the world" as their home page boasts, but it is unquestionably up there. Launched in early July 1996 by UK partners Mark Bernstein and Hermann Hauser, E-Online is a fresh, new, kaleidoscopic and informative mega-site. E-Online promises to be the definitive online entertainment channel for

the entire family. On the downside, however, there is a pay option for formal subscription, which carries the bulk of the Web site's gaming offerings. With reliance on sleek design powered by Silicon Graphics Webforce, this may very well be one of the premiere entertainment sites to look for in the years to come.

Escapade
http://www.escapade.com/

This Web e-zine describes itself as "The No-nonsense Guide to Interactive Electronic Entertainment," and that is *exactly* what it is. No logging in or subscribing is necessary—just up-to-date information to satisfy your multiplayer gaming needs. Provocative articles and amusing features spice up this site. While visiting this page you get the warm sense of a tight online gaming community. There is a lot to see and do here and this site proves you don't need a lot of advertising or money behind you to produce a concise specialized gaming site. A job well done!

Fun Online
http://www.egmont.de/:///www.egmont.de/

A German e-zine dedicated to covering PC games directed at kids. This site is heavy on selling these CD-ROMs but also includes a Hints n' Tips section, tech support, and a modem list of others like-minded for some head-to-head action. A cartoon alligator is your host here for Fun Online!, who will take you to other fun areas such as real-time Java games and a Top 10 list.

Other German E-Zines

PC Player Magazine
http://www.pcplayer.de/

SpieleNews
http://www.spielenews.com/

Zox-Up
http://www.heiend.com/zoxup/

Power Play
http://www.magnamedia.de/powplay/index.html

In Fusion
http://www.infusion.de/

GamesMania: German Edition
http://www.gamesmania.com/cgi-bin/german/
default.cgx

click for the full story. The Game Stuff area has some interesting trinkets such as game music, Hocus Pocus (cheats/codes), and reader survey Most Wanted games by platform.

Game Cabinet, The
http://www.gamecabinet.com/

Ken Tidwell's monthly gaming Web zine covers many other forms of amusement rather than computer games. Family, strategy, role-playing, board, and miniature games are featured here. With a dozen or so contributors, this is a *different* Web site worthy of a closer look. Game news, reviews, language game rules translations, an interactive mail box, and purchase information for most of the games highlighted.

Game Fan Online
http://www.gamefan.com/

Another impressive online counterpart to the colorful Game Fan publication focusing on console, hand-held, and PC games. Right off the bat a clickable large graphical image takes the surfer to the various pages: Hot Info, Reviews, Downloads, Mailroom, and Game Stuff. News is broken up into daily industry headlines and is laid out chronologically, so if a caption appeals to you,

Game Japan
http://www.rcp.co.jp/recca/

A weekly English and Japanese e-zine from Tokyo, Japan. Every issue has a top story, gossip section, game archive, links, mailing list, and a "hot release" area. Don't mind if the English isn't completely up-to-par—you'll get the gist of the what the articles are getting at. This crisp 'n colorful PC- and Mac-based publication is brought to you by Recca-sha Inc. Also note their PC Top 40 download page and Top 100 Video game chart.

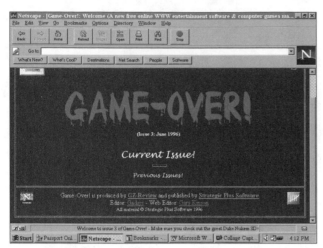

Game-Over!
http://www.ftech.net/~strat/index.htm

A cool free UK-based online zine dedicated to computer gaming. A scrolling newsreel runs at the bottom of your browser, and large screen shot graphics grace the main page. This e-zine contains PC game reviews, and other features (The War Room, Re-boot, and On the Grapevine) are broken into the specific games themselves. Game-Over! is designed well and its Links section contains some serious game-related lists.

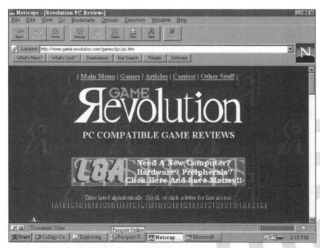

Game Revolution Magazine
http://www.game-revolution.com/

An e-zine glorifying Saturn, PlayStation, Mac, and PC games. The Revolution is a fun site with personalized

options such as frames and a keyword search to get right to games of interest. Dividing between computer and console games, this page provides gaming news, reviews, contests and other tidbits such as a Q & A, press releases, and hot links. The Game Revolution magazine is an elementary and descriptive Web page. Check out their Quake bestiary section.

Game Review, The
http://ns2.clever.net/~ionizer/

The Game Review is a weekly gaming mag released every Sunday at 5pm EST. This ambitious online zine contains raw and unbiased opinions on the PC game products available today. A neat option here is that you can download the edition you are interested in to read offline if you wish, *or* you can submit your e-mail address if you wish to have it automatically sent to you. The Game Review is proud to be the longest running and most popular weekly *Warez* (hacked or cracked game available on the Net) mag/review publication. The issues themselves are bare-bones text, but the flavor and cunning approach to these games keep you not only interested, but enthralled.

Gamers Online
http://www.neca.com/~online/gamers-online.htm

Platform systems such as Nintendo, Sega, and Sony consoles are highlighted here, and the staff of Gamers Online offer previews, reviews, features, and game listings on all the hottest TV systems today. This site is easy to navigate through and game fans can download movie clips or save screen shots on new titles or older classic standbys. Cheats and Top 10 lists are also available, as well as a small PC section.

Gamer's Zone
http://www.worldvillage.com/wv/gamezone/html/gamezone.htm

World Village's popular online gaming section caters to almost 1,000,000 registered citizens! For those of you who are not familiar with World Village, it is a

World Wide Web society allowing members to enjoy, for free, its many areas…facets of a real community such as a Chapel (religious studies), Café (chat groups), School House (educational software and articles), and of course, the Gamer's Zone. Enjoy cool online real-time games such as Web Jotto, Mozart's Musical Dice, MYST Trivia Challenge, and the new online graphical epic adventure entitled Sanctuary. Great World Village exclusive games in a modern and friendly entertaining environment.

Games First

http://www.turbonet.com/games/

This online publication caters to the computer game fanatic. The Just Out and PC Tech Tips sections are handy and informative, as are the huge game indices broken into numerous categories. Games First has a five-member staff not including the contributing authors. This Web site is arranged well, and I particularly liked the classic shareware, new demos, and PC charts of download distinctions.

GamesMaster

http://www.futurenet.co.uk/

Welcome to Britain's best-selling video games magazine. This Web site is fairly plain considering its colorful paper cousin, but the cutting-edge reviews, news, and major strategy section are rich in content. PC, Amiga,

AUTHOR'S PICK

GamesMania

http://www.gamesmania.com/cgi-bin/ english/default.cgx

GamesMania is a crisp and colorful multilingual gaming e-zine. Whether your preference is English, Italian, Japanese, or German, you can access insightful gaming news, reviews and previews, contests, demos, and a great Tech Support and Developers page. The layout and design of this cutting-edge page is bright and attractive, and I could see why this site has been rewarded with "the most resourceful" gaming site on the Net. Definitely one to bookmark as a favorite to keep up-to-date on all your computer gaming news and more. Much more…

and console systems are all equally attended to, and the many articles will provide many hours of material to sift through for the electronic gaming enthusiast. As with other FutureNet products here, you can order a subscription or read past issues online.

Games Online Zine
http://www.magicnet.net/~postman/games_online/

An e-zine devoted to games of all sorts. PC, Mac, console, and online RPG games are covered and reviewed by various writers. Heavy on feedback and reader interaction, this site focuses on providing the visitor with an all-around comprehensive gaming encounter. Not much to look at, but heavy on filling and variety.

Games Update
http://www.gamesupdate.com/

You know you're in for a treat when you are notified right away what browser plug-ins you will need to get the most out of a site. The Games Update Web zine gives the gamer current news and gossip, downloads, videos, a top 10, and give-aways—all related to home console, handheld, and PC games. Other non-game-related articles were found in the news section as a bonus (e.g. DVD technology and other high-tech movie and educational happenings). Check out the N-64 movies to download.

Game Wire
http://www.gamepen.com/gamewire/

Joshua Arnold, Editor-in-Chief's, e-zine is affiliated with The Game Pen site at http://www.gamepen.com/, so you know this site *has* to be good. Game Wire is a gamer's mecca, with attractive laid-out sections: downloads, news, reviews, links, interviews, and more. Sleek design and informative articles grace this zine's pages. Mac, PC, and console game fans will have lots to see and do here. Cool sections include Center Stage (inside industry news) and the Wall (bios, Game Wire networks, screen shots, etc.).

Geracao Digital—Revista de Games
http://www.roadnet.com.br/gd/

Geracao Digital is a Brazilian magazine's Web site honoring PC, console, and arcade games. Completely in Spanish, this page is a hip, modern site with colorful graphics, animations, and frames (if you choose). Many

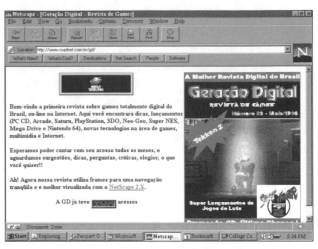

in-depth reviews, online chats, strategy tips, and links are available here if you have Netscape 2.0 or higher as a browser.

Inside Mac Games
http://www.imgmagazine.com/

Inside Mac Games is a beautifully detailed magazine site whose sleek appearance is only second to its content. Mac addicts can access the newest info on their favorite games, flip through the online archives of past issues, order games directly, contribute to the voting booth, or scan the many game and Mac-related links around the world. Readers and subscribers of the paper editions (and bundled CD-ROM) will find other useful and entertaining information here.

Other Related Mac Sites of Interest

Apple Computer
http://www.info.apple.com/

Networkable Mac Games
http://www.AmbrosiaSW.com/netgames/

MacWorld
http://www.macworld.com/

MacSense
http://www.macsense.com/home.html

MacUser
http://www.zdnet.com/macuser/

MacWeek
http://www.macweek.com/

Cyberian Outpost
http://www.cybout.com/cyberian.html

Intelligent Gamer Online, The
http://igonline.escape.com/

This is the online counterpart to the printed magazine most noteworthy for its industry news and console-gaming previews. IGO offers those without fast connections a text-only option of their page—a rare consideration these days. IGO is a light site with not much content, but the Discussion Forums for Sega, 3DO, Atari, Nintendo, or Playstation games may be of interest.

NEXT Generation
http://www.next-generation.com/

The online version of Imagine Publishing's successful print mag is a solid and resourceful console and computer gamer's Eden. The NEXT page is constantly updated and tweaked for its many visitors and boasts news, reviews, previews, screen shots, forums, charts, demos, contests, and Q & A sections. Heavily leaning toward TV console systems, this is a worthwhile site for any 32- or 64-bit systems such as the Sony PlayStation, Sega Saturn, Nintendo 64, or Matsushita M2 player. PC and Mac gamers really need not apply here.

Online Gaming Review
http://www.ogr.com/

A savvy page that gets thousands of hits per day. Dedicated to the mature PC Gamer, Online Game Review (OGR) started out in the fall of 1995 with a mission to provide up-to-date and honest reviews and news of PC games for their many visitors. Columns, editorials, and in-depth coverage on the gaming industry and Internet happenings as a whole are also looked at among cheats, hints, tips, and FAQs for games of all genres. A very good Web zine site.

OS/2 Games Home Page
http://www.austin.ibm.com:80/os2games/

IBM sponsors this much-needed games page for OS/2 Warp users and programmers. Their goal is to offer OS/2 game-related information tips to both game players and developers wishing to combine the power of OS/2 Warp with PC-based games. Important sections are "Running DOS & Windows games on OS/2" and "Native OS/2 Consumer Products" (such as SimCity and SimCity 2000).

PC ACE Online
http://www.fogstudios.com/pcace/pcace.html

An online counterpart to the print mag PC Ace. Read reviews of the hottest PC flight sim games (among other genres), get behind-the-scenes news on current and upcoming titles, find out how to tweak your Windows 95 to support better flight sticks, or fill out subscription information. PC ACE Online lets you preview what you'd find in their paper publication with readable columns such as "Over There" and "PC ACE Academy."

PC Firestorm
http://wings.buffalo.edu/~mfs2/

Headed by Max Stewart and Jeff White, PC Firestorm is one of the more down-to-earth and non-intimidating e-zines around, written by University of Buffalo students. They maintain their PC game reviews are unbiased since these are the same people buying the games—the articles are honest and accurate. Their downloads section has been influenced (and contributed to) by the folks at the mega Games Domain site. Don't forget to check out the far-reaching links area as well.

PC Gamer—UK edition
http://www.futurenet.co.uk/

Another worldwide magazine giant has an excellent Web page (as with all the other FutureNet paper gaming publications: Sega Power, Amiga Format, Edge). Big colorful buttons, charming graphics, and acute game reviews grace these pages. These extensive sections (Hot Lists, Classics, Best of the Rest, Guidelines, Hardware, and more) are comparable to how big the paper edition of this magazine is (have you ever held one of these puppies?). Past issues and an online subscription (with valid credit card) are also available.

AUTHOR'S PICK
PC Gamer

http://www.pcgamer.com/

One of the better magazine sites on the Web today. This is the online counterpart to the North American version of the PC Gamer mag from Imagine publishing. Keen and discerning writers preview and review the hottest games and provide many strategy tips for their guests. A newspaper feel on their front page is effective (columns, headlines), and their left-framed sidebar allows the visitor to steer to 20 or so destinations. These include the contents of the current paper issue, next issue, and bundled CD-ROM. Moreover, chats, forums, downloads, cheat codes, links, feedback, and industry news are all available…and more. This is a Grade-A Web site worthy of countless returns.

PC Games Online
http://www.pcgamesmag.com/

Another nicely arranged Web site to serve as a supplement to a fine print magazine. A good use of frames organizes the many game reviews, cheats, behind-the-scenes developments, and a rich archive section. As with most of the other Web sites that have paper counterparts, you can subscribe online and offer useful feedback for the publishers. A clean and user-friendly PC games site, especially for newer gamers or computer novices.

PC Industry and Entertainment News
http://www.mbay.net/~dtingley/

Scott Tingley has created a fairly humble online center for game news, reviews, previews, demos, patches, and links. Most sections have stated "Under Construction" for some time now, but perhaps Scott will finish off his computer gaming pages sooner than later.

PlayStation Power
http://www.futurenet.co.uk/

UK magazine's shrine to the Sony PlayStation console system. The paper press is heavily geared toward previews, reviews, and playing tips, but PlayStation Power's online relative is very light and scarce in content. A few articles are available for perusal, but not much else is here. I thought this might be a ploy to purchase the glossy paper mag, but even the past issues have little substance. I would stick to FutureNet's other related magazine, Official UK PlayStation Magazine, also at http://www.futurenet.co.uk/.

AUTHOR'S PICK

PC Multimedia and Entertainment Magazine

http://www.mortimer.com/users/pcme/

Award-winning PCME site is an avid gamer's heaven. Tons of content and graphics in many areas of gaming will keep any visitor's attention for quite a long time here. Besides up-to-the-minute news and behind-the-scenes previews, you can also capture downloads, reviews, strategy guides, chat and discussion forums, exclusives, patches, interviews, links, and give-aways (catch all that?). Depending on your tastes, zap over to the Adrenaline Zone (3D games), Fantasy Zone (Adventure and RPGs), Strike Zone (Simulation and Combat games), and others. Sections on hardware and educational/children's software are an added asset here. Michael Bendner exhibits his acute know-how on the PC gaming scene and delivers it with sleek organization. This site is optimized for Netscape 2.0+ in 640x480 mode using at least 64,000 colors.

Pulse and The Puppy Press, The

http://www.happypuppy.com/pulse/
index.html

An informative and interactive zine brought to you by the people at Happy Puppy headquarters. PC, Mac, and TV console reviews, Q & A, strategy advice, and older archived collections are accessible here. Internal quick-links shoot to other sections of the Happy Puppy realm of gaming goodies. Plain-looking site but wealthy in content and relevance to what's hot.

Sega Power

http://www.futurenet.co.uk/

Another FutureNet magazine publication that has gone online. Sega products, news, game reviews, and pre-views are all covered here on Sega Power's online counterpart. There are many other features here, but Sega Power's most notable areas (and probably most accessed) are their hints, tips, walkthroughs, and cheat codes for all the toughest games. Sega Power online also claims they have more reviews than any other Sega magazine. If a Sega Mega Drive, Master System, Game Gear, 32X, or Saturn is your current gaming system, hit the Sega Power Web site and see why it is Britain's best-selling *Sega* magazine. Note: Also check out the Sega WWW links section.

Titania Magazine

http://www.bluestar.net/programs/titania/

This online publication contains current and past is-sues, GameBytes (news and reviews), Interactive Fo-rums, a Quake Chamber, and FTP archives (shareware, FAQs, patches, and editors). Titania mag-azine is a graphically clean-looking site with a fast load rate between pages. The content on all the hot PC games is worth reading, downloading, or printing out. Good articles on War and strategy titles by editor Martin Kozicki.

Top Secret Home Page

http://www.atm.com.pl/~ts/ or http://
www.atm.com.pl/~ts/2000.htm (English
version)

A Polish e-zine Web site for computer games fanatics. Cute animation and a colorful layout help lift the gam-ing reviews, tips and tricks, and screen shots. A variety of games are highlighted—not just one particular genre—and a lengthy links area is provided with mainly corporate and developer sites.

Total!

http://www.futurenet.co.uk/

This time FutureNet brings us their Web page to com-plement their #1 Nintendo magazine. Forwarded by Rob Pegley, Total!'s editor, find out all the current go-ing-ons in the Nintendo sphere. Game previews, re-views, and strategy tips make up the bulk of this site, but there are also links, cheats, past issues, and other feature articles on the future of 64-bit gaming. Meet the team that produces the UK paper mag, or start your subscription online with a valid credit card.

VrE Online

http://biz.swcp.com/coach/vre/frames_
index.html

A modern e-zine dedicated to Virtual Reality worlds with many games-related section. Optimized for Netscape 3.x, music, frames, and animation fill your eyes and ears with vibrant color and climactic music (from Interplay's Shattered Steel game). View the "Most Popular PC Games in the World" (or download the Top 40 of them), see what's In The Pipe (news, previews, and the rumor mill), read new or past arti-cles, peruse links, access hints or cheats for tough games, indulge in forums, or enter for free stuff. Bonus feature: Download VrE Online to read offline.

Will's Wonderful Game Magazine
www.hipark.austin.isd.tenet.edu/pub/cns95/ wogame2/game2.html

A tribute to Mac gaming, this site has downloads, cheats, and hints for a few strategy and action titles. Besides the area on SimCity 2000, this page is designed more for kids, with the average age suggestion of 9 to 13 years old. Many links and much shareware/freeware are accessible from Will's page.

15

ARCHIVED OR MEGA SITES

AS with the FTP sites we looked at in Chapter 10, this section is devoted to listing cool mega sites that archive tons of shareware, freeware, and game demos across all genres. In most cases there is a lot more available at these huge gaming emporiums than just games themselves: add-on levels/scenarios, hints or walkthroughs (complete solutions), patches (game "fixes" or updates), cheats, codes, links (related Web sites), chat groups, screen shots, maps (if applicable), movies, slide shows, news, previews, interviews, and reviews—all under one roof! Some of these sites may also be listed here because they do not fit into any one specific category. Note that many of these pages are *mirrored* at other locations; that is, more than one computer contains the exact Web site elsewhere, and you should choose the URL closer to you since it will be faster to access. What shopping malls did for individual stores is what these mega sites did with all specific categories of gaming and game accessories. The success and longevity of many of these Web pages prove that convenience and selection go a long way for us online gamers.

3D Gaming Scene, The
http://www.pol.umu.se/html/ac/spel.htm

A massive site honoring the latest trend in action PC entertainment—3D, first-person perspective gaming. Spend hours here downloading demos and shareware or accessing hints, cheats, and codes for all your favorite shooters. You may preview upcoming 3D games complete with screen shots and descriptions. A What's New section and a broad link list is also worth browsing through. For more information, read the 3D Gaming Scene FAQ at http://www.pol.umu.se/html/ac/faq/3dfaq.htm.

Absolutely Games!
http://www.clicked.com/shareware/games/allgames.html

A collection of over 350 shareware and demo games are offered here to download. A simple yet organized list of games is laid out alphabetically for a painless search of current hits and past classics. If you don't have time to download or wish to keep it off your hard drive, you may visit the Java or Shockwave Arcades available. A jump to the hottest 20 titles, or best sports games, is also just a click away. Part of the Clicked.com family of Web sites, Absolutely Games! is a convenient gaming site, but you'll probably spend more time in the real-time interactive arcade than in the downloadable section, as there are many other more worthy shareware Web sites to visit.

Abstract Funhouse, The
http://starcreations.com/abstract/funhouse/index.htm

Let Psycho the Clown (the official mascot of the Funhouse) take you through the various sections such as the Game Downer (links to live games [almost 100!], interactive real-time games [Shockwave, Java], and games which you have to download first), the Laugh Riot page for comedy links, and Kidzweb—gaming pages for children ages 3 to 9. Good site for the novice or advanced gamer.

All Good Things
http://www.bf.rmit.edu.au/~blee/agt.html

All Good Things (AGT) is designed to give the gamer just what it sounds like—only the best of Internet shareware and game demos. Classics such as Doom, Warcraft, Magic Carpet, and NASCAR racing are provided for download, along with newer hits such as D, Quake, Command & Conquer, and Close Combat. A section entitled "Close But No Cigar" gives an interesting, and often humorous, look on popular games that didn't make AGT's "A" list, and why.

Apolon's Software
http://www.netcom.com/~apolon/
index.html

A host of downloadable PC and Mac titles, a Top 10 (with product descriptions), utilities, a space for independent programmers, Java-based games chat area, and a links collection. Apolon's page is littered with graphics of hot titles, and their demo section has a handy letter bar ("click on the first letter of the game"), or you can follow along alphabetically.

Arcadium
http://game.factory.net/

Upon free registration you are invited to partake in the many discussion forums and chat groups offered to "hard-core" PC or console gamers. There are also posting and voting areas, online surveys and profiles, Mac games, Internet games, and other exclusive features. Arcadium is a very modern-looking site that has some pretty serious gaming reviews, screen/product shots, and links. Oddly enough, no demos or shareware are available for download, so if you read or chat with someone about a game you may be interested in you will have to go elsewhere on the Net in order to try it out for yourself. Be forewarned: Travel time within the Arcadium site has proven slow, and loading time between pages is tediously high.

Asterix Game Page
http://members.tripod.com/~game29/

A clever and well-designed page, but be patient for the long loading time. An icon-based graphic front page allows the gamer to choose his/her *operating system* (OS). A list of online games, cheat codes, demos, links, a voter's corner, and a problem-solving page can all be found here. Once inside your desired OS, each game genre is alphabetically listed and the number of games per category is shown. A noteworthy section has cool computer game previews (non-playable demos and screen shots) from some of the hot games due out in

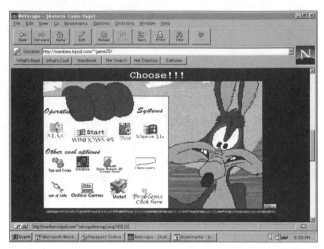

the future. Other utilities and miscellaneous software can also be downloaded.

Cheat Machine
http://www.sliceoflife.com/official/Aforest/
CM.HTM

Cheat Machine is a program of cheats for various PC games and is updated monthly. Cheat Machine will either tell you how to cheat in a given game (codes or actions), or it will change your game files automatically. It is free, but the registered version includes a program to allow you to develop and write your own cheats. Cheat Machine has one of the biggest collections of cheats, codes, patches, tips, secrets, and hints for cheating on shareware or commercial PC games.

Cheat Page, The
http://members.aol.com/formula73/webpg/
cheats.htm

Are *Orcs* getting to you? Having trouble controlling your *'Mech*? Well, don't buy anything just yet (strategy mags, hint books, or a 1-900 call)—just point your browser to The Cheat Page and find out all the programmer's tricks to cracking the hottest PC games today. From Alone in the Dark to X-Com, what you need is here. Part of the bigger Game Center (http://members.aol.com/formula73/webpg/gamecntr.htm#games), this site is a handy and much-needed Web page for all gamers.

Classic Video Game Nexus
http://iquest.com/~lkseitz/cvg_nexus.html

Another cool Web site devoted to gamers whose childhood or early teenage memories lie in the first wave of video arcades and home console systems. If names like Atari, Intellivision, and Colecovision strike a chord with you, or the familiar sounds of video games like Q-bert, Pac-man, Defender, and Pole Position make you smile, then point your browser here for a taste of early 80s nostalgia. Heavy on links to other places around the Net for related interests. Chomp-chomp.

.cONsoLe .WOrLd
http://www.cm.cf.ac.uk/Games/

A UK site dedicated to most TV console systems: Sega (Genesis/MegaDrive, 32X, Genesis CD/Mega CD, Game Gear), Nintendo (SNES, NES, Game Boy), Atari (Jaguar, Lynx), 3DO, and the CD-i. .cONsoLe .WOrLd carries almost 2,000 individual titles along with news, cheats, game specs, FAQs, images, and useful links (newsgroups and FTPs, too).

Cutting Edge Games
http://www.flash.net/~shogun/

A page designed by Shogun's Lair to bring you the creme de la creme of downloadable PC games from the Net. Choose between his Top Picks, Doom-Style Games, Simulations (i.e. space, flight, and racing sims), Role-Playing, Adventure, Strategy/War games, Family Fun (education, arcade, board, and casino games), and Sports games (including the Fighting genre). Cool links are also provided.

Digital Nostalgia
http://www.umich.edu/~webspin/games/

If you spent the late 70s and early 80s with a pocket full of quarters or tokens at an arcade, or playing Atari's Pit-fall on your TV, then you'll love this site paying homage to classic arcade and computer games. From Pac-man to Space Invaders, Donkey Kong to Centipede, these downloadable favorites fill up each of these nostalgic

AUTHOR'S PICK

CNET Game Center

http://www.cnet.com/Gamecenter/

Some WWW companies have managed to build colossal empires online that cater to your every need. The C-Net Network is one of those Mecca sites deserving of every drop of positive recognition from the online, and offline, community. Their Gaming Center itself has many excellent writers covering game reviews, news, gaming guides, sneak peaks, exclusives—not to mention thousands of tested and tried freeware, shareware, and demos for your home collection. If you are serious about gaming this is a "bookmark" must, brought to you by one of the most reliable all-around sources on the Net. C-Net is the main front desk to the Virtual Software Library (VSL)—the most powerful tool for searching for shareware and freeware on the Internet housing over 160,000 files available free for download. Through VSL, find out what are the most popular downloads from the Internet, as well as the newest files; or browse through the archives using keywords or by directory. Although C-Net is the master site for VSL, see below for other mirrored sites around the globe. Make sure you also bookmark the C-Net main page for all of your other computer necessities at http://www.cnet.com/.

Mirrored VSL Sites

Australasia

Telstra Corporation, Melbourne, Australia
http://www.telstra.com.au/cgi-bin/vsl-front

The Hong Kong University of Science and Technology, HongKong
http://sunsite.ust.hk/cgi-bin/vsl-front

Europe

University of Ljubljana, Slovenia
http://www.fagg.uni-lj.si/cgi-bin/vsl-front

Imperial College of Science, Technology and Medicine London, England
http://shase.doc.ic.ac.uk/cgi-bin/vsl-front

University of Vaasa, Finland
http://garbo.uwasa.fi/cgi-bin/vsl-front

Technical University of Chemnitz-Zwickau, Germany
http://www1.tu-chemnitz.de/cgi-bin/vsl-front

North America

C|net: the computer network, San Francisco, USA
http://vsl.cnet.com/

OAK Repository, Oakland University, Michigan, USA
http://castor.acs.oakland.edu/cgi-bin/vsl-front

Computerlink/Internet Direct, Toronto, Canada
http://abyss.idirect.com/cgi-bin/vsl-front

Compusult Limited in Mount Pearl, Newfoundland, Canada
http://www.compusult.nf.ca:80/cgi-bin/vsl-front

pages. Looking for a Colecovision or Commodore 64 Emulator? Well, you can find those here as well. Tons of freeware and shareware goodies to choose from for PCs (sorry, no Mac games). Many cool links, too.

Download Games Now!
http://166.93.8.14/~bwood/bwgames.html

Yes, that's what this page is called. Part of Brent Wood's home page, you can download both new and classic shareware and game demos. Each choice is accompanied by a screen shot, file size, and brief description. Other assets of this page are the informative links collection for PC and Mac games and the "Other Fun Stuff" section. How many other non-corporate game pages out there reach almost a million hits in one year?

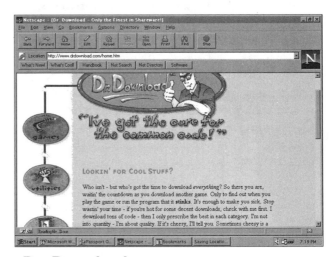

Dr. Download
http://www.drdownload.com/home.htm

The Doc has set out to provide his game-hungry guests only with worthy shareware. He reasons there is too much junk out there, so this Web master takes it upon himself to bring you, the gamer, only the cream of the crop. With all of his online hours under his belt the Good Doctor has earned respect from his visitors for his self-proclaimed gaming knowledge and discernment. Nice-and-simple page design and user-friendly animated colorful buttons.

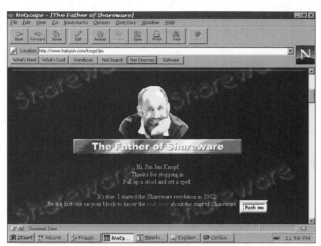

Father of Shareware, The
http://www.halcyon.com/knopf/jim

Jim Knopf, the now retired "father of shareware," started the "try-before-you-buy" software revolution back in 1982 in Bellevue, Washington. This award-winning site, which receives over 3,000 hits a day, is a tribute to the realm of shareware and freeware as a whole. Crescendo sings out tunes on your visit, such as Dolly Parton's "9 to 5" or the Coca-Cola theme song, while you rummage through the informative links to worldwide software resources. Most of Jim's more recent freeware creations are available for download, leaning toward varied Windows utilities. If nothing else, I think this Web page is important for any Internet gamer to visit to see where our shareware practices originated.

Fun Game Domain
http://www.fungame.com/

The Fun Game Domain (FGD) contains almost 1,000 downloads and nearly 1,500 cool links. Every new day will bring you a "Fun Site of the Day" to link to, or you can view the daily demo pick. Add the FGD button to your own home page and they'll send you Mutant Space Bats of Doom for free. Use the "PC Game Finder" section to track down Web sites, demos, previews, reviews, cheats, and fan sites for an abundant number of commercial PC games.

AUTHOR'S PICK

File Factory, The

http://www.filefactory.com/

The File Factory is a preview of the features to be found in GameScape, the game resource center of the Total Entertainment Network (see Chapter 13). A visit here requires a frames- and Java Script-compatible browser such as Netscape 2.0+ or Microsoft Explorer 3.0+. This page claims they have "nothing but PC game files," and a whole slew of them, too: patches, news, shareware, FAQs, uploads, cracks, secrets, utilities, and an e-mail message notification for any new changes (optional). Literally thousands of files available—all for free. I guess Santa found out I've been good all year!

G1—The GameMasters
http://www.gttweb.com/game/

A links-happy site providing their visitors with, in their opinion, the top 5% of all Internet gaming sites. The theme from those Charlie Brown cartoons fills the background while you surf through their game links: action, strategy, simulations, land warfare, naval warfare, air warfare, space and fantasy sites...and more. Commercial companies and gaming hardware manufacturer sites are also provided. Check out the moving color marquee for current news and contest information.

Galaxy Games

http://www.galaxygames.com/

The world's largest online game store…and more. This Netscape 3.0-enhanced site sells 3DO, IBM, MAC, Nintendo, PlayStation, and Sega games straight to your door for $5.00 a pop ($12.00 outside of the U.S.). This Web page also offers free demo downloads, company and unofficial game links (aptly called "Jump Gate"), a resource center (pre-release hype), and information on their World Group BBS (claiming 25,000 game downloads, 20 online live multiplayer games, and a huge game classified section).

Galt Shareware Zone

http://www.galttech.com/

A very Windows-oriented design graces this Web site's pages and offers quite a selection for the enterprising gamer. Sign up for a free newsletter or read extensive game reviews before you go out and blow some dough on the newest game. Even better, for $40.00 you can order any of the Mega CDs and have it delivered to your door (over 55 countries served). The CD is packed with over 600MB of games or, if you have the time, download them all right here from their archives. By the time you read this, the Galt Shareware Zone may well have celebrated its millionth or so visitor. Congrats to a well-arranged and charming Web page.

Gamelan Java Games on the Web

http://www.gamelan.com/pages/
Gamelan.arts.game.html

Earthweb's Gamelan's Arts and Entertainment Games section links you to the hottest real-time gaming around the world using Java Applets. Each directory is separated into arcade games (121 entries), board games (75 entries), card games (33 entries), multiplayer (56 entries), puzzles (99 entries), and resources (131 entries). If you prefer an alphabetical list encompassing all formats, it is provided here as well.

Games and Utilities for Windows 95

http://www.ryerson.ca/~j1leung/

As his home page indicates, John Leung has prepared an alphabetical listing of cool Windows 95 games to download for free. They are all presented alphabetically along with file size and brief description. Useful utilities and hot links are also supplied in this Canadian frames-enhanced Web site. Make sure you grab Hangman 2.0 (only 145K) and The Scent of War 1.

Game Head

http://gamehead.com/index.stm

Pacific HiTech's gaming emporium Game Head is an attractive and resourceful site designed to get you what you want quickly and effortlessly. This frame-enhanced site allows you to hot link to your fave gaming genre (role-playing, action, strategy, etc.) or use their convenient search engine to zap you to a particular game you have in mind. The seemingly never-ending list of shareware, freeware, and demos available for download also contain handy game descriptions. Game Head features a Top 100 Downloads section or a Top 10 Downloads list per gaming genre. Multiplayer and 3D games also have their own section for easy reference. Game Head is one of the better-looking and more comprehensive archive sites on the Web.

AUTHOR'S PICK

Games Domain

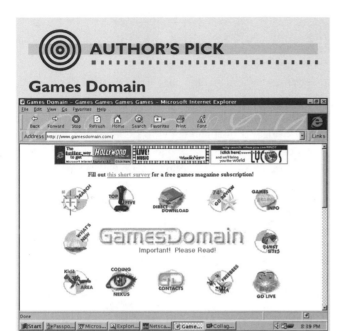

www.gamesdomain.co.uk

Possibly the world's finest collection of free games to download whether you own a PC, Mac, or an Amiga. Games Domain contains thousands of shareware and freeware games (yes, I said *thousands*) with an easy-to-use search engine, daily gaming news, and exciting contests—not to mention their many column and feature sections. Hey, where else can you get over 50 different versions of Tetris?! Bookmark this site for more free games than your hard drive can handle.

Mirrored Sites:
http://www.gamesdomain.com (USA)
http://www.gamesdomain.ru (Russia)
http://gamesdomain.dstc.edu.au (Australia)

Game Link
http://ccwf.cc.utexas.edu/~hristos/
gamelink.html

An easy-to-use Web site housing a few hundred popular shareware games and game demos. Separated alphabetically by game name, this site lists not only the file size and game category but allows you to view the *read.me* text prior to download—a feature many other

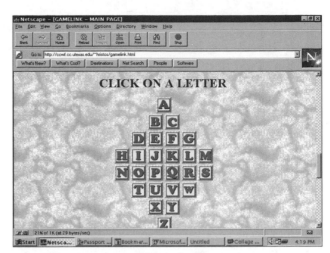

Web sites should consider. If the game sounds like it is for you—click away and it's yours. Easy as pie.

Mirrored Sites:
USA: http://piglet.cc.utexas.edu/~hristos/
gamelink.html
Italy: http://www.vol.it/mirror/GAMELINK/
gamelink.html

Game List, The
http://moose.erie.net/~bobby/

Bobby Wellington's well-known games page is designed to give the surfer a links selection of games listed alphabetically. Great for inexperienced or younger computer gamers, most titles are given a description, system requirements, and a screen shot and file size count. The FTP sites are right there ready for hot linking and downloading. A simple framed design is effective and easy to navigate back and forth.

Game Oasis
http://www.cyberspace.com/acroft/

The Game Oasis Web page is a plain front door to a game-rich FTP site and is broken down into FAQs, Cheats, Hints, and Demos. Many to choose from in all genres, these games are presented by name; but read the *INDEX* file first prior to sifting through the list. Instead of spending $20.00 on a hint or walk through book—see what the Game Oasis has in store first.

AUTHOR'S PICK

GameLords

http://www.gamelords.com/

By pooling collective talents, the Game Lords have set out to give you a complete comprehensive PC gaming experience. To use their own words, this Web page is a place where "weary virtual warriors can return to, to rest, recoup, exchange a few words, regroup, re-arm, pick a fight, and get ready for the next battle." Download tons of files (levels, patches, editors, and utilities) or view FAQs, strategy, screen shots, and secrets to all the hottest single-player and multiplayer titles: Quake, Duke Nukem 3D, Warcraft II, Mech-warrior 2, and Descent. This page is young (debuted end of August '96) and has a very strong future.

Game Page, The
http://www.xs4all.nl/~gzbrn/GamePage.html

This B&W-looking page contains many useful sections and features. Peruse though the links to the Internet PC games charts, news, reviews, downloads, codes, and a voting corner. The best part of this European page is the thousands of add-on levels designed for Doom, Doom 2, Descent, Quake, Command & Conquer, Warcraft II, Heretic, and Hexen.

Game Page of the Universe
http://www.pht.com/game/universe/index.html

Yet another cool gaming page from Pacific HiTech's growing online presence. Peruse through a multitude of "Best of" lists and articles on what's hot in the gaming world. A thorough list of links connecting to corporate sites and popular e-zines is also illustrated here. Their immense FTP site contains zip file size and you can even look at the contents of the file prior to download. Game enthusiasts can also add to the archive collection by uploading beloved shareware or rare game demos. PHT does it again with yet another useful site to keep you engaged for hours.

Game Shack
http://www.jorsm.com/~dbrtos/

Dave Brtos started Uncle Billy Bob's Game Shack in November, 1995 as a hobby, but little did he know he'd have over 100,000 hits less than six months later. This re-vamped Web site contains shareware games to download, cool links, prizes, and more. Any games page that start's with "Hi Y'All!" can't steer you wrong.

Game Time! All Games Radio Network
http://www.vn1.com/menu.htm

Game Time! is an interesting Web site containing ten radio shows all to do with electronic gaming, leaning toward PCs. Real Audio software is necessary (available at http://www.realaudio.com/) to listen to these "radio" broadcasts, broken up into daily shows and specialized sections. Mondays has sports news, Tuesdays are Sims, Wednesdays are reserved for action and adventure games, Thursdays are slotted for strategy and role-playing news, and Fridays zoom in on multiplayer and Internet gaming information. There are also family gaming radio news, a developer's show, and more. Also check out the Java Chat Lounge to exchange your views and strategy opinions with fellow gamers. It's cool to hear gaming news, reviews, and playing tips through audio for a change, and, of course, you can still surf the Net while listening at the same time. Great site with a promising future.

GamePen, The

http://www.gamepen.com/

One of the Web's most informative computer game sites offering many facets of gaming interest and trade-marked sections. Areas such as "UnderD" (under development) gives you the latest gossip and behind-the-scene news, "CheatMe" (a cheat, hint, and code listing), "Group Therapy" (the latest demos and news direct from game-drenched Newsgroups), MultiplayerPen, and more. GamePen's "Game Time News Express" is a great Real Audio gaming news service with all the latest inside scoops. Simply minimize the Real Audio window and continue to check out this site while you listen to radio-like broadcasting on current electronic gaming happenings. GamePen has a nice effective layout and Web page design that is a cross between a comic book and a newspaper. What makes GamePen worthwhile are the accurate and reliable sources for news and strategy suggestions on the latest and greatest computer games.

Game Warehouse

http://www.iguide.com/genuine/sharewar/index.htm

A extensive list of "classic" shareware or freeware titles from the past couple of years. Remember games such as Aquaman, Pickle Wars, Brix, Catacomb Abyss 3D, and 1992's Spear of Destiny? Each of the 200 games available for download here is complete with honest reviews and ratings. The Games Warehouse is part of I-Guide's large online presence (the "Making sense of the 'Net' people"). Here's a place with no flashy graphics or animations, but you can find hidden gems and lost gaming classics.

Gamer's Inn, The

http://www.gamersinn.com/

Very few Web sites actually make you feel like you are in another time or place. Although the games they offer sometimes help you escape for a while, hardly do you get a *real* experience out of the Web site environment itself. The Gamer's Inn is that rare exception, where the sights and sounds of medieval Europe come alive in a friendly pub atmosphere (complete with corset-wearing maidens serving ale and cider). Happy Celtic music flows in the background while you make your selections exclusive to the Gamer's Inn: the Arena, Curio Shoppe, Gallery, Chronicles, Hall of Mystics, the Trysting place, etc. Java and downloadable games are available. Game demos, shareware, and freeware are separated into genre, operating system, Net games, multiplayer, tips, tricks, and more. Real-time chat groups, computer game artwork, game developments, accessories, and news are also provided. Words cannot describe this page well enough—this is a must see (and hear) to believe. An all-around A+ Web site.

⊚ AUTHOR'S PICK

GameSpot

http://www.gamespot.com/

You may have seen GameSpot advertised in any of the leading Internet magazines over the past few months. A lot of money and time has gone into this PC gaming mega site, but the end result is a sleek, colorful, and informative gaming resource center to gratify all tastes. Exhaustive game reviews are broken down into eight gaming genres, but they also include company information, screen shots, difficulty rating, player's reviews, and an accumulated tally by the GameSpot staff for an overall score—per game! GameSpot also has exclusive features and departments as well as current gaming news with an option to e-mail you the updates. Related links, contests, chat forums, and a strategy section are also provided here. The only drawback to the site is the overflow of advertisements, but at least they are gaming related (and when you see this site for yourself, you'll know why they needed the investments and advertising sponsors!). One of the "Top 10" gaming sites anywhere.

⊚ AUTHOR'S PICK

Happy Puppy

http://www.happypuppy.com/

Would you believe that this Web site receives almost *two million* hits per month?! Happy Puppy (HP) is indisputably the most popular gaming site on the World Wide Web and is deserving of their inconceivable number of visitors. Created by long-time game designer Jennifer Diane Reitz, HP offers may sections and columns that cover every aspect of gaming imaginable: PC Hit 100 Games, WWW and FTP gaming guides, Cheats, Patches & Solutions, Online Web Games, Reviews, Real Audio Radio Shows, Pages for Youngsters, Web Mags, and more. HP also features pages by recruits Lord Soth (with over 1,200 games to play) and Hank "Doom" Leukart (Doom FAQ ver 6.666 writer and author of the *Doom Hacker's Guide*). As if this wasn't enough, there's Game Newsgroups, a developer's page, 50 recent top game hits, Jennifer's Critique, and an exhaustive list of game-related and other interesting links in and around the Web. Truly one of the best gaming sites available. Not just a bookmark *must*, but how about HP as a start-up page for when you log on to the Net?

Game Zone, The

http://www.gamezone.net/

This otherwise plain site serves as a database of downloadable freeware and shareware games. A simple yet attractive main page fronts this out-of-date gaming assortment with a surprising number of hits well into six figures. This is basically a modest FTP site with a Web shell, but unfortunately there are far too many bigger and better pages offering the same games and more. Yet UNIX/Linux game-searchers may find some interest here.

Internet Charts—PC and Video Games

http://www.xs4all.nl/~jojo/index.html

JoJo's World Internet Charts (IC) document the hottest PC and video games on the Web. IC is constantly updated (with an option to vote), and each list highlights the game name and developer, genre, position, weeks on chart, and number of points awarded. Each entry into the Top 100 Commercial games and Top 40 downloads charts are all hot-linked to the Happy Puppy site so the surfer can download the game demo or access strategy tips, tricks, and codes. Cool site to find out what is popular in the expanding PC and video game industry, with multiple mirrors.

Mirrored Sites

USA: http://www.tiac.net/users/top100/
Malaysia: http://cyberhq.net.my/top100/
UK: www.futurenet.co.uk/,pcgamer1,pcgamer,/computing/worldcharts

King Link & Games

http://www.kinglink.com/

When was the last time you visited a Web site and saw and heard fireworks? I didn't think so. King Link & Games is a gaming kingdom housing online forums, anonymous FTP access, top games, and Windows applications for download (complete with reviews of each product), hot links, and a gaming news section. The best part of this frame-enhanced site is its "What's New?" section (daily additions of games and news) and

Jumbo!

http://www.jumbo.com/

Would you believe me if I told you there was a Web site where you can download, for free, over 200,000 files?! One of the largest collection of freeware and shareware on our green earth is found here courtesy of the folks at Jumbo. Search by name, date, operating system, or file-type in order to find what you need fast and efficiently. This is truly a gamer's paradise as you can read the product's full description before you start to download. The appropriately named Jumbo! Web site is also a treat for Mac, Amiga, or UNIX gamers, since they have their own section in the games subdivision. This Web page simply screams, "bookmark me!"

the Site Map illustrating what there is at this Web page and where exactly to find it. With all these pages here you'll be glad to know it is a fast site to navigate through (they boast using super fast multiple T3s). With the exception of the intro fireworks, this page is not much to look at, but it is definitely one of the best gaming archives and news/reviews sources around.

Lord Soth's Games on the Internet
www.happypuppy.com/games/lordsoth/
index.html

One of the more respected resources on the Net in the realm of computer gaming. Lord Soth provides his visitors guide links to almost 2,000 games and also includes extensive cheats, hints and tips, walkthroughs, FAQs, add-ons, patches, and level editors. There are also sections highlighting non-playable demos, archived lists, and online multiplayer gaming. Games are broken down alphabetically or by gaming genre. Lord Soth is part of the Happy Puppy family, which is one of the most popular gaming-related Web sites across the globe at http://www.happypuppy.com/.

Mecca, The
http://www.mm.com/user/tcdmntia/wwd/

Slick design and hearty content make up this PC gamer's page. Sections include news (of the day, too), downloads, links, Game of the Week, levels, codes, On the Horizon (previews), Net games, Top 10s and more. Optimized for Internet Explorer 3.0, this savvy page is great for 3D action and real-time strategy titles such as Quake, Duke Nukem 3D, Warcraft II, and Mechwarrior 2.

Nuke InterNETWORK Page
http://www.nuke.com/

A huge resource for computer and video gaming news, reviews, and downloads brought to you by Ziff-Davis publishing. Excellent features such as The Nuke Gaming Minute presented in VDOLive format, a Java Chat room, a Doom WAD and Duke Nukem MAP file listing, and a downloadable gaming library (almost 2,000 available); you can also subscribe to an e-mail "video or computer game mailing list" with up-to-the-minute happenings, or view the recent uploads from the last seven days. Use Nuke as a springboard to launch you to the greatest computer magazines from ZD like *Computer Life, PC Computing, Computer Gaming World, PC Week, Family PC, Computer Shopper, Windows,* and more! Nuke brings you the wild and exciting world of gaming at your fingertips.

Online Games Directory
http://www.tc.umn.edu/nlhome/m041/
fran0264/games.htm

Following in the trend to make all the latest and greatest PC games multiplayer (and thank heavens for that), the Online Games Directory features genre-specific information on multiplayer games. Game description, where to play them, how much it'll cost you, and a screen shot are available for all games. Categories are War, Strategy, RPG's, MUD's, Casino, Java, and Board games. Complete with crescendo tunes by Queen ("Another One Bites the Dust")—how appropriate for fierce head-to-head action! A Game of the Month section is also offered. Optimized for Netscape 3.0+. Hell, stay just for the midi tunes!

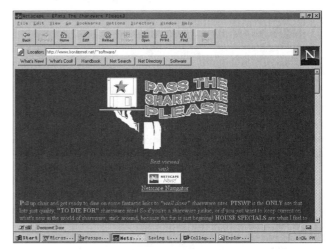

Pass the Shareware Please
http://www.frontiernet.net/~software/

Another site dedicated to providing the time-conscious Web gamer the definitive list of worthwhile games to download and links to visit. Heavy on shareware as a whole, but their gaming section has the infamous Bekki Swartz's lists of cheats to all your favorite games. This is a good Web site to visit if you're stuck on your newest CD-ROM purchase. Simply pore over the alphabetical list provided and choose your poison. This site also features a cool (utility) tool of the day to download.

AUTHOR'S PICK

Pacific HiTech

http://www.pht.com/

I wouldn't quite say they have "over one zillion files" as their main page maintains, but you do get the idea they must have one of the biggest collections of software in the galaxy! PHT is an online game purchaser's dream because they have all you need under one roof. Surfers can order multimedia products direct to their door and pick up free CDs in the process. This Web site has a handy map outlining their enormous site—a feature other large Web sites should consider! For a more exhaustive look at their gaming division, point your browser to PHT's GameHead page (http://www.gamehead.com/index.stm).

PC Release List, The
http://www.avault.com/pcrl/ or
http://pc-release.ukonline.co.uk/

Hosted by Adrenaline Vault (see Chapter 14), this page is devoted to gaming lists of all kinds such as Classic Games, New Games (by the day), and a Hall of Fame chart. Hot gaming news and a handy in-site search engine is also provided. Download game demos and shareware, or browse through the past month's charts. A gaming category section (arcade, strategy, Sims, etc.) is also available for those who prefer to look for games by specific genre. Slideshow previews and useful game patches can be downloaded as well.

Queue's World
http://www.thequeue.com/

Queue's Adventures is designed to share new Virtual Reality worlds on the Web with their visitors (like Worlds Chat and Alphaworld) as well as providing you the best in Adventure, RPG, Online Gaming, and 3D Action game reviews, demos, news, screen-shots, and links. Complete with a scrolling color marquee, other sections include "Queue's 5-star Sites," "Queue's VR Worlds," "Queue's Adventures," and "Queue's Game Site." Game demos are also mirrored to the Adrenaline Vault Web page.

Rasener Software Archive
http://metro.turnpike.net/~dusty/

Although the MS-DOS game section was closed upon my visits, the Windows games archive contained 20+ pages of shareware and freeware titles. Don't look for Duke Nukem 3D or Quake here—games found here listed alphabetically are more the traditional or classic titles. When a selection is chosen you are linked to the FTP site (Oregon State University) for quick and easy download. No graphics, no games description, and no cheats, hints, patches, or add-ons. Simply Windows games and lots of 'em.

Riddler
http://www.riddler.com/

Some of you may remember seeing the Riddler "caps" or icon button on various Web pages early in 1996. That was part of their free "caps" contest that gave away a cruise, cash, and a weekend away for two. Riddler is a sleek and colorful Web experience housing many exclusive games and prizes.

Try your luck with real-time mind-bending graphical games such as Mental Floss, The Daily Riddle, Bloodhound, Gridlock, Checkered Flag, King of the Hill, and Aha! Registration is free but is required to play.

Sandbox—The Interactive Entertainment Network
http://www.sandbox.net/

A gaming network housing very cool original games and prizes. Immerse yourself in episodic tales of intrigue, virtual road trips, and real-life courtroom dramas; or compete head-to-head with players from around the world for daily prizes. Games include the riddle-heavy Cyberhunt (an interactive thriller!), The Court of Last

Resort, The Best of Arizona Super Bowl Road Trip, and Speedbump. Registration is free, so take advantage of this fun Web site.

Shareware.com
http://www.shareware.com/

One of the most popular shareware sources on the Net. Part of the mega C-Net family (see their "Game Center, " above), Shareware.com is a modern page chock-full of shareware, freeware, and game demos. Lists titles by popularity (generated by the Virtual Software Library people), operating system, or by time (specific week, month, or year). Articles, news, and reviews can be found at the C-Net front page—but for those of you ONLY interested in shareware (and tons of it), point your browser to http://www.shareware.com/.

Shareware Games and Demos
http://games.mgweb.com/

A popular no-frills site (almost half a million hits so far in 1996 alone) supplying the Web surfer with chat and discussion forums to help you get through those tough games. Nominate your picks for the best and worst three games of all times. Add your e-mail address to the list to be automatically notified when the site has something new to see. A fair Web page with a myriad of downloads to try out. Heavily weighted in the 3D action game genres.

Italian Mirrored Site:
http://www.vol.it/MIRROR4/EN/bc.cybernex.net/pub/users/paladine/games/
or
http://www.vol.it/UK/EN/VIDEOGAMES/

Software Net
http://www.software.net/quick.htm

Basically an online shopping network for all computer-related software products (over 20,000 overall). Typing **games** in their own search engine will pull educational, puzzle, and strategy titles for sale. This site is for the gamers who would rather have their CD-ROMs delivered right to their door. Listed by company name and operating system.

Software Site, The
http://www.softsite.com/

Winner of Point Communication's "Top 5% of all Web Sites," The Software Site is a Windows gamer's paradise. News, downloads, and cool links make up the bulk of this page, with a rich Windows 95 Games section. From here on in, click on the desired game category and each game comes complete with description, system requirements, and often company notes. UltiSoft, a small Windows game developer, has their home page on The Software Site and offers their own shareware games for either Windows 3.1+ or Windows 95. Featured programs are also highlighted.

Spoiler Centre, The
http://spoiler.et.ee/

Thank heavens there are places like this. I remember a not-too-long-ago experience spending tons of money calling a 1-900 line to California for PC game hints. The Spoiler Centre (SC) is set up for those of you who have pulled your hair out trying to find solutions to those tough games in the wee hours of the morning. Veikko Danilas's SC breaks up computer games in five categories (Action, Strategy, RPG, Adventure and Other), or you can use their handy built-in search engine ("Zork" brought up *Return To Zork, Zork Nemesis, Beyond Zork, Zork 1, Zork 2,* and *Zork 3*). Most often there will be more than one spoiler per game as well.

A very useful site, mirrored through Games Domain all around the world.

Mirrored Sites:
USA: http://www.gamesdomain.com/spoiler/
UK: http://www.gamesdomain.co.uk/spoiler/
Russia: http://www.gamesdomain.ru/spoiler/
South Africa: http://www.gamesdomain.co.za/spoiler/

Starbase Triton
http://www.striton.com/

An attractive modern page with big colorful graphics and many sections: Gaming forums/discussion groups, Demos (non-interactive movie or playable), Information Center, Patches, Companies Databank, Gaming Accessories, Official Game Pages, and Game-Related Sites (links). Best part of the page is the Demos section—a huge listing of free offerings all key-coded with necessary information.

Tikkabik's Mac Games Page
http://www.tikkabik.com/mac_arcade.html

Fan of the coin-op arcade games from the "good old days"? Do you, as a Mac player, feel shunned for the lack of good game clones or emulators? Well, thanks to Boston's Peter A. Cohen, this collection of classic favorites is linked in alphabetical order, and each game is similar (or even almost identical) to the original. From Arkanoid to Xevious, it's all here and linked to

FTP sites and Web pages around the globe. The Mac addict can download these variations of classics for free or peruse through the long list of Mac- and game-related links.

Tim's Clubhouse
http://www.heatersworld.com/
timspage.html

An all-in-one site. Sections include: Strategy and Tactics, Universal Hint System, Tipswap (exchange tricks with others), Demo Download (over 100 choices), Game Sites (links), Magazines, Newsgroups, Hardware, and more. The Universal Hint System and Tipswap areas makes this page worthwhile alone, but there are other endearing qualities like a Live Game Chat and a scrolling Java newsreel.

Ultimate Gaming Resource
http://www.nai.net/~duane/home.htm

A good fix for all your PC- and console-based information. Many sections cover all facets of electronic gaming: What's New, News, Reviews, Rumors, Previews, PC Release Dates, Console Release Dates, Cheat Codes, Walkthroughs, Demos, Patches, Software Companies, Hardware Companies, Feedback, and Links. On a good note: This page is constantly updated and expanding...but on a bad one: The gray background they use on their page makes it very hard to read against the black and blue print.

Video Game Lair/Computer Game Central
http://www.pcgames.net/vgl/

This site is primarily two things. First, it is a voter's corner where you nominate the five top PC games today. Second, a links-section sends you to other large gaming centers on the World Wide Web. If you want to have your say on what's hot and what's not, then drop in here for your two-cent's worth. You may find little else here to spark your interest. This plain page is part of the larger, more impressive PC Games network site (http://www.pcgames.net).

Video Game Yellow Pages
http://www.gamepen.com/yellowpages/

VGYP is a comprehensive computer and video gaming page offering links to gaming manufactures, magazines, Newsgroups, cheats and hints, patches and fixes, demos, and more. A handy search engine is included along with an organized choose-by-genre option for your favorite computer gaming types (Action, RPGs, Sims, Strategy, etc.) and platform systems (Nintendo 64, Sega Saturn, 3D0, PlayStation). Also included here is "News Express," a daily gaming news forum, and "Addicted to Games," a humorous weekly comic strip. All-around impressive Web site with lots to offer for the avid gamer. Part of the larger GamePen Web site (http://www.gamepen.com/).

Wild Side Gaming Page
http://arachnid.colgate.edu/alewis/
games.html

A plain, clean gaming site complete with demos, cheats, FTP lists and company WWW links, reviews, and news. Web surfers can also keep up on gaming gossip and industry happenings through an automatic e-mail free subscription if preferred. All shareware games available are of the 3D-perspective action genre such as Quake, Doom 1.9, Strife, and Duke Nukem 3D. Pick up the Ultimate Doom patch here as well.

AUTHOR'S PICK

Virtual Arcade, The

http://www.thearcade.com/

Toronto, Canada's Webwurx Multimedia opened this fantastic virtual coin-op arcade at the close of summer 1996. VRML, CGI, Java, and Shockwave programmers from around the world have contributed games to these six centers: Arcade 1, Arcade 2, Strategy, RPG, Board, and Elite rooms. Beautiful music fills the air while you navigate through the rooms (only with Internet Explorer 3.0) and play variations of Galaxian, Dig Dug, and other early 80s classics. A 3D first-perspective site worth visiting to see the latest and greatest browser technology.

Windows 95.com
http://www.windows95.com/apps/ games.html

It's only appropriate that Stephen Jenkins, ex beta-tester for Windows 95 and founding member of the Bill Gates Fan Club (egad!), would create a Web site honoring the most anticipated computer operating system in the history of mankind. Needless to say, Windows 95.com should be viewed with Microsoft Internet Explorer 3.0+ for the great music on every page

(not found on the Netscape browser). It has many sections, but the URL above heads right to the games section with plenty o' downloads to adds to your gaming collection. A thorough Action category also containing many great Quake utilities.

WINDOWS SHAREWARE ARCHIVE: GAMES SECTION

California State Univeristy, San Marcos
http://coyote.csusm.edu/cwis/winworld/ games.html

Over 50 HTML pages of Windows games, each listed alphabetically with a description, file size, and date. This FTP-like archive is not much to look at but is loaded with games heavily weighing toward card, puzzle, and arcade classic titles. Cool solitaire variations and rare strategy games can be found here. A very *different* Web page with hard-to-find treats.

WinSite Archive
http://www.winsite.com/

An extravagant collection of Windows-only software. Use the search engine or browse the top 100 uploads (Windows 3.1x, 95, or NT) or hottest downloads. Many games and game utilities available from the WinSite FTP servers are presented here with text and file

AUTHOR'S PICK

ZD Net

http://www.zdnet.com/ or http://206.66.184.176/home/filters/ main.html

Another powerhouse site from the giant computer magazine and newspaper publishers Ziff-Davis. Zap to any of the popular magazines such as *Computer Gaming World, Windows, Computer Shopper, Computer Life, PC Week, PC Computing, Yahoo! Life, Family PC,* and more. I suggest you simply click on the Software Library icon to view, and download, the over 10,000 shareware files available! Each are broken up into gaming genre (Action, Strategy, Classics) or platform (Windows 95, Mac, DOS), or some games or commercial gaming companies have features and reviews in headline format. A gorgeous, modern site worthy of many visits to increase your personal games demos and shareware collection. In a rush? Click on http://www.hot-files.com/games.html to access ZD's "Top Rated Shareware Games."

size descriptions. It seems the reigning most popular downloads to date are strip poker variations. Games dominate the Top 100 lists, but you may also find really cool utilities and other multimedia add-ons.

Zone, The
http://www.thezone.pair.com/game/list.htm

This section of The Zone houses a gigantic collection of PC games to play for free. By employing a simple click 'n download execution—all the shareware, freeware, and demo games listed alphabetically here are yours to keep. Try out classics like I-Motion's creepy Alone in the Dark, or test your skill with Origin's Wing Commander IV. Looking for more game links around the Web? Then use The Zone's gaming resources list for places on the Net to hit (http://www.thezone.pair .com/game/biglist.htm).

16

COMPUTER GAME COMPANY SITES

THE advent of the World Wide Web has opened a marvelous communication channel through which businesses can present news and information about their products to potential consumers. This is especially true for computer game developers and publishers, who can use the medium to literally demonstrate their products and provide online support, both technical and general, for their customers. Quite a boon for game-players, this development has made it possible, and almost standard procedure, for enthusiasts to first try out games in one form or another before spending money on them.

The following computer software companies are some of the biggest names, selling the biggest games. Whether a developer or a publisher, most offer downloadable bits and bytes—playable demos, screen shots, patches, hints, videos, or audio files—from the games in their product lines. These are free samples for the taking, and you don't even have to say please. Enjoy.

A DIRECTORY OF GAME COMPANY SITES WORTH SEEING

3D Realms Entertainment
http://www.3drealms.com/

This division of Apogee software specializes in developing, you guessed it, 3D technology games. Review the 3D Realms catalog of current and future products with titles such as Terminal Velocity and Duke Nukem 3D, check out the file areas and message bases, and find out how to order products. Registration for full access to site options is required, but a guest pass is available.

7th Level, Inc.
http://www.7thlevel.com/

The creator of the arcade series Tracer and Battle Beast, as well as the strategy series Monty Python & the Quest for the Holy Grail and Monty Python's Complete Waste of Time, 7th Level hosts this virtual playroom offering demos and a look at the company's product line. Official company briefs and bios can also be found, along with an online shopping center and a place to sign up as an official 7th Level family member.

Access Software Inc.
http://www.accesssoftware.com/

The maker of golf simulators and interactive movies such as "The Pandora Directive" and "Under a Killing Moon," Access Software promotes its products with this look "behind the box," so to speak. Enjoy screen shots and other background material supporting the company's products. Ordering information and technical support are available.

Acclaim Nation
http://www.acclaimnation.com/

The developer of crossover interactive games for titles such as Magic: The Gathering, Iron Blood, and Dragon-Heart, Acclaim/Nation promotes its wares and shares demo downloads. General company news is also on tap for those with a mind to drink it in.

Action Games
http://users.aol.com/actiongame/
actionzz.htm

Find out what the folks at Action Games have been up to over the past several months and download flight simulator games. Discover what it's like to cruise a spaceplane at Mach 2 through the atmosphere on Mars. Also find A-10 and F-16 sims.

Activision
http://www.activision.com

Promoting titles such as MechWarrior 2 and its sequel, MechWarrior 2: The Mercenaries; Interstate '76; and the NetMech: Eight Player Pack, Activision offers links and loads geared to stimulate players' "gotta have it" reaction. Also online, find customer support, company news, and other general company information. For those in the mood to order, the Activision Shop promotes a toll-free number as well as retail outlets where the products are available, and promises online ordering soon.

Accolade
http://www.accolade.com

Come to play and download demos of the company's newest titles, including the multiplayer Deadlock and the 3D action game Eradicator. Also find tech support and the usual company promotional material.

Ambrosia Software
http://www.ambrosiasw.com/

The maker of Apeiron, Barrak, Chiral, Escape Velocity, and other titles, Ambrosia Software invites players to explore the world of its games. Download demos, read FAQs, and check into utilities, add-ons, and upgrades. For those who wish to make purchases online, secure ordering is available. Other site features include company news, technical support, and links to selected cool sites.

Anarchy Entertainment Inc.
http://www.anarchyent.com/

Find demos, previews, and other efforts promoting the Anarchy line of titles. Among the featured games find the 3D puzzle Too Many Geckos, the graphical adventure Dread, and the Viking fighting game Valhalla. Information about ordering the games is online, as is an opportunity to be added to the company mailing list. Those curious about Anarchy can read the profile, which recounts the company's history and core philosophy.

Apogee
http://www.3drealms.com/

Promoting its software hits like Wolfenstein 3D and Rise of Triad, Apogee Software hosts this showcase for its current and future products. Stop by for the latest company news, cheat codes, and a look "behind the scenes." Those who are registered can also download game files, user add-ons, and patches. Be sure to check out the message boards.

Argonaut
http://www.argonaut.com/

The creator of 3D titles such as FX Fighter and Star Glider, Argonaut hosts this look at the company's past and peek at its future. Read a company profile, review its catalog of titles, stop by the Music Studio for a bit on sound, and check out the Technology Lab for a look at the company's achievements. There's not much to do here, but loads to read.

Bethesda Softworks
http://www.bethsoft.com/

The developer of such hit titles as the Wayne Gretzky Hockey series, the Delta-V flight simulator, and The Terminator series, Bethesda hosts this open house where visitors can learn about the company and download game demos. Also find technical support, patches, updates, and utilities. The Emporium is open for those who'd like to make purchases, and job-seekers can check out available opportunities.

Bio Ware
http://www.bioware.com/

Meet the joint creator (along with Interplay) of Shattered Steel, a big bot 3D action game, and Forgotten Realms, a single-user AD&D role-playing game. Stop by the Shattered Steel area for a download, a background on the game's story, and development notes. Those who are interested can also see why they call this company Bio Ware. Medical education software, anyone?

Blizzard Entertainment
http://www.blizzard.com/

The maker of the Warcraft series of fantasy combat games, Starcraft, and the role-paying adventure Diablo, Blizzard Entertainment treats its visitors to game demos, patches, cheat codes, and support files. Also online find company information and development news, technical support, and information on purchasing the company's games and licensed products.

Brøderbund Software
http://www.broderbund.com/

Where in the World is Carmen Sandiego?, Myst, and Prince of Persia are just a few of the game titles from this mega-marketer of educational, entertainment, and home-use software. Browse the company's catalog of titles, read about the company's history and prospects for the future, research job opportunities, and find out how to submit ideas for possible development.

Bullfrog Productions Ltd.
http://www.bullfrog.co.uk/

From the creator of Hi Octane, Populous and Populous 2, Syndicate, and Theme Park, this development update promotes Bullfrog's newest and soon-to-be-released titles. Find information on Dungeon Keeper, Syndicate Wars, Gene Wars, and Theme Hospital. Also find cheats for older games, interviews, and gaming hints and tips.

Bungie Software
http://www.bungie.com/

Check out the latest from the creator of the Marathon series, Pathways Into Darkness, and Abuse. Review the company's product catalog, download demos, and stop by the Bungie Store for special Web-only offers. Need to register a product? No problem; do it online. Other site features include letters from players, company news, and a challenge to "find Ling Ling's head."

Class6 Interactive
http://www.class6.com/

Promoting its Windows 95-only ware, Class6 Interactive pitches its CD-ROM role-playing adventure, Creature Crunch, and its interactive animated adventure, Cosmo's Rocket. Read all about the games and where they're available for purchase. General information about the company is also featured.

Cyan Inc.
http://www.cyan.com/

The creator of Myst, Cyan Inc., promotes the game by answering players' most Frequently Asked Questions about future game releases, the possibility of a movie, and the potential for other Myst-related entertainment such as books. A catalog of Myst paraphernalia is online offering mousepads, clothing, mugs, and calendars. And a link to Brøderbund, the game's publisher, leads to technical support. Finally, links pointing to players' pages and other Myst-related sites round out the offerings.

CyberDreams Inc.
http://www.cyberdreams.com/

Discover why the interactive, nightmarish adventure game I Have No Mouth, And I Must Scream, based on the short story of the same name by Harlan Ellison, won *Computer Gaming World* magazine's Adventure Game of the Year Award. And find out how Dark Seed II picks up where Dark Seed, the SPA's Best Fantasy Role Playing/Adventure Program of 1993, left off. Then look ahead to upcoming CyberDreams releases: Noir, Reverence, and The Incredible Shrinking Man.

CyberFlix Inc.
http://www.cyberflix.com/

The maker of Dust: A Tale of the Wired West, Lunicus, and Jump Raven, CyberFlix promotes its released titles with story background and downloads of the latest updates or a product demo. Look ahead to the company's future releases and get the early word on titles such as Skull Cracker, Titanic: Adventure Out of Time, and Red Jack's Revenge.

Deadly Games
http://www.deadlygames.com/

Offering downloadable demos and updates, Deadly Games promotes its line of WW II air, land, and sea battle simulation games. Check out Drumbeat, M4, The Battle of Britain, Bomber, and U-Boat. Background on each of the games offers a graphical introduction to play, while critical reviews support each game's quality. A section called Dispatches From the Front previews the company's latest title, U-Boat II (downloadable demo available), and features letters from players.

Destiny Software Productions, Inc.
http://www.destiny-software.com/destiny/

Discover what is new at Destiny, the developer of computer games like Creepers, Solitaire's Journey, TOS Basketball and Baseball, Blood Bowl, and Dark Seed II. Download an addictive puzzle shareware game called Jam, check out the company's Internet Radio Software, and try out the featured 3D Demo.

Digital Image Design Ltd.
http://www.did.com/

Home base for *Computer Gaming World's* 1996 winner of the Simulation of the Year award, Digital Image Design promotes its star product, EF2000. Read background on the game where players fly missions in NATO's most intense jet fighter, the Eurofighter 2000; review the specs and capabilities of the aircraft; peruse the EF2000 technical FAQ; check out screen shots from the game; and download the latest patches. Those

interested can also learn more about the company and preview upcoming DID releases.

Digital Pictures
http://www.digipix.com/

A developer of photo-realistic interactive games for multiple platforms, Digital Pictures promotes its titles with plot synopses and screen shots. Find games like Quarterback Attack with Mike Ditka, Maximum Surge with Yasmine Bleeth, and the controversial teenage slasher spoof, NightTrap.

Domark Software
http://www.domark.com/

Find out what's old, what's new, and what's soon to come out from the folks at Domark. Better yet, demo many of the titles they have. Plus, win prizes and enjoy special offers. A sampling of the titles with downloadable demos includes: Shellshock, Big Red Racing, Total Mayhem, and Bud Tucker in Real Trouble. Games are good for stand-alone play, and some support multiuser networked fun. This corporate site's a real player's bonanza!

Electronic Arts Online
http://www.ea.com/

This big name develops, publishes, and distributes big brand names like Bullfrog, Origin, EA Sports, EA Studios, and Jane's Combat Simulations. Surf the site by platform or label, and take the Web survey. Some demos and movies are available, but not where expected; check the suit-and-tie stuff. Also find a company profile, current company news, and customer support.

Elite Systems
http://www.elite-systems.co.uk/

With gaming hits like Airwolf, Commando, Paperboy, and Dragon's Lair, Elite promotes its latest opportunities both for employment and play. Download demos of the company's newest releases, Strike Point and Onside. Also find details about its Dirt Racer and Virtuoso games. Those curious about working at this family-owned business can look into the situations currently available.

Empire Interactive
http://www.empire-us.com/

The maker of Terry Bradshaw Fantasy Football, Dawn Patrol Head to Head, and Dreamweb promotes these and other games at this corporate home page. Find FAQs for many of the war theme games, preview upcoming releases, and review the company's current titles. Press releases, technical support, and an introduction to the EI staff are also featured.

Enlight Software
http://www.enlight.com/

Discover what Capitalism is all about. Enlight Software promotes its real-time, business strategy game based on the economic system that made America what it is today. Download a demo and patch, read the FAQs and strategy tips, and find out how to order a copy of the game. The critics are raving about the game; see what they're saying and why.

Epic MegaGames
http://www.epicgames.com/

Promoting Fire Fight, Extreme Pinball, Radix: Beyond the Void, and other older action attractions, Epic also turns attention to new titles like UNREAL, Jazz 2, and Curly's Adventure. Download demos and shareware, get the FAQs, and read the latest company news. Those curious about what's coming up can certainly find out, and anyone ready to buy can shop the onsite Epic MegaStore.

FormGen
http://www.formgen.com/

Bragging it publishes the "hottest" computer games from the world's "best" PC game developers, FormGen sets out to prove the claim. Visit the product gallery for information on the company's product line, including Duke Nukem 3D and Space Dude. Stop by the shareware library to download versions of Duke

Nukem 3D, Terminal Velocity, Black Knight, and other titles. Check out the support area for patches and other game information. Or rummage through the company files for news and general corporate data.

GameTek
http://www.gametek.com/

Reviews, previews, demos, FAQs, hints, patches, and much more are online from the folks who've brought out games like Road Warrior, Jeopardy, and Super Street Fighter 2 Turbo. Check out the latest and expect to spend some time exploring. There's plenty to do and see, and there's a promise that there's more to come!

Goldentree Enterprises
http://www.goldtree.com//welcome.htm

This Web page promotes Goldentree's star release, Cylindrix, a 360 degree, 3-on-3 battle to the death. Download the demo, or check out the shots of ships and aliens. Also find technical support, company news, and the game's reviews. Onsite contests add prizes to the mix of excitement and entertainment.

GT Interactive Software
http://www.gtinteractive.com/
homepage.html

Promising not just games but experiences, GT Interactive promotes its line of intensity games that includes mega-titles like DOOM II, Ultimate DOOM, Wolfenstein 3D, and Mortal Kombat 3. Download demos, check out Cool Extras, and seek online support. Those who want to stay in touch can add their name to the mailing list. There's plenty to do and see; plan to explore.

GTE Entertainment
http://www.im.gte.com/

New titles include Titanic: Adventure Out of Time, NCAA Championship Basketball, and Siege. Older titles include FX Fighter, EF 2000, and Dust. Check out the games, find technical support, and get the latest company information.

id Software
http://www.idsoftware.com/

The developer of titles like Quake, DOOM, DOOM II, Ultimate DOOM, and other "killer" games hosts this welcome to its world of death and destruction. Stop by to play with the corpses—download demos, shareware, upgrades, and patches. Or visit the Shopping Maul to find out how to order. Those curious about the company can read all about it, and anyone so possessed can link to companies considered "Friends of id."

I-Motion
http://www.imotion.com/

The developer of Alone in the Dark previews coming titles including Knight's Chase and Virtual Chess, and promotes current releases like C.E.O. and Prisoner of Ice, based on H. P. Lovecraft's writings. Explore the games, enjoy the available downloads, and check out the Hints Corner for quick tips on play. Those looking to buy games can also find out how to order a product.

Infogrames
http://www.infogrames.com

This multilingual site promotes the products available through this international producer of interactive games. Find adventure, action, simulation, and discovery games including titles like Alone in the Dark, Knight's Chase, Solar Crusade, and International Tennis Open. Find out what's new with the company and what's coming soon. Those just rooting around should check out the Goodies page for fabulous downloads.

Interactive Magic
http://www.imagicgames.com/

A developer and publisher, Interactive Magic promotes its simulation and strategy games at this corporate site. Check out the demos available for downloading: American Civil War, Decathlon, Apache, Star Rangers, Hind, and more. Also find company news and informa-

tion, technical support, and ordering information. Feeling lucky? Take a chance in the online contests.

Interplay Productions
http://www.interplay.com/

Between what's coming, what's just arrived, and what was already here, this super site sparks enough excitement to enthrall most any game-player. Check out this small sampling from the dozens of titles promoted: Battle Chess, Descent, Jetfighter III, Normality, Shattered Steel, Star Trek: Starfleet Academy, and Zombie Dinos from the Planet Zeltoid. Stop by to download a wide range of demos, and while onsite, look into placing orders.

Intracorp Entertainment
http://www.intracorp.com/

A developer, publisher, and distributor of multimedia entertainment software under the labels Capstone, Three-Sixty, and The Next Move, Intracorp titles include Witchaven and Witchaven II, Roger Zelazny's Chronomaster, William Shatner's Tekwar, plus chess, casino, and cards titles. Stop by for demos, support, and additional company information.

Kinesoft Development
http://www.kinesoft.com/

The developer of Earthworm Jim, Pitfall, Knight Moves, and Comedy Classics struts its stuff at this promotional site. Learn all about the company, how to pronounce a few relevant terms, and what Kinesoft opportunities are available for fun and profit. Links lead to the promotional pages for each of the company's games.

Looking Glass Technologies
http://www.lglass.com/

The result of a merger between Blue Sky Productions and Lerner Research, Looking Glass Technologies is a developer and publisher of interactive games and simulation software. Its current titles include Flight Unlimited and Terra Nova; its future titles will include British Open Golf. Find out more about these games and the company behind them.

LucasArts
http://www.lucasarts.com/

Download demos and other product fun from the gaming company which has grown out of the empire built by the man behind the *Star Wars* legend. Among the titles in the Product Spotlights find Dark Forces, Rebel Assault II, and Jedi Knight. Other site features include press releases, the current company newsletter, and a link to the company store. Those needing technical support can also find an online hand.

Magnet Interactive Studios
http://www.magnet.com/mis.html

Explore the interactive gaming fun available from this subsidiary of the Magnet Interactive Group, Inc. Current titles featured include Beyond the Wall: Stories Beyond the Vietnam Wall, Comedians, Chop Suey, and ICEBREAKER. Download demos and other gaming promotional material. Also catch a preview of an upcoming title, BLUESTAR.

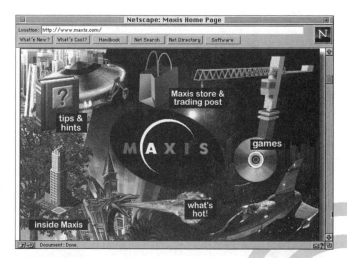

Maxis
http://www.maxis.com/

Simulations, creativity, adventure, and action games are all on tap at this user-friendly, try-me, buy-me gaming stop. Find titles like A-Train, the various SimCity editions, RoboSport, and Full Tilt! Pinball. Those who want to chat about the games can visit the BBS forums. Tips and hints support play. And of course, the company

previews what's coming down the pike. This site is worth a look.

Microforum
http://www.microforum.com/

Screaming Skies, Mind Grind, and Virtual Corporation only head the list of titles touted here. Demo games like Expect No Mercy, Shakii The Wolf, and Iron Blood. Also find patches, FAQs with cheats and hints, customer service, and online ordering. Register to win prizes, read game reviews, and drop by the Coffee Shop to render an opinion or two.

Microsoft Games
http://www.microsoft.com/games/

A page from the Microsoft corporate site, this directory points to games Windows' users play. Download a free trial of Monster Truck Madness, preview upcoming releases like Deadly Tide, and check out older offerings like the flight and space sims and the sports games. A link to information about Microsoft's Internet Gaming Zone points to online, real-time play.

Mindscape
http://www.mindscape.com/

Offering games that cover the action, adventure, military combat, and fantasy role-playing genres, Mindscape promotes its multiplatform releases. Find titles like Air Power: Battle of the Skies, Warhammer: Shadow of the Horned Rate, Angel Devoid: Face of the Enemy, and Chessmaster 5000. Download demos for Azrael's Tear, Fantasy General, Panzer General, and more. Other site features include company news and an online store open 24 hours a day.

New World Computing
http://www.nwcomputing.com/

Download playable demos for Chaos Overlords and Empire II, plus find game patches for about a dozen more titles such as Anvil Dawn, Might and Magic, and Hammer of the Gods. Online FAQs answer the most common technical and non-technical questions about the games, and the customer service area tells how to reach the company for support.

NovLogic

http://www.novalogic.com/

This site is for those who number combat sims among their games of choice. Check out these titles for waging war: Werewolf vs. Comanche 2.0, Armored Fist, Comanche, and Wolfpack. Find complete product ordering information, press quotes, and customer support. Visitors can also sign up to receive the company newsletter and preview the titles on their way.

Ocean Software

http://www.ocean.co.uk/

Surf the Ocean Software site for a look at the company's current and future releases. Find titles like Worms, True Pinball, The Killing Grounds Alien Breed 3DII, World Rally Fever, and Zero Divide. Game information, screen shots, and some demos are available to download. Site features also include an insightful look at the company and its in-house team, information on contests, online help, and other customer services.

Oxford Softworks

http://www.demon.co.uk/oxford-soft/

Specializing in classic games of strategy and skill, Oxford Softworks promotes its line of chess, backgammon, Othello, go, checkers, and 4-in-a-row software. Explore the company's gaming options, review its history and services, or place orders online.

Parallax Software

http://www.pxsoftware.com/

Those looking for the latest news, information, and updates on Descent II need look no further. Download the latest here. Plus find playable demos, shareware, demo movies, screen shots, and levels for both I and II. These folks hold the copyright for the game; they should know best how to treat the game's players!

Pixel Storm Entertainment

http://www.sy-systems.com/

This multimedia production company offers its clients many services, and it develops games to boot. Download free demos of two strategic puzzle games: MegaMotion and PlasmaZone. For those who enjoy these games' challenges, ordering information is also online.

Playmates Interactive Entertainment

http://www.playmatestoys.com/
piehome.htm

Care for a piece of free PIE? Download product information and playable demos for Battle Arena Toshinden, Earthworm Jim 1 & 2, and Powerslave. Also find product profiles for MDK, Into the Void, and Mutant Chronicles: The Mortificator. Contests, press releases, and technical support information add to the balance of features that build out this site.

Pop Rocket

http://www.poprocket.com/

Here's the home of Total Distortion, the music video adventure game. Play mini-games taken from Total Distortion CD-ROM, download some of the tunes and sound loops, check out the graphics, or take a guided tour of the game's characters, places, and other things. Need hints? Stop by the Hints Forum. Want videos? Try the Video Trading area. Looking for something different? Stop by the Shockwave gaming area.

Presto Studios

http://www.prestostudios.com/

Read the story of how a rag-tag band of merry hackers overcame all odds to…Oh, never mind that. Skip to the list of The Journeyman Project games that have come from the effort, and explore how hard work and dedication can turn into fun.

Psygnosis
http://www.psygnosis.com/

Known for its award-winning Lemmings series, this acquired subsidiary of Sony Corporation of America is an international game developer and publisher with over 100 titles for a variety of computer platforms. Rummage the files for information on what's out, preview what's in the pipeline to come, and check out those "e-clips"—videos, screen shots, demos, and more! Titles currently in the e-clip spotlight include: Destruction Derby 2, Wipeout XL, Lemmings Paintball, Krazy Ivan, and over a half dozen more.

Raven Software Company
http://www.ravensoft.com/

Visitors are cordially invited to take a look around the site, download some demo material, and offer the company feedback. Find action and adventure titles like Hexen, Heretic, Cyclones, ShadowCaster, and Black Crypt. Other site features include a technical support area and the company's online profile.

ReadySoft
http://www.readysoft.com/

ReadySoft promotes its roster of titles including Shadoan, The Music in Me, Dragon's Lair and Dragon's Lair II, Space Ace, and Robinson's Requiem. Downloads offered include hints for various games, instructions for running the games on Windows 95, and a BrainDead 13 screen saver. Also find movies for Brain-Dead 13, Dragon's Lair, and Space Ace. Company information and technical support round out the available offerings.

Reality Bytes
http://www.realbytes.com/

A developer and publisher, Reality Bytes promotes its multiplayer arcade action game, Havoc, and previews its upcoming 3D action adventure, Dark Vengeance. Link to the "official" Havoc Web site, check out the Reality Bytes technical support area, read press clips,

and review the company's history. Those looking can also check into job opportunities with the company.

Revolution Software Ltd.
http://www.revolution.co.uk/

Developing graphical adventure gaming fun, Revolution promotes its titles: Lure of the Temptress, Beneath a Steel Sky, Broken Sword: The Shadow of the Templars, and Circle of Blood. Enjoy game overviews, walkthroughs, and screen shots.

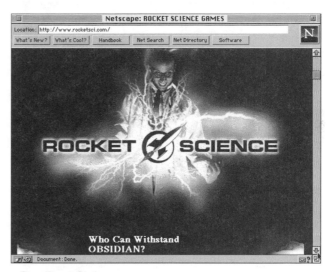

Rocket Science
http://www.rocketsci.com

Unlike most gaming company sites, which are often too "corporate," this one is actually fun. The site itself is a kind of game, with a great personality and a great look. But its presentation isn't all that recommends it. Check out the company's newer titles: The Space Bar, Rocket Jockey, and Obsidian; plus, find information on its older titles: Cadillacs and Dinosaurs, Loadstar, and Wingnuts. Enjoy demos, cheat codes, screen shots, and tech support.

Scavenger, Inc.
http://www.mcb.net/parsec/scavenger_page.html

Find Into the Shadows, A.M.O.K., Scorcher, Kicker, and Terminus in the spotlight at this game developer's home page. Download a rolling demo and demo editor for Into the Shadows, an animation file for Terminus, and screen shots from Scorcher. Stop by the online gallery for "exclusive" pictures, and check out the What's New? files for the latest news. Contact information and a calendar of release dates round out the items offered.

Shiny Entertainment
http://www2.shiny.com/shiny/

The Earthworm Jim series and MDK are the featured titles on these pages. Find information, demos, screen shots, and more. The company also posts job opportunities and a bit about itself.

Sierra
http://www.sierra.com/

Action and arcade, adventure, sports, simulations, strategy, and even family entertainment games are all featured in the diverse titles at Sierra. Browse and buy. Or download freebies including demos of the latest games, Larry pop-ups, and a Sierra Diving Adventure screen saver. Also find live, online gaming opportunities, news about upcoming releases, and customer services such as technical support.

Sir-tech Sofware, Inc.
http://www.sir-tech.com/

Spotlighting its mythical titles like Star Trail—Realms of Arkania, Wizardry Trilogies, Jagged Alliance, Druid—Daemons of the Mind, and Wizardry Gold, Sir-tech hosts this promotional page. Get in on the weekly game giveaways and contests, see what's new in the way of hints and screen shots, and check out what titles are on the way from the folks who are proud official sponsors of the U.S. Bobsled Team.

Spectrum Holobyte - MicroProse
http://www.microprose.com/

Visit two of the four development studios owned by Spectrum Holobyte, a developer and publisher whose games include Sid Meier's Civilization, X-COM, F15

Strike Eagle, and Fleet Defender, as well as Falcon 3.0. Star Trek: TNG "A Final Unity," and Top Gun: Fire at Will. Check out the latest and greatest from these two leading design studios. Enjoy demos, updates, and new versions. Plus, find the expected corporate profiles and press clippings.

Stormfront Studios
http://www.stormfront.com/

The creator of the Tony La Russa Baseball series and Old Time Baseball promotes these and other interactive entertainment titles. Read all about the games, download patches, and link to the EA store to order online. Company information and online support are also available for those needing additional assistance.

Strategic Studies Group: GHQ
http://www.ssg.com.au/

Boasting the "world's best" games of strategy, this game maker promotes its latest, previews its future, and glories in its past. Find titles like Total War, Warlords II, Carriers at War, the Battlefront series, and the Civil War series. Visit these games' pages for product news, available downloads, FAQs, and other gaming aids. The Scenario Library also offers downloads worth checking out.

Take2 Interactive Software
http://www.take2games.com/

Find out what's new from the folks responsible for titles like Ripper, Hell, Maximum Roadkill, Master of Orion, Star Crusader, and Millennia. Explore the latest: Battlecruiser 3000AD and Iron & Blood. Plus, find game overviews and promotional matter like screen shots, patches, and FAQ files for all the company's games. Those in need of support can consult the Frequently Asked Technical Questions file or e-mail the company any questions.

Team 17 Software Ltd.
http://www.team17.com/

Looking for demos? Look here and find a dozen or so! Demo titles like Worms, AlienBreed3D II—The Killing Ground, Kingpin Bowling, Superfrog, Arcade Pool, Project X, and World Rally Fever. Also enjoy game patches, hints and tips, plus a T17 FAQ. Worm fans will find a link to the official World Wide Worm site. And there is other free game-related stuff to download out of the Goodie Bag. Need more reasons to stop by? Two words: Beer Garden.

Trimark Interactive
http://www.trimarkint.com/

Promoting its latest and soon-to-be-released games, Trimark opens the information vault on: The Hive, Magzone, Halls of the Dead, and Galaxis. A playable demo of The Hive is currently available for download, and the others should come online soon. In addition to game news, also find information on technical support and the company's other customer services.

Twenty First Century Entertainment
http://www.21stcent.com/

A publisher of pinball sims including Pinball World and the new Total Pinball 3D, Twenty First Century hosts

this virtual product showroom. Check out the company's product line, download playable demos and screen shots, review a cheat code, and find out how to order products. Technical support is also available.

Ubi Soft Entertainment
http://www.ubisoft.com/

Pick a country from the seven listed and let the exploration of this international distributor and software developer begin. Ubi does so much more than games, but in that area of this site find a demo of Rayman and screen shots from POD. Those with ideas for Rayman 2 are encouraged to enter the company's current contest. And anyone curious about the company will find plenty to ponder in the corporate profile.

US Gold
http://www.usgold.com/

Find out what's glittering at the home page of this subsidiary of Eidos PLC. Check out the company's exclusive line of sports video games commemorating the Summer 1996 Olympics in Atlanta, including an adventure title featuring IZZY, the official mascot everyone tried to forget. Also find technical information for Desert/Jungle Strike, Dominus, and Slipstream 5000, along with a demo for Shellshock, a new tank combat game.

Viacom New Media
http://www.viacomnewmedia.com/

Fans of games based on movies and television programs can't go wrong with the current features at the Viacom Game Zone. Titles in the spotlight include Zoop, Congo The Movie: Descent into Zinj, Phantom, Star Trek: Deep Space Nine—Harbinger, and Beavis and Butt-head in Virtual Stupidity. Catch the latest "buzz," sneak hints, and find help for all. Also find previews for the titles currently under development and read interviews with people relating the ideas behind the games.

Vic Tokai Inc.
http://www.victokai.com/

Explore the product line-up of Nova Spring PC Games. Titles include Defcon 5, Alien Virus, Deadline, Silverload, The Scroll, Extractors, and Virtuoso. Find game overviews and screen shots, but watch for tips and tricks, video downloads, game specials, and giveaways coming soon.

Virgin Interactive Entertainment
http://www.vie.com/

Virgin promotes its Hot List of games which includes titles like The 7th Guest and its sequel, The 11th Hour; Command & Conquer and C&C: The Cover Operation; Agile Warrior: F-111X; Hyper 3-D Pinball; and Zone Raiders. Find game overviews and downloadable goodies. Those curious about what's coming down the pike can look to see what's in the works, while those needing technical assistance can access the Ultra Tech Matrix for hints, FAQs, patches, and demos.

WarnerActive
http://www.warneractive.com/index.html

Anyone who is still wondering "Where's Waldo?" need only drop by this site for an answer. He's at the circus and he's exploring geography. Download playable demos for both of these "Where's Waldo?" interactive games.

Westwood Studios
http://www.westwood.com

A division of Virgin Games, Westwood Studios is a developer and publisher of interactive entertainment software, with such titles such as BattleTech, Dune II, Command & Conquer, Kyrandia, and the first commercial Internet-supported version of Monopoly to its credit. Read the company's history, review its gaming products, shop online, or visit the chat area and talk tactics.

 **AUTHOR'S PICK**

Interactive Entertainment Industry Links
http://herb.algonet.se/~hegge-t/ieil.htm

It seems hardly fair to pick one company over another as an Editor's Choice when the selection basically boils down to a preference for the games a company has to offer. So instead of choosing one, I choose them all. And I choose them via this indispensable resource—a regularly updated who's who of the companies involved in the Interactive Entertainment Industry. Visitors to this page will find the names (big and little) who work to make the video and computer games industry the unyielding and pioneering success it is today. Organized by company type, the hyperlinked directory points to the home pages of the organizations concerned with: consoles, software, hardware, development, business, media, and miscellaneous concerns. Through it, players can scout the latest releases from their favorite companies, keep abreast of corporate developments, and perhaps anticipate where the future will take the industry and those who enjoy its wares. Thanks, Henrik!

Zombie Virtual Reality Entertainment
http://www.zombie.com/

Demo and/or preview the coming attractions from the company promising cutting edge 3D audio, 3D graphics, and multiplayer networking. Check out Locus, Ice and Fire, and ZPG (Zero Population Growth). Be sure to stop by the technical support area, too. There you'll find patches, useful files, and tips.

Developer Resources
http://www.neversoft.com/christer/GR/ developer.html

Here's another directory aimed at game developers, but a good resource for gamers as well. Find the companies who make gaming magic organized by category and type. Under Hardware Manufacturers find Computer, Chips, and Operating Systems; Consoles; Peripherals; and Miscellaneous. Under Software Manufacturers find Development Systems and Tools; Graphics Systems and Programs; Code Libraries; Services; Schools, Organizations, and Associations; Developers and Publishers. Also find Trade Magazines and Book/Magazine Publishers. Many of the directory listings are annotated, and all are hyperlinked to the company home pages.

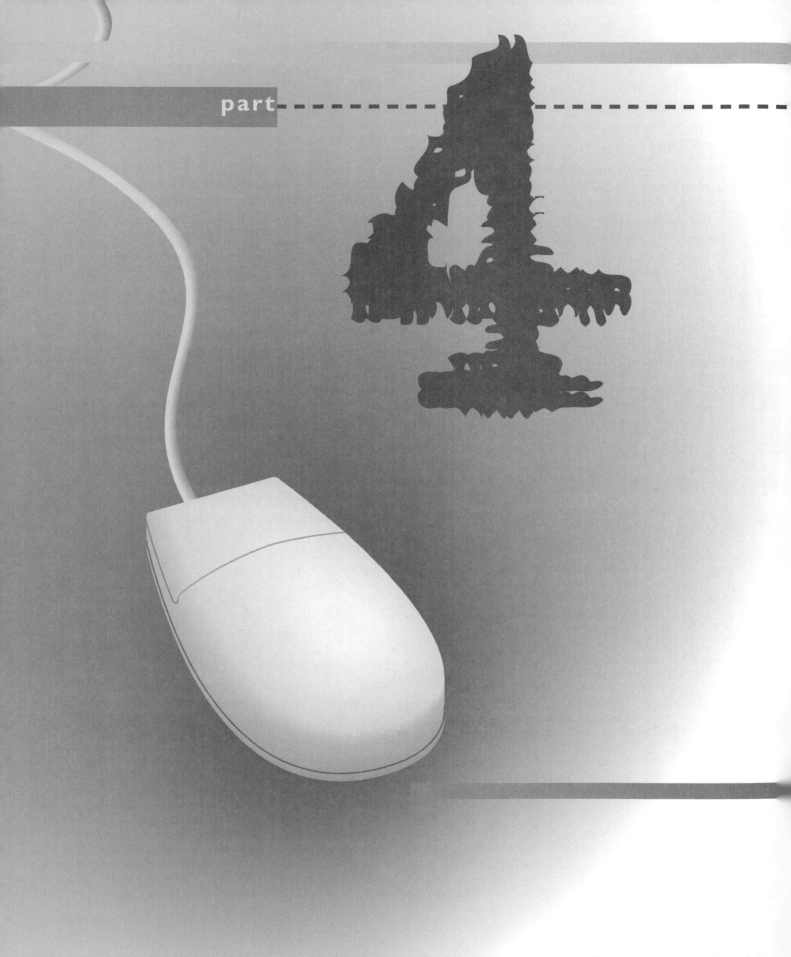

HOW TO PLAY. . .

QUAKE

DUKE NUKEM 3D

DOOM, DOOM II, AND
ULTIMATE DOOM

CIVNET

WARCRAFT II:
TIDES OF DARKNESS

MECHWARRIOR 2 AND
NETMECH

chapter 17

QUAKE

THEY *had* to do it to us, huh? They couldn't hold back a little longer. I think many of us were happy playing our 3D games of past (Duke Nukem 3D, Rise of the Triad, and Doom 95), since custom levels and multiplayer play made for high replayability. But the folks at id software just had to throw a cyber monkey wrench into everything on Saturday, June 22, 1996, when the shareware version of Quake quietly surfaced on the Net (in true id style…no fanfare). It didn't take long for word of mouth to catch up with the release (um, maybe *seconds*…) until every computer game fanatic had a working copy on their hard drive. Qtest—a Deathmatch multiplayer Quake beta that had floated around for a while proved to be pale in comparison to the polished seven-level shareware release. Now with the full version shipped, the creators of such revolutionary 3D titles as Wolfenstein 3D and Doom, Quake has set, once again, new advancements in graphics, sound, and networked gameplay.

The Internet is chock-full of Quake files, FAQs, screen shots, discussion groups, strategies, bonus levels, and more, but for beginners it's easy to find secrets, cheat codes, and notes on how to get set up for an Internet multiplayer game. Links to various Quake sites around the Web can be found in Chapter 4 of this book.

QUAKE SYSTEM REQUIREMENTS

Quake is only available for DOS. It will run in a Windows 95 box, but you will need 16MB RAM to do so. You must have MS DOS 5.0 or higher, a 60MHz Pentium processor, 8MB RAM minimum, 40MB hard drive/disk space for the shareware game (yes, 40MB!), or 75MB for the full version. There is VGA and SVGA graphics support, and Quake also supports Sound Blaster cards and 100% compatibles, modem, network, and IP (Internet) play. Mouse and joystick are optional.

A CD-ROM is required if you buy the full game in the stores. However, there is another way to get the full game. To purchase Quake online at their Web site, download the encrypted package and follow the installation procedure. You'll be prompted to call an 800 number at some point along the line and you'll be given a password to unlock your copy of the game after id has received your credit card details.

The shareware version of Quake will have sound effects—but no music—since the CD is required. Trent Reznor, the brawn behind "Nine Inch Nails" fame, provides an eerie backdrop to the game. The 11 songs are fascinating and appropriate to the Quake environment, and to put it best, it's like Industrial Music meets Tangerine Dream. Shareware players, don't be disappointed—if you put another music CD in your drive during gameplay, it will play it and change tracks with each new level you complete!

QUAKE QUEST: BASIC OUTLINE AND FEATURES

The best way to describe the *feel* of Quake is to compare it to a medieval yet futuristic theme, where *slip gates* (teleportation machines) are being used for malevolent purposes by the evil "Quake" from another dimension.

Your primary goal is to stay alive in this dark, gothic environment against the Quake's deadly

army of Rottweilers, Grunts, Enforcers, Death Knights, Ogres, Shamblers, Fiends, and more.

The secondary goal is to make it to the slip gates at the end of each level until you return back to the start of the episode (after five to eight levels) and enter a new dimension. There are four episodes, or dimensions, and four skill levels to choose from (one really tough "Nightmare" skill, if you can find it—it's hidden). The shareware version contains only one episode, *Dimension of the Doomed* and the other three episodes are *Realm of Black Magic, Netherworld,* and *The Elder World.* I suggest you play these in consecutive order as the dimensions get progressively more difficult.

Quake features a full six degrees of freedom (you can look up and down now—as opposed to Doom), a revamped keyboard layout (although somewhat similar to Doom/Doom II) and 3D polygon-based, texture-mapped items. Enemies in Doom may look like they are in real 3D since you're looking at them from a first-person perspective—but they really are 2D. Each object, monster, and weapon in Quake are in true 3D.

I DIDN'T KNOW THAT!

If you have the shareware or full version of Quake, there are a lot of text files to read in your directory that will brief you on the basics of gameplay, controls, weapons, bad guys, and single-player or multiplayer set-up. Read these or print them out to supplement this chapter: Help.txt, Licinfo.txt, Manual.txt, Order.txt, Readme.txt, Slicnse.txt, and Techinfo.txt.

SELECTED SECRETS EPISODE ONE

Try these out with your Episode 1, Level 1 (shareware or registered), and you'll get the hang of where to look in future levels for more secrets:

1 Forward and to the right of the start is a ledge with flashing lights. Jump up on the ledge and shoot the red design on the wall (to your right). There will be a box of shells behind it.

2 Under the first bridge you come to a river. It goes into a cavern. Jump into the river and follow it along into the cavern. Go up the steps—there will be a 100 health item

and a door to the end of the level; the game will register a secret. At the end of the cavern is a lift taking you back up to the start.

3   Past the first bridge is a door. Enter the door and kill the monsters. To the right of the entrance is a column and a ledge. Go to the corner between the two and shoot the globe texture high up on the column. A platform will rise and you will be on the ledge. Turn to your right and shoot the globe texture on the ledge. The wall behind the globe will open, leading to a quad damage item.

4   To the left of the door past the bridge is a hall. Follow it to the right and there is a button on the wall; when the button is pressed, a platform will slide out from the wall. Halfway across the platform, turn to your left. There will be a red target slightly above the level of your head. Shoot it and turn to your left. A door in a wall will open, revealing a double-barreled shotgun.

5   Past the platform over the pool is a door. Go through the door and head forward and to the right. Go down the walkway and turn left. Follow down the walkway again and turn left again. There will be a button and a light in front of you.

6   Jump onto the banister, then jump onto the light. Either step or jump onto the button and look at the wall in front of you. There will be a ledge and two blocks sticking out. Jump to the lowest block, then up to the next block and to the ledge. Inside is a 100 health item.

7   Go all the way down the walkway. There is a door. To the right and behind a column (where it's real dark) will be a biosuit. Take it. Be quick, as the biosuit doesn't give you much more time than you need. Jump into the slime and swim underneath the door. Follow the tunnel until it opens into a larger area and there will be a platform overhead.

8   Swim up to the opening in the platform. If you are running low on air, you can swim up to the platform from the tunnel, but you must step over the opening before the game registers the secret. There will be a platform with a yellow armor and some health on it. There is also a slipgate to the area over the door past the bridge (back around to secret #3).

QUAKE AND BAKE: CHEAT CODES

Press the console key (the tilde, or "~"), type in the code of interest, and press Enter.

Code	Action
GOD	Invincibility toggled on or off
FLY	Up to the rafters! (toggle)
NOCLIP	Go through walls
NOTARGET	Monsters won't attack you unless provoked
GIVE S #	Gives you # Shells
GIVE N #	Gives you # Nails
GIVE R #	Gives you # Rockets
GIVE C #	Gives you # Cells
GIVE H #	Gives you Health # 1–999
GIVE #	Gives you weapon # (8 is the lightning gun, etc.)
IMPULSE 9	All Weapons
IMPULSE 11	Escape from the console for each use
IMPULSE 255	Quad Damage!

Code	Action
REGISTERED 1	Makes the game think it's registered. You can get the lightning gun, and open the doors to the registered levels. (It will hang if you enter registered slip gates.)
R_FULLBRIGHT 1	No more shadows

INTERNET PLAY

As in most games, the AI in Quake doesn't compare to real human opposition, so get hooked on Death-match play, a.k.a. Frag-Fests (note: you're competing for *Frags*—get one when you take a life, lose one if you die…the person with the most Frags wins).

There are many ways to play Quake online (with up to 15 others via modem, LAN, serial connection, or Internet), but most of us do not have access to a network, and modem play restricts you to opponents in your city (or the long-distance costs would be astronomical). If you want to play Quake over the Internet, you absolutely need a 28.8 Kbps or better modem. Generally speaking, the more people in the game, the slower and less smooth the game will be (but there are other relevant variables to consider such as bandwidth, latency, current load, etc.).

There are a few ways to set up Quake to play on the Net, but the easiest would be to use the TCP/IP under Windows 95 and edit the Q95.BAT file (although playing in Windows 95 may slow frame rate down—read the *Techinfo.txt* file that comes with Quake on how to configure properly). Once up and running, you will need to find the IP address of a Quake server near you. You can find one by going to various Quake Server lists. If you're so inclined, other methods will work such as the Beame & Whiteside DOS TCP/IP stack or Novell's

ODI IPX stack under DOS, PDIPX with packet drivers under DOS, and the Microsoft IPX stack in a Win95 DOS box. Instructions on setting it up are also in the *Techinfo.txt* file.

Quake has two kinds of servers: Listen and Dedicated. A Listen server should run on the faster of the players' machines, which acts as the server while running the game. The best scenario is if you have an extra PC that has some kick to it, it can act as a Dedicated server, i.e., handle all server duties and leaving the players' machines free of the added unnecessary work. Quake will allow up to eight players on a Listen server, and double that on a Dedicated server. Type **Quake-listen** to launch a Listen server, and **Quake-dedicated 16** to launch a Dedicated server.

Another fairly easy way to set up on the Net is through a dedicated Internet game service such as Kali or MPlayer Gameway (see Chapter 13). For Kali, download the free software from http://www.axxis.com/kali/ and run Quake as if it was on an IPX network. The Web site MPlayer Gameway also allows you to play Quake on their network at http://www.mplayer.com./ First download their client software, create an account, and connect to the Internet via your ISP (complete instructions are in the free kit).

There are many options in playing multiplayer Quake. Variations in Deathmatch, cooperative play, teamplay (different color pants), difficulty level, and starting point—are all considerations. I do suggest you at least finish the first episode in a single-player stand-alone game before you decide to tackle others from around the globe.

So turn the lights down low, the speakers up high, and be careful soldier, 'cause some heads are gonna roll!

QUAKE SERVER LISTS

Quake Command
http://www.nuc.net/quake/

The Legions of Quake
http://www.legions.com/search.htm

The Quake Stomping Grounds
http://www.stomped.com/servers.html

Gamelords.com
http://gamelords.com/quake/

Deicide's Quake Domain
http://www.monmouth.com/~vfuks/servers.html

World Online
http://www.worldonline.nl/quake/

The Arena
http://www.the-pages.com/quake/

Grizzly's Quake Lair
http://www.geocities.com/Hollywood/7710/quake.html

DeathStar Quake Pages
http://www.abm.com/quake/

Elgrande's
http://members.aol.com/elgrande1/server.htm

PIPO Quake Server List
http://www.pipo.com/quake/

NAZ Inc.
http://www.naz.com/quake/quake.html

SSI Micro Servers
http://www.ssimicro.com/ssipages/ssi-bin/quak

18

DUKE NUKEM 3D

COME GET SOME!

The knockout game of 1996 took many die-hard computer gamers by surprise, and by storm. Who would have ever thought that the third installment in the Duke Nukem series would be the true Doom-killer? Time and time again, countless titles found their way to store shelves over the years all claiming to be "the next Doom." However, all but a few proved to be creatively (and often, technologically) inferior. Some have come close, such as Dark Forces or Rise of the Triad, but for the most part, many were bland, unimaginative clones with nothing new to offer.

The original Duke Nukem was released by Apogee in 1991 and the sequel two years later. 3D Realms, Apogee's label for their 3D titles, fired out Duke Nukem 3D, which picks up where Duke Nukem II left off—the Duke heads back to Earth after his long and violent blast-fest only to find that it has been taken over by aliens (who took all the women away…that makes Duke MAD!!).

There are three episodes in the full version of Duke Nukem 3D: "L.A. Meltdown," "Lunar Apocalypse," and "Shrapnel City." They run chronologically but you don't have to play them in consecutive order. Each of the three episodes contain about 10 or 12 levels, but there are hidden levels scattered throughout them all. L.A. Meltdown begins in the 21st century in downtown Angeles, completely deserted with the exception of our alien rivals, other creepy characters, and a few Earth women tied and bound in slimy pods. Lunar Apocalypse takes place just above Earth in a giant space station, and the final episode, Shrapnel City, takes Duke back to Earth. To finish the job off, Duke is to obliterate the rest of the extra-terrestrials complete with a climactic ending—a battle-to-the-death against one helluva beast in an outdoor football stadium.

Duke Nukem 3D can be played solo or head-to-head via a modem or network (appropriately called DukeMatch games). As with many other computer games over the past few years—playing against another player (or many others) is both thrilling and highly addictive. This is especially true with Duke Nukem, and nothing gets your heart racing like challenging *real* live human opponents on the other end.

GETTING STARTED

The minimum system requirements to run Duke Nukem 3D are listed as follows: a 486 with 8MG RAM and VGA graphics (486DX2/66 with a local bus video card is suggested). SVGA mode requires a Pentium with 16MG RAM and a PCI local bus and VESA compliant video card. 30MG disk space and a CD-ROM are also necessary. A compatible sound card is an option but is highly recommended for a good all-around experience. A modem, joystick, mouse, Gravis GamePad, Cyberman, VFX1 Headgear unit, and Space Player are all supported but not necessary. (Note: The modem *is* necessary for multiplayer games.)

For more information, read or download, the official Duke Nukem 3D FAQ (http://www.3drealms.com/duke3d.html).

ADULT CONTENT: BE FOREWARNED

The violent and sexual content in this game is no secret. You can disembowel your enemies in ways never before imagined: eyeballs and guts fly across the room, blood drips down walls, and pleas for mercy can be heard from your almost-dead opponents (in between choking on their own blood, of course). Strippers will flash you their goods if you wave a few dollars at them, while Japanese geisha girls will do it for fun. Racy comments fly from the

Duke's mouth including, profanities, sexual innu-endoes, and violent one-liners from popular R-rated movies.

How many games do you think would sell if your character was a suit-wearing accountant who goes to work and counts numbers all day? Exactly. Duke Nukem 3D is an exciting, fast-paced world with a completely interactive FANTASY environment. If you are a concerned adult, you do have the choice for toning down some of the adult features in the game from the Options menu upon regular start-up (which also includes a password protection)(see Figure 18.1).

PATCHES

You want to check your version of Duke Nukem 3D, because there are three patches available. One brings you from v1.0 to 1.1 (DN3D11PT.ZIP), the second upgrades your v1.1 to 1.3d (called DNSW13PT.ZIP), and the third is version 1.4. Find them at http://www.3drealms.com/.

MULTIPLAYER SETUP: DUKEMATCH CHOICES

Duke Nukem 3D supports an IPX-based network—you don't need to be logged onto a server, you just need to have an IPX protocol stack running. If you are lucky enough to have access to a networked system of computers in your office, Duke Nukem 3D is *the* game to have. To play against up to eight opponents, simply run the *setup.exe* program and select the menu option "Network Game." Choose the number of players involved and leave the socket number as "Default." You may select a player name if you like, then click on the "Launch Duke Nukem 3D" menu item under the "Network Game" menu. That's it!

Figure 18.1
RASC Advisory Label

MODEM

Run *setup.exe* and select "Modem Game" from the Options menu. Select whether you are to wait for a call or dial your opponent (it makes no difference). Set up the COM port for your modem (you only have to do this once), and under "Setup Modem" choose your modem type (the default should work in most cases). Select a name for yourself under "Player Name, " and if you are the "caller," then type your friend's phone number under "Phone Number List." Back under "Modem Game" click on "Launch Duke Nukem 3D," and the modem initialization will begin.

SERIAL GAMES

Run *setup.exe* and select "Serial Game" from the Option menu. Select "COM Port" and choose which COM port you use; leave the other options for now. Select a player name, then the "Launch Duke Nukem 3D" under the "Serial Game" menu.

INTERNET PLAY

The Total Entertainment Network (TEN) carries different games on their Network that allow you to play your favorite CD-ROMs on the Internet against others. Although there are a few of these gaming networks, TEN carries the exclusive rights for the game Duke Nukem 3D on the whole Internet.

Through their service (at time of press, still FREE!) you can challenge other Duke players from all over the world. To run Duke on the Net you'll need Windows 95, a Pentium 60MHz (minimum), 16MG RAM, a VLB (VESA local Bus) PCI SVGA card, and a 14.4 modem (28.8 minimum recommended). Select "TEN" from the Main Menu setup and install TEN on your hard drive.

Click on the Ten icon on your Windows 95 desktop and follow the start-up instructions from there. Check out TEN's Web page for more information (http://www.ten.net/), call 1-800-8040-TEN, or e-mail them at questions@ten.net.

COMMUNICATING WITH YOUR OPPONENTS

Apogee/3D Realm's trademarked "RemoteRidicule" (or RTS) feature is a handy (and fun) way to taunt your opponents. By pressing the Alt key and F1 to F10 during play, your opponents will hear different pre-recorded taunts ("You Suck!"). The sounds come from a file called *duke3d.rts* and you can select what exactly you want to "say"—or use the free utility included on the Duke Nukem 3D to create your own!

You may also type at your opponents during DukeMatches by pressing the "T" key and then your message. It is a good way to either tease your opponents or simply communicate back and forth during play (e.g., "Let's get outta here and try level 8 next!").

The most comprehensive list of RTS files on the Net is available at The Unofficial RTS File Distribution Center (http://www.cyberhighway.net/~srogers/duke/index.html).

DUKE NUKEM 3D AND THE INTERNET—A MATCH MADE IN HEAVEN

The shareware version of Duke Nukem 3D will go down as one of the hottest downloads in the history of the Internet. You can grab it from many places including the 3D Realms Web page (http://www.3drealms.com/duke3d.html). Version 1.4 will probably be the last of the shareware updates.

But the Internet is not just for downloading the shareware version of the game or to find and compete with others via DukeMatch (TEN Network). The Internet has many other exciting offerings for Duke Nukem fans including thousands of bonus levels, editors, screen shots, midi songs, animations, FAQs, strategy tips, secrets, cheats, patches/fixes, chat groups, news, reviews, discussion forums, art (to use for wallpaper), e-mail lists, screen savers, icons, and more!

HOW TO USE CUSTOM-MADE MAPS

I have to admit that the most useful benefit of the marriage between Duke Nukem 3D and the Internet is that you can make and trade your "user maps" or custom-built levels. The Build software is available for free on the Duke Nukem CD-ROM, and you can create your very own worlds!

The are many places on the Net to get these cool levels made by others, and this is how to use them: download the ones that sound interesting to your "temp" directory (or equivalent) on your hard drive (some may appeal to multiplayer play or may have a "theme" you like). Expand the zip file (e.g. *volcano.map*) into your Duke Nukem 3D directory and click on *setup.exe* in Windows Explorer (if using Windows 95). Choose the "Select User Lever" option and then highlight the map name you just downloaded. Then choose "Save and Launch Duke Nukem 3D," and that's it! With the amount of interesting maps out there, the possibility for repetitive gameplay is next to none. There are literally thousands—but some cool maps to look for include "Le Rock," "Anarchy," "Paintball," "Sand," "The Pond," "Factory," "Island 1," "BlockWar," "AirMobil," and "55." With such a wide variety of game additions out there, Duke Nukem 3D will remain as a resident on your hard drive for ages, even when you've completed the original full game. There is also a free utility on the Duke CD-ROM that will allow you to convert Doom WADs (custom levels) into Duke Nukem 3D Maps!

DUKE LINKS HOTLIST

Many of the cool Web sites worthy of a visit are mentioned in Chapter 4, but here is a quick reference guide of just a small sampling.

Official Duke Nukem 3D Home Page
http://www.3drealms.com/duke3d.html

Gamelords
http://www.gamelords.com/

Tribute to Duke
http://duke.intersphere.com/

Don's Duke Nukem 3D Page
http://www2.awinc.com/users/dgronlun/duke3d/duke3d.html

Mike Miller's Duke Nukem Site
http://www.bayserve.net/~mike/duke/

Andy's Duke Nukem 3D Site
http://www.empnet.com/andy/duke3d/

The Definitive Duke Nukem 3D DukeMatch Repository
http://nukem.apk.net/

The Adrenaline Vault Duke Nukem 3D Site
http://www.avault.com/duke.html

My Favorite Duke Nukem 3D Site!
http://www.wesnet.com/kevinfin/game/duke3d.htm

Stefan's Duke Nukem 3D World
http://www.erlangen.netsurf.de/stefan.welker/duke3d.htm

The 3D Gaming Scene
http://www.pol.umu.se/html/ac/split/dukenukem.html

The Duke 3D Pages
http://members.tripod.com/~duke3d/

Undernet's #Duke3D Web Page (USA Site)
http://www.acs.oakland.edu/~klmatero/duke3d/

Yahoo's List of Duke Nukem 3D related Sites
http://www.yahoo.com/Recreation/Games/Computer_Games/Titles/Duke_Nukem_3D/

DUKE NUKEM 3D CHEAT CODES

Monsters getting to you? Can't seem to keep enough ammo for your glorious weapons? Health just not up to par? Don't sweat…here is the complete list of cheats to help you through the game.

First pause the game (press the Pause key) and type in the following codes (see Table 18.1). Listed beside them are the desired outcomes. You may not have to type anything first at all for the Shareware version.

Table 18.1: Duke Nukem 3D Cheat Codes

Cheat Code	Outcome
DNGODLY	God Mode on
DNUNGODLY	God Mode off
DNCORNHOLIO	God mode (toggles)
DNKROZ	Same as DNCORNHOLIO
DNWARP <episode><level>	Jump to other episode and level
DNSCOTTY <episode><level>	Jump to other episode and level
DNAMMO	Full ammo (cool!)
DNVIEW	"Follow" Duke mode (like F7 key)
DNWEAPONS	All available weapons
DNUNLOCK	Unlock locked doors
DNITEMS	Keys, items, etc.
DNSTUFF	Keys, weapons, ammo, items
DNRATE	Shows frame rate (top of screen)
DNSKILL <skill level 1-5>	Restart level with skill #
DNCLIP	Walk-through-walls (v1.1)
DNHYPER	Steroids
DNENDING	Ends the episode
DNCASHMAN	Throws out cash with <Spacebar>
DNBETA	"Pirates suck" message
DNMONSTERS	Makes monsters disappear when you get near them
DNCOSMO	Register "Cosmo" message
DNALLEN	? message

BASIC STRATEGY TIPS

Duke Nukem 3D is not a tough game to learn, but there is definitely more to it than just running and shooting at everything. If you're perceptive enough during game play, you can learn a lot about your enemies and your environment. These beginner skills will help you persevere even with the deadliest of all aliens or in the most challenging of all levels.

Some of these suggestions may sound obvious, but they may just extend your lifespan!

Save often—and make back-ups. There is no worse feeling for any computer gamer than achieving so much and then getting your bits blown apart without saving the game. Name your saved games appropriately so if you return after a few days you'll know exactly where you left off.

Get to know your controls—well. Press F1 during gameplay for an overview of your Control menu. As with the game of Doom, strafing is very important, especially in keeping alive in multiplayer gaming. Strafing refers to "sliding" side-to-side or "side-stepping" by holding down the Alt key and the desired right or left arrow. Your ability to dodge bullets and lasers will ultimately determine your fate. In Duke Nukem 3D you can also crouch ("Z" key), jump ("A" key), run (Shift key), and look up and down (Home and End key, respectively). Also, get familiar with your ten weapons—note which ones work well with certain creatures and get to know which ones not to fire so close. Use these, and practice.

When in doubt—RUN! Don't be afraid to leave a room or city square if you're outnumbered, out of ammo, or need to devise a better plan to defeat your opponents. I've seen people exhaust their weaponry and proceed to try to "kick" a dozen or so armed aliens. Not a good idea.

Keep an eye on your health. Always look for med-kits lying around, and don't forget to drink from a broken fire hydrant (or even from a broken pipe behind a bathroom urinal if need be!) to increase your health.

Use the security cameras. Press the Spacebar to flip through the various camera angles around your environment and see where those pesky aliens are hiding.

Use your inventory efficiently. Scroll through what you've pickup along the way. Do this with the "{[" and "}]" keys. Steroids, a jet pack, night-vision goggles, a med-kit, protective boots, scuba gear, or a HoloDuke may just buy you some more time in the game.

Try out fun stuff: play billiards in the nightclub (Episode 1, Level 2), leave bloody footprints after stepping on a body, or use your jet pack and take a look at your level from above (or turn it off from way up above and hear yourself scream all the way down to your death!). You can also look for monsters in the can—yep, throw a pipe bomb in from above and watch him explode on the toilet! (Sick, eh?) There are of course, secret rooms and bonus levels hidden throughout the game—keep an eye open for a suspicious crack in a wall or a slanted ledge of a building. For a complete list of secrets, hidden jokes and references, and colorful maps for the entire game, point your browser to the mega-site Gamelords (http://gamelords.com/duke3d/).

BONUS GOODIES

The Duke Nukem 3D Commercial CD-ROM also contains some extras that not very many people are aware of. First of all, the original complete Duke Nukem and Duke Nukem II games are on the CD for free. In addition, shareware versions of other Apogee/3D Realms titles such as Realms of Chaos, Raptor, Rise of the Triad, Wacky Wheels, Terminal Velocity, and others are provided. Other goodies include a collection of midi tunes, pictures, preview shots of games Blood, Prey, and Shadow Warrior, and other utilities such as the WAD-to-map maker, an RTS maker, and the Build engine to make your own levels.

There's quite a lot to see and do in the world where Duke rules—so regardless of whether you're playing Duke solo or head-to-head—have fun, and "kick some ass!!"

19

DOOM, DOOM II, AND ULTIMATE DOOM

ON December 10, 1993, id Software established a new standard for computer gaming with its first shareware release, the highly anticipated 3D combat action game DOOM. Voted the 1994 Game of the Year by both *PC Gamer* and *Computer Gaming World*, DOOM is touted as the single most installed piece of software ever—an indication of its intense popularity with gamers worldwide. Using seamless, textured environments, the game is played in a three-dimensional rendered maze where realistic lighting, sound effects, and other animated features add to the overall experience.

Less than a year later, on "DOOMSDAY," October 10, 1994, the record-breaking DOOM II: Hell on Earth was released for sale. Considered as both the commercial version of DOOM and its sequel, the game presented players a new scenario, even more realistic 3D graphics, twice the demons, and more weapons. In 1995, The Ultimate DOOM hit the retail stores. Offering players the original 27 levels found on the shareware version of DOOM, this commercial version also included a brand new episode with nine additional levels. Also that year, Master Levels for DOOM II was released and extended play with 20 additional, independently designed but id-supervised levels. Through all its releases, the DOOM series has continued to perform well beyond expectation.

THE SCENARIOS

DOOM

Players take on the persona of the sole survivor of a space marine detail. Sent to Phobos, a Martian moon, the detail's mission was to answer a garbled distress call from a remote facility of the Union Aerospace Corporation, where the military had been conducting secret projects in inter-dimensional travel. The message warned of something evil coming through the gateway. Players must face the horror with only a pistol and the hope of finding better weapons inside the station, where the rest of the detail has apparently died.

DOOM II

Having survived the Martian moon, the space marine returns to Earth, only to find a situation far worse than that on the Phobos. On Earth, there are more demons both in number and variety, and the fate of humanity rests squarely on the shoulders of the intrepid space marine, who must clear the way to transport the remaining few humans alive off the planet and into safety.

WEAPONS AND ENEMY TARGETS

Weapons

Each version of the game allows different weapons, or combinations of weapons, from the overall arsenal used in the series. Weapons which are used include the space marine's fist, pistol, shotgun, super shotgun, chain gun, chain saw, rocket launcher, plasma rifle, and BFG9000 ("Big Fraggin Gun").

Enemy Targets

As with the weapons, each version of the game features different creatures bent on impeding the space marine's progress through the various game levels. These creatures include undead or former humans, undead human sergeants, brown thorny imps, horned demons, spectres, lost souls, fire-breathing cacodemons, plasma-flinging Barons of Hell, rocket-shooting cyberdemons, large robotic shooting spiders, chain gun-toting undead human sergeants, Hell Knights, smaller shooting spiders, bad-tempered skeletons, and fiery spirits.

SECRETS, HINTS, AND CHEATS

Those who prefer the advantage in a game, or simply find themselves stuck and needing assistance to advance through the games' levels, should refer to the Official DOOM and DOOM II FAQ. Written by Hank Leukart, the document provides an invaluable resource for exploring (on paper) the DOOM that awaits players in the game.

A whole section of the FAQ is devoted to cheats and spoilers, answering questions like: What command line parameters exist?; Where are the DOOM secret levels?; Where are the secret doors in DOOM?; How many enemies are in the entire game?; and, of course, What are the DOOM cheat codes?

Obviously, this is way too much information to reprint here, particularly since the FAQ is easily attainable online. A hypertext version may be found at http://doomgate.cs.buffalo.edu/docs/FAQ/doomfaq/. In the spirit of generosity and to whet the taste for more, however, here's a cheat code to get things rolling. Simply type: **idbehold** (Get it? id behold). A menu of six letters will then appear, representing a variety of defensive gear, attributes, or aids—"**S**" (**S**trength), "**V**" (in**V**ulnerability), "**I**" (partial **I**nvisibility), "**R**" (anti-**R**adiation suit), "**L**" (**L**ight amplification visor), and "**A**" (full **A**uto-mapping). Choose and proceed.

KEYSTROKES: MAKING MOVES

For an action-packed game, DOOM requires very little dexterity on the keypad for a player to score well. Place one hand on the arrow or directional keys, and use the other hand to press the Control key and the Spacebar. In this position, you're poised to shoot up the place.

Obviously, the arrow keys move the character through the game: up = forward, left = left, right = right, and down = backward. Alt-left arrow and Alt-right arrow move the character side to side. The Control key fires the weapon that is currently in use, and the Spacebar is used to open doors and manipulate switches. The number keys change the weapon in use—players select from the various weapons they find and pick up along the way. The Tab key shows the map, and the Escape key returns players to the game's menu.

TYPES OF PLAY AND RESOURCES

DOOM supports stand-alone or individual play, as well as two different multiplayer action options. Multiple players can either combine forces to scour the mazes and fight the monsters as a team, or they can go it alone and combat one another (in addition to the monsters) in the DeathMatch mode. Multiplayer action is possible via direct serial connection (or null modem), a modem connection, or a network connection. In fact, the only thing required to play DOOM (v.1.6 or greater) via modem is two players with identical (registered) versions of the game. However, as with most things, there are steps players can take to increase their enjoyment level and decrease their frustration levels when attempting to launch a multiplayer game. To aid in this effort, The Doom2 Modem Information Page (http://www.sscf.ucsb.edu/~duncan/doom/index.html) provides players step-by-step assistance in connecting themselves (and their friends) for local DOOM action.

In order to enjoy DOOM over the Internet, players must go beyond the basic programming provided by the game and seek out additional resources. One such resource is a handy piece of freeware called iFrag. The TCP/IP Internet DOOMer's FAQ, written by Scott Coleman and Jay Cotton, discusses the installation and use of this program and points to where the program can be downloaded. (A hypertext version of the Coleman/Cotton document can be found on the iFrag FAQ page http://dirac.bcm.tmc.edu/ifrag20.html.) Though a direct Ethernet connection is best when using iFrag, acceptable levels of play can be achieved with 28.8Kbps modems.

To explore other options for multiplayer DOOM fun, check out the section of this book on Network Gaming, Chapter 13. DWANGO (http://www.dwango.com/enter.html), the Kali service (http://www.axxis.com/kali/), and XBAND PC (http://www.xband.com) all support DOOM action in one form or another.

For additional DOOM-related resources, refer to the Web and Usenet newsgroup sections of this book (Chapters 4 and 11 respectively). There are a number of Internet sites offering relevant material and interesting insights into the game. Among these resources, perhaps the first place any player should look in searching out additional DOOM bits and bytes is Piotr Kapiszewski's DoomGate collection found at http://doomgate.cs.buffalo.edu/. The downloads, documents, and forums offered will prove a valuable asset to anyone interested in advancing in skill and knowledge of the game. To get the official word on DOOM, players can visit the id Software corporate site at http://www.idsoftware.com; and to find quick answers to otherwise plaguing questions, again, The Official DOOM and DOOM II FAQ is available at http://doomgate.cs.buffalo.edu/docs/FAQ/doomfaq/.

20

CIVNET

"Everybody Wants to Rule the World"
—Tears For Fears, 1985

The original Civilization, by MicroProse, revolutionized the computer gaming industry in 1991. It was the first computer strategy game which demanded a combination of the political interrelationships of military strength, science/technology, and cultural and economic exigencies. Highly addictive with a high replayability (since it could always be a different game), it was available on many platforms (which was rare for the time). It was the first true *God game,* taking off where Sim City (Maxis, 1987) left us.

Sid Meier's strategic game has won a handful of acknowledgments including the Software Publishers Association's "Best Entertainment Program" and Computer Gaming World's "Overall Game of the Year" and "Hall of Fame" award. The premise to this *God game* is as follows. Choose a nomadic tribe, pick a suitable location, settle them, and try to create a civilization. In the process you develop new technologies, meet your neighbors (aggressive or passive local tribes), and eventually visit new lands. Your goal is to be the most dominant civilization in the world…all the way down the timeline to the space age. Opposed to fast-paced action/arcade games, or *twitch* games, Civilization is a true thinking game, utilizing the classic turn-based strategy/war game fashion. With every minor decision you choose your citizens' destinies. No two games ever play the same, which makes for great re-playability—a feat many computer games cannot claim. The success of this game is second to none (almost one million copies sold), and all closet megalomaniacs alike (me, included) have never really shelved the game—in fact, it has been a current resident on my hard drive for some time. Until CivNet came along.

Over five years later the strategy game of all games has been upgraded to support the two newest aspects of modern computer gaming—multimedia technology (with Civilization II and Civ2000 in the works) and network multiplayer play (CivNet). MicroProse's Civilization II, also designed by Sid Meier, has received a massive facelift—SVGA high-res graphics, CD-quality audio, mini-movie animations, and a new multimedia "Wonders of the World" feature. Other improvements, such as technology and city advancements, a new map editor, an expanded diplomatic system, and new pre-set scenarios are also in place. This brings us to the second, and more exciting, of the two sequels—CivNet (see Figure 20.1).

CivNet plays similarly to Civilization, but besides solo play it now features head-to-head gaming via your modem. One problem with the original is that your computer opponent's actions were often predictable or, at times, unrealistic (this is common with most games that rely on AI). With CivNet, however, you can now challenge two to six *real* players through the Internet, a local network, or BBS. New options also include

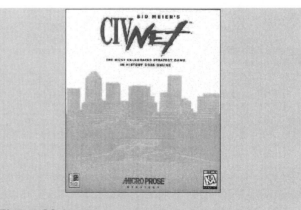

Figure 20.1
CivNet

a revamped Windows interface, turn-based or si-multaneous play mode choice, a chat mode where you can talk to other players, a customizable on-line character, and a new map editor to create new worlds (which allows you to view multiple maps simultaneously).

GETTING STARTED

The goals of CivNet are the same as its predecessor. A discerning balance of the four main impulses of real civilization is your key to success: exploration, economics, knowledge, and conquest. Your main objective is to survive, while your secondary goal is to *thrive*. If you choose Earth as your planet you be-gin with a small band of colonists in the year 4,000 B.C. (Figure 20.2). From there you develop towns, discover science and technologies, raise armies, send out diplomats and merchants and meet with other civilizations. Co-exist, interact (trade goods or exchange knowledge), or fight with others while you continue to expand into bigger cities. *Where* you choose to develop your civilization plays a key role in your success—various resources and land terrain will prove different benefits and obstacles.

OFFICIAL GAME SPECS

Requirements to play CivNet are Windows 3.1 or greater, an IBM PC or compatible, 486 or Pentium processor, 8MB RAM, SVGA 256-color graphics, and a Microsoft-compatible mouse.

A CD-ROM drive with MSCDEX 2.2 or later with 12MB of hard drive space is also required. Civ-Net supports an MPC Level 2 compliant system, CD Audio, and, for modem multiplay, a 14.4 baud modem, IPX/SPX, NetBIOS, TCP/IP(Winsock), Win 95 Dial-Up Networking, Hotseat, and Game Connection. A standard PPP Internet with an Inter-net Service Provider connection is recommended.

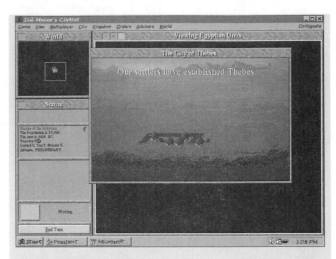

Figure 20.2
Settlers in CivNet

FIRST THINGS FIRST

There is a patch for CivNet available on the Inter-net to fix minor bugs in the game. Before you do anything, get the file called *civnetp3.zip*, which can be found at ftp://ftp.microprose.com/. This up-date is for all languages and replaces all previous versions, including the older patch *civnetv1.zip* (December 1995). Additional information is pro-vided for CivNet in general, including the official CivNet FAQ (http://www.microprose.com/civ-net/civnet.faq.html), the Official CivNet Internet Info FAQ (http://www.microprose.com/civnet/civintfq.html), and the unofficial CivNet FAQ (http://www.iag.net/~jlehett/civtech.html).

BEGINNERS, SOLO PLAY, AND THE MANUAL

CivNet is a very challenging game, to say the least. It is ambitious to learn and very tough to master. If you're a newcomer to Civilization or this type of gaming genre, then I suggest you load the Tutorial game (*tutorial.sav*) until you get in the swing of things (see Figure 20.3). Follow along the Tutorial game with the Instruction Manual (pages 7 through 20). Having done that, you should still play a few times by yourself before tackling real-life opponents. Choose to be a Chieftain (the easiest difficulty level) with no more than three civilizations. Do yourself a favor—put a pot of coffee on (or grab a soda) and sit down and *read* this manual. I have to admit, I haven't even broken the spine on most of the manuals I have for games. Let's face it—most of us tear open the wrapper of a CD-ROM, pop it into our beloved computers and learn how to play as we go along. That's half the fun, but this ain't no Doom—CivNet can be quite complicated, and you may miss out on key points if you don't know how to properly build and defend, explore and conquer. The manual covers basic game setups, city concepts, managing your cities (resource development, protection), managing your trade, terrain and movement, mobile units and combat, natural disasters (yup, just as in SimCity!), diplomacy, and notes on winning the space race. Multiplayer info and setup, a reference guide, how to create new worlds, and a hearty appendix are also included here. If time isn't on your side to read the 200+ page manual, make sure you at least run and read the Tutorial and keep the handy additional Advances Chart and Player Aid card.

The game is controlled mainly with a mouse, but there are hot-keys or short-cut keys for faster gameplay (e.g. "R" to build roads, "E" to end turn, or "Q" to quit, etc.). Get to know these, as they will save you quite a bit of time; once you get the basics down, you'll be well on your way.

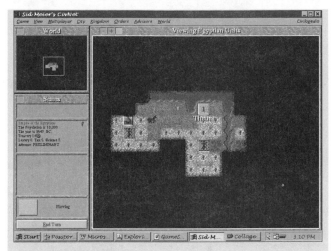

Figure 20.3
Solo play

TIPS FOR MULTIPLAYER GAMES

If you are experienced with TCP/IP games on the Internet, then you are aware of the potential crashes, lags/hangs, and reboots you may have to face. This is the unfortunate reality about the current status of online games right now, regardless of your operating system (see Figure 20.4).

On top of this, I found CivNet to be a relatively slow game to play online against others. Most of the head-to-head strategy games on the market today (such as Warcraft II and Command & Conquer) use a real-time combat engine, so you may get a little antsy at first, but here are ten things you can do to help make your multiplayer CivNet game flow more smoothly and swiftly.

1   Get the patch.
2   Turn off all other applications on your computer, shut down your browser, or close any FTP software you may be using.

Figure 20.4
Multiplayer play

3 Play during *off-peak* hours—anywhere from 11 p.m. to 7 a.m. (of course, these times vary according to the time zones of the players).

4 Call your Internet Service Provider to get your IP address and, if possible, "ping" times for your opponents (see #5).

5 Each player should "ping" the other's player's IP addresses to make sure there isn't too long of a lag time (more than 400ms or 500ms lag time is not recommended). "Ping" refers to the time it takes for information to travel through the Internet connection from one computer to another. If using Windows 95, you can get a selection of ping software at http://www.windows95.com/apps/finger.html.

6 Minimize the number of players in the game.

7 Try not to minimize the CivNet window; you can move it to the background, but

closing and opening this window may cause the game to crash.

8 Do NOT click on a city after you have clicked "end turn."

9 Turn-based games will take longer to play than simultaneous games (and in simultaneous games the host will have an unnatural advantage in head-to-head combat).

10 Be patient—multiplayer will take much longer to play than stand-alone games.

More help is offered at the MicroProse CivNet Technical Support page (http://www.microprose.com/civnet/civtech.html).

CIVNET CHEAT CODES

To activate the cheat mode, wait until the *end turn* bar is flashing in the lower-left corner. Then type **CTRL** once, then **A O D B A M F** in sequence. The Cheat menu "Extras" will appear next to the World menu. And away you go

Code	Outcome
ScaleIt	Increases your production
ArmyInfo	See information about the other races
MoneyAndPower	Self-explanatory
AllSeeingEye	Reveal the whole map!
GetRichQuick	Self-explanatory
GetSmartQuick	Self-explanatory
MissileCrisis	Creates the production of nuclear missiles
SettlersHo!	Creates settlers
Nukestorms	Causes Global Warming
Automode	The computer moves for you
Armaggedon	The best one, nukes the whole world!

FINDING PLAYERS

If you're looking to find players, or if you want others to know you're ready for a game, there are a few places on the Net you can go.

Register and visit the Microprose CivNet Player Registry—they have a list of e-mail addresses of people interested in playing CivNet, divided into geographical area. To register, point your browser to http://www.holobyte.com/civnet/players/register.html or view the directory at http://www.holobyte.com/civnet/players/directory.html.

The CivNet challenge board (http://www.wizweb.com/arena/civnet/) allows you to post a challenge or check your area code to find potential opponents. You may also visit and register at CivNet at ICV.Net. The purpose of the mailing list here is to get a group of people out together one night a week on the Internet to play an online game. This site is free and open to all who like to play the game online (http://www.icv.net/~williams/civnet/civnet.html) (see Figure 20.5).

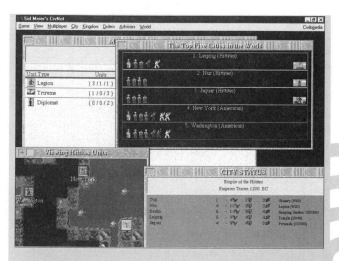

Figure 20.5
Top 5 CivNet player cities

Chat with others via IRC with #civnet http://www2.undernet.org:8080/~cs93jtl/IRC.html.

LINKS TO OTHER CIVNET SOURCES ON THE NET

Here are a few CivNet WWW pages around the Net that carry cool pictures, sounds, reviews, strategies, and more.

Some of these sites are covered more in depth in Chapter 7.

MicroProse CivNet Page
http://www.microprose.com/civnet/

CivNet Pictures, Icons, and a Map
http://www.wam.umd.edu/~tjsjr/civpics.html

CivNet Review - Coming Soon Magazine
http://www.megatoon.com/~t15/issue16/civnet.htm

DM's CivNET Page
http://www.ncweb.com/users/dm/civnet.html

RYYT's CivNET Page
http://www.ualberta.ca/~wtsang/civnet.html

Games First!
http://cypher.turbonet.com/GAMES/1TITLE/C/CIV_NET/CIVNET.STM

The Heggen Pages
http://www.teleport.com/~twisted/CivNET/

CivNet Challenge Board
http://www.wizweb.com/arena/civnet/

#CivNET's Homepage
http://www.radix.net/~mikes/civnet.html

CivNet Player's List
http://www.zorda.com/playlst/civplay.htm

The Civilization Page
http://www.lilback.com/civilization/

So whether you start off as Honest Abe, Elizabeth I, Ramses, Caesar, or one of your own creations, remember you now have to ability to change history, but it won't happen overnight. Take the time to *learn* CivNet, and be patient with the online multi-player lag times…don't forget—Rome wasn't built in a day!

WARCRAFT II: TIDES OF DARKNESS

THE battle for control of the mythical kingdom of Azeroth begun in Warcraft: Orcs & Humans continues in Blizzard Entertainment's wildly popular and award-winning sequel, Warcraft II: Tides of Darkness. A game of strategic planning, tactical operations, and resource management, Warcraft II offers 28 campaign scenarios played out in a fantastic world where magic spells can raise the dead and dragons rain fire from the sky.

THE SCENARIO

Following the deaths of the Orcish Warchief Blackhand and King Llane of Azeroth during the First War, Orgrim Doomhammer has risen to rule the Orcish forces occupying Azeroth, and Sir Lothar has risen to lead an alliance of nations forged to repel the continuing Orcish advance and beat back the evil forces all the way to the Portal whence they came.

Players choose for which side they wish to command troops, the Clans of the Horde or the Alliance of Lordaeron. In either case, players are given campaign missions with specific objectives, which must be carried out fully in order to win the level. The key to commanding a successful mission is ensuring you have adequate forces (which you must create and/or train) and the resources necessary to sustain them (which you must find and harvest).

Throughout the game, three natural resources are fundamental: gold, lumber, and oil. It takes money to make anything (and most everything must be made), lumber to build anything (and most everything must be built), and oil to power ships (even though many of the ships have sails). In other words, there are basic things you must

have in order to get the things you really need to complete a mission. And the dependencies grow more and more complex as the game advances.

For example: To get an Elven Archer (one of the ground units for the Alliance), you need to have a barracks; but to have a barracks, you need to have a lumber mill; and to have a lumber mill, you need to have a peasant to build it; and the peasant comes from the Town Hall. Do you have one of those? And once you have your Elven Archer, do you have enough food to feed him *and* the peasant? Things can get complicated real fast, especially if you're under attack and you haven't trained any footmen.

COMPARING FORCES

The sides are fairly evenly matched, though in the upper levels of play the styles of fighting begin to differ. Commanding the Alliance forces requires a more sophisticated approach to Warcraft because of the types of spells that come into play. Commanding the Orcish Horde, on the other hand, requires little subtlety at all. These forces are brutes and they fight best that way.

Alliance Ground Units	Orcish Horde
Peasant	Peon
Footman	Grunt
Elven Archer	Troll Axethrower
Elven Ranger	Troll Berserker
Knight	Ogre
Palladin	Ogre Mage
Ballista	Catapult
Mage	Death Knight
Demolition Squad	Goblin Sappers

Alliance Air and Naval Units	Orcish Horde
Gnomish Flying Machine	Goblin Zeppelin
Gryphon Rider	Dragon
Oil Tanker	Oil Tanker
Elven Destroyer	Troll Destroyer
Transport	Transport
Battleship	Ogre Juggernaught
Gnomish Submarine	Giant Turtle

COMMANDS AND CONTROLS

The game utilizes a point-and-click interface for issuing general commands. The left quarter of the screen features a mini map of the campaign area, under which are two boxes: the first describing the unit (building, being, or craft) currently in play, and the second graphically indicating the command options available with that unit. Players simply click on the command icon and the order is carried out, provided of course the player has enough resources in store. Messages appear throughout the command sequence and prompt players unsure of what to do next.

The right three-quarters of the screen is the command map, or campaign area where the game is actually played out. It is here that players point and click to select the units they wish to order into action.

CHEAT CODES

To enable a cheat, press the Enter key. The prompt "Message:" will appear in the bottom left border of the campaign map. Type the code for the cheat desired and press Enter. The message

"CHEAT ENABLE" will be displayed when the code is entered correctly. To disable a cheat (if applicable) simply enter the code again. These cheat codes are for the full version of the game; the game demo has different codes, which can be found in that version's documentation.

Code	Action
GLITTERING PRIZES	Adds 10,000 gold, 5,000 lumber, and 5,000 oil to reserves
VALDEZ	Adds 5,000 oil to reserves
EVERY LITTLE THING SHE DOES	Upgrades your magic users with all spells
DECK ME OUT	Upgrades all technologies
ON SCREEN	Displays the entire game map
MAKE IT SO	Accelerates pace of building, training, and upgrading
HATCHET	Accelerates tree harvesting
IT IS A GOOD DAY TO DIE	Renders units invulnerable to all computer opponent attacks, except magical attacks
UNITE THE CLANS	Results in instant victory
YOU PITIFUL WORM	Results in instant defeat
NEVER A WINNER	Prevents a victory at the level
TIGERLILY	Allows player to jump between levels using additional code: HUMANx or ORCx, where the "x" is replaced by the desired level, 1 to 14

THE MAP AND SOUND EDITOR

One of the game's outstanding features is that it comes equipped with an editor that allows players to create additional levels of play, or PUDs. By editing together units (buildings, beings, and craft), topographical features, and sounds, customized scenarios can be created, saved, played, and shared system to system. Detailed help files assist players and provide them all the options they need to extend their enjoyment of the game long into the future.

MULTIPLAYER FEATURES

In addition to its single-player campaign mode, Warcraft II also supports a variety of multiplayer protocols that allows up to eight people to play simultaneously. Players can go head-to-head via a direct serial connection (null modem), a modem connection, and an IPX network connection. To find out how to connect and play over the Internet, stop by the Warcraft 2 Unofficial FAQ List by Dan Zerkle (a.k.a. Trouble) at http://www.ogr.com/faqs/warcraft2.faq. The FAQ offers a helpful look at using the Kali service to play.

For more information on the game in general and playing head-to-head, try Geoff Fraizer's Shlonglor's War 2 Page at http://www.andrews.edu/~fraizer/war2.cgi. Geoff offers playing strategies, PUDs, and other items of interest to Warcraft II fans. Another page to visit is Methos' Warcraft II Strategy Page at http://www.mtsu.edu/~csc10001/strat.html. Along with strategy tips, this page also offers a compiled list of links to other game fans' pages.

22

MECHWARRIOR 2 AND NETMECH

VOTED by *PC Entertainment* as 1995's "Game of the Year", MechWarrior® 2 combines arcade action with elements of role-playing and simulation games to create an intense virtual battle experience through texture-mapped 3D animation and realistic sound. Generally based on the FASA board games BattleTech® and MechWarrior, the game's scenario derives more specifically from the Trial of Refusal depicted in the novel *Bred for War* by Michael Stackpole.

THE SCENARIO

The year is the distant future, 3057, and two rival Clans vie for supremacy. Clan Jade Falcon fights for the forceful domination of Terra; The Wolf Clan fights to protect Terra from the scourges of war. Both Clans are mighty; each is determined it fights for right.

Players assume the role of MechWarriors, an elite group of fighters who "strap on" and pilot the Clans' BattleMechs, two-legged fighting machines laden with armor and a complement of brutal weaponry. The Clan for which a player chooses to fight during any session of play is up to the player. An equal number of missions is included for both Clans, so players can play one side and then the other, meeting each Clan's very different mission objectives.

The game allows for two modes of play. In the career mode, players garner honor points and compete for rank within the Clans. In the instant action mode, the play is the thing—the play action that is, with no concern for rank, career, or honor, just destruction and coming back alive.

STRATEGIC APPROACHES TO THE GAME

New recruits to the game will do fine if they keep one thing in mind before they go rushing into the fray: Battles are not won and lost on the battlefield, but instead on the training field. And MechWarrior 2 offers a superior training program complete with training missions. It is on the Clan training grounds where players can experiment with the 15 different BattleMech models and the 20 different pieces of weaponry available for use.

As each weapon offers different capabilities, so too the BattleMechs differ in their size and maneuverability. Since a MechWarrior must select, customize, and configure the BattleMech he will take into each mission, an intelligence of the machinery and weaponry, plus savvy skills, will be vital to surviving.

The Clan assigns missions, the MechWarrior does not choose. It is important, therefore, for the player to read the mission briefing and understand the mission objectives before preparing a BattleMech and adventuring out of the Clan hall. Know, too, the missions are timed, and though it is possible to run through a mission dodging exchanges with the enemy Clan, this in-and-out tactic garners few honor points.

When engaged in combat, keep in mind that a legless BattleMech is a lame BattleMech and an armless BattleMech is often disarmed. Also, be aware that the armor on the back of a BattleMech is the weakest—this is true of your BattleMech as well as your enemy's. Watch your back and aim for your opponent's.

Lastly, recognize that with all the fire power (emphasis on *fire*) a BattleMech normally carries, the machine can heat up rather quickly and become a hazard to the MechWarrior at the controls. Take care not to overheat; the results can be fatal.

GAME CONTROLS

The action in MechWarrior 2 is fast and furious, so it is no surprise that a player's reactions on the keyboard need to be somewhat fast and furious, too. In fact, the computer keyboard control codes are somewhat as complicated as the controls That might be expected inside an actual BattleMech. Tables 22.1 through 22.6 lists the codes.

Table 22.1: Cockpit Weapon Controls

Code	Action
Spacebar	Fires the selected weapon
Enter	Cycles through available options to select a weapon or weapons group
\ (backslash)	Toggles between chain fire and group fire
Shift+1, 2, or 3	Adds a weapon to a weapons group
Num Lock, /, * (on the keypad)	Fires weapons group
K	Jettisons ammunition
T	Cycles through all targets
R	Returns to previous target
E	Targets nearest enemy
F	Identifies nearest friend, or Starmate
Q	Targets object in reticle
I	Inspects targeted object
Ctrl+T	Turns targeting off

Table 22.2: Heads Up Display (HUD) System Controls

F1	Cycles through the multifunctional display
F2	Toggles the radar display between normal and full screen
F5	Toggles damage display; indicates any damage the BattleMech has sustained
F6	Toggles HTAL (Head/Torso/Arms/Legs) damage display; reports any damage to armor
F11	Toggles HUD (Heads Up Display); enables/disables HUD
U	Uses menu; reports systems status
F12	Reviews mission objectives

Table 22.3: Camera Controls

F4	Toggles target display; targets angle
F7	Toggles rear view
F8	Down view
F9	Weapon view
F10	Weapon view after launch

Table 22.4: BattleMech Pilot Controls

1 through 0	Accelerates the BattleMech (0 = 100%) and slows the BattleMech to a stop
+, -	Increases, decreases throttle
Left and Right Arrows	Steers left and right
Backspace	Reverses direction
< or >	Twists the BattleMech's torso
/	Recenters the BattleMech's torso
M	Recenters the BattleMech's legs under its torso
J	Engages jump jets (when applicable)
	To steer the jump jets, use the 6-key "home" portion of the keypad

Table 22.4: BattleMech Pilot Controls (Cont.)

N	Selects a NAVigation point
A	Turns autopilot on and off
V	Turns MASC on and off
S	Engages manual shutdown or restart
O	Overrides automatic thermal shutdown
Ctrl+Alt+E	Ejects the MechWarrior pilot from the BattleMech
Ctrl+E	Turns auto-ejection on and off
Ctrl+Alt+X	Initiates self-destruct
Ctrl+F1 or Ctrl+B	Allows MechWarrior to command Starmates
Ctrl+F2 or Ctrl+F3	Determines command point 1 or 2

Table 22.5: Pilot View Controls

Z	Zooms in
Shift+Z	Zooms out
Ctrl+Z	Resets zoom magnification
7 (on the keypad)	Glance to the left
9 (on the keypad)	Glance to the right
Ctrl+Arrow Keys	Controls pilot line of vision
L	Turns low light amplification on and off
W	Turns enhanced imaging on and off
F3	Turns satellite uplink on and off
X	Zooms in on satellite uplink image
Shift+X	Zooms out on satellite uplink image
C	Turns External Tracking Cameras (XTC) on and off
Ctrl+Arrow Keys	Controls External Tracking Cameras's line of vision

Table 22.6: Other Controls

Esc	Reveals options/battle parameters menu
Alt+P or Alt+Pause	Pauses game
Ctrl+Q	Aborts or exits a mission
Ctrl+P	Snaps a screen shot

CHEAT CODES

To a MechWarrior, "war is life" and honor is all. There is no honor in cheating, but here are some of the game's cheat codes just the same. To activate these cheats, a player must be actively involved in a mission, and the codes must be typed while the Ctrl+Alt+Shift keys are depressed (see Table 22.7).

Table 22.7: Cheat Codes

Code	Action
BLORB	Turns invulnerability on and off
CIA	Provides unlimited ammunition
COLDMISER	Turns heat tracking on and off
DORCS	Introduces the "dorcs" who created the game
ENOLAGAY	Nukes the area, killing everything vulnerable
FLYGIRL	Installs jump jets on BattleMechs without them
FRONT	Makes rearview camera a frontview camera
Ctrl+Left Arrow	Turn left
Ctrl+Right Arrow	Turn right
Ctrl+Up Arrow	Increase altitude
Ctrl+Down Arrow	Decrease altitude
Z	Zoom in
Shift+Z	Zoom out

Table 22.7: Cheat Codes (Cont.)

Code	Action
GANKEM	Destroys the object targeted
HANGAROUND	Enables player to stay at mission site after the mission has been completed or time has run out
MEEPMEEP	Enables time compression
UNMEEPMEEP	Disables time compression
MICHELIN	Displays bounding spheres on targets
MIGHTYMOUSE	Provides unlimited jump jet power
TINKERBELL	Positions external camera to view a fixed area
XRAY	Provides ability to see through objects
ZMACK	Enables time expansion

NETMECH AND MULTIPLAYER ACTION

You must run MechWarrior 2 along with Net-Mech in order for 2 or more users to play. With NetMech true multiplayer action in MechWarrior 2 is possible, allowing up to eight players to simultaneously shoot it out for the honor and glory of their respective Clans. In addition to opening up the multiplayer capability of the game, NetMech also includes 15 new missions.

While every player in a multiplayer session must each be running the same version of Net-Mech, only one player needs to have a full copy of MechWarrior 2 to host the other players participating in the session. The MS-DOS version of Net-Mech is currently available free for download from the Activision corporate site at http://www.activision.com/netmech/index.html.

NetMech/Mechwarrior 2 play is currently supported at DWANGO (http://www.dwango.com/enter.html) and by Kali (http://www.axxis.com/kali/). Mechwarrior 2 head-to-head action can be found at MPlayer Gameway (http://www.mplayer.com/). For more information on these services see Chapter 13 on network gaming.

APPENDIX
USING THE CD-ROM

THE CD-ROM that's packaged with this book includes software for you to use. The software will not only allow you to explore the Internet and search the Web, but will also allow you to view the fully hyperlinked HTML version of the book that's contained on the CD-ROM. Before you can use the software, however, you will need to install it on your computer. This is a simple procedure that will take only a few minutes.

WHAT'S ON THE CD-ROM?
The CD-ROM includes the following software that can be installed on your computer:

- Hyperlinked HTML version of the book for PCs and Macs

- Microsoft Internet Explorer Web browser for PCs and Macs

- Netcom NetCruiser software for PCs only

- Shareware versions of Doom, MechWarrior 2, and Quake

VIEWING THE HYPERLINKED HTML VERSION OF THE BOOK
The CD-ROM contains the fully hyperlinked text of the book, including approximately 2500 Web site descriptions and Internet addresses. Every section of the CD allows you to select an Internet address and instantly connect to the actual site. Otherwise you'll need an Internet connection to link to anything on the Web. The CD-ROM also contains a hot button to connect directly to the Lycos search engine.

Using the CD-ROM
To view the hyperlinked HTML version of the book that's included on this CD-ROM, you will need to run a Web browser. Simply follow the steps below.

Running Most Web Browsers (Including Netscape Navigator)

1   Place the CD-ROM in your CD-ROM drive.

2   Launch your Web browser.

3   Choose **Open File** from the File menu.

4   Select your CD-ROM drive. For PC users, this is usually drive **D**. Mac users: Double-click on the **CD-ROM icon**.

5   Double-click the file named **Welcome.htm**.

Running Microsoft Internet Explorer

1   Place the CD-ROM in your CD-ROM drive.

2   Launch **Internet Explorer**.

3   Choose **Open** from the File menu.

4   Click the **Browse** button.

5   Select your CD-ROM drive. For PC users, this is usually drive **D**. Mac users: Double-click on the **CD-ROM icon**.

6   Double-click the file named **Welcome .htm**.

7   Click on **OK**.

INSTALLING WEB BROWSER SOFTWARE

If you do not have a Web browser currently installed on your computer, we have included Microsoft's Internet Explorer and Netcom's NetCruiser on this CD. The steps for installing the programs are described below.

Recommended PC System

- 486 PC (Pentium PC preferred)
- Windows (3.x, 95, or NT) operating system
- 8MB RAM (16MB preferred)
- 8MB free space on your hard drive (15MB preferred)
- 2x CD-ROM drive (4x recommended)

Macintosh System Requirements

- Apple Macintosh or Power Macintosh (or clone) running System 7.0.1 or later
- Apple Open Transport of Mac TCP and Thread Manager
- Minimum of 8MB RAM (16MB preferred)
- 2x CD-ROM drive (4x preferred)

For all systems

A modem (14.4 BPS or faster is recommended for optimum performance)

INSTALLING INTERNET EXPLORER

Internet Explorer Version 3.0 for Windows 95

You must be using Microsoft Windows 95 to run Microsoft Internet Explorer 3.0. Locate the Win95 folder in the MSIE directory on the CD. Create a temporary directory on your computer. Copy the MSIE30M.EXE file from the Win95 folder on the CD and paste it in the temporary folder on your hard disk.

Double-click on the file. Follow the instructions that appear on your screen to complete the installation.

Internet Explorer Version 2.1 for Windows 3.1

You must be using Microsoft Windows 3.1 to run Microsoft Internet Explorer 2.1. Locate the Win3.1 folder in the MSIE directory on the CD. Create a temporary directory on your computer. Copy the DIMINI21.EXE file from the Win3.1 folder on the CD and paste it in the temporary folder on your hard disk.

Double-click the file. Follow the instructions that appear on your screen to complete the installation.

Internet Explorer Version 3.8 for Windows NT 4.0

You must be using Microsoft Windows NT 4.0 to run Microsoft Internet Explorer 3.8. Locate the WINNTI38 folder in the MSIE directory on the CD. Create a temporary directory on your computer. Copy the LENT351X.EXE file from the WINNTI38 folder on the CD and paste it in the temporary folder on your hard disk.

Double-click the file. Follow the instructions that appear on your screen to complete the installation.

Internet Explorer Version 2.0 for the Macintosh

Double click the Internet Explorer Installer icon to install.

Note: Eudora Light is an Internet Mail client application that is included in Microsoft Internet

Explorer 2.0 for the Macintosh. Documentation for Eudora Light is not included. To download the Eudora Light Manual separately, visit the Microsoft Internet Explorer Web site at http://www.microsoft.com/ie/iedl.htm#mac

INSTALLING NETCOM

Netcom's NetCruiser software (for Windows users only) includes everything you need to get your own Internet account with Netcom, explore the Internet, and peruse the contents of the CD-ROM that's included with this book. Before you can use it, however, you'll have to install the tools on your computer. It's a simple procedure that will take you just a few minutes.

Minimum System Requirements

Before installing NetCruiser on your computer, check to be sure your computer and modem meet the following requirements:

- Minimum 386DX 33 MHz processor
- Minimum 4MB of RAM
- Windows 3.1 and MS-DOS 5.0 (or greater) or Windows 95
- 12MB available hard-disk space
- 14.4 BPS or better modem
- A mouse, trackball, or other pointing device

Windows 3.1 Installation Instructions

1 Insert the CD into CD-ROM drive.
2 From Program Manager, select the **File** menu.
3 Choose **Run**.
4 In the command line, type **d:\netcom\setup** (where d is your CD-ROM drive).
5 Click on **OK**.

Windows 95 Installation Instructions

1 Insert the CD into CD-ROM drive.
2 From the Start menu click on the **Settings** menu.
3 Click on the **Control Panel** menu.
4 Select the **Add/Remove Programs** icon.
5 Click on the **Install** button and follow the instructions that appear on-screen to complete the installation. You will find the setup file in the NETCOM folder on the CD-ROM.

Note: You may need to disable any anti-virus or screen saver programs during installation.

RUNNING THE SHAREWARE GAMES ON THE CD-ROM

We've included shareware versions of Doom, MechWarrior 2, and Quake on the CD-ROM. To run the games, follow the instructions below.

Doom Version 1.9

To run DOOM, you need an IBM compatible 386 or better machine with 4MB of RAM, a VGA graphics card, and a hard-disk drive. A 486 or better processor and a Sound Blaster Pro(TM) or 100 percent compatible sound card are recommended.

Installation Instructions for DOS

Insert the CD into your CD-ROM drive. If you're running DOS, simply change to the letter of your CD-ROM drive (most likely D: or E:), then type **CD DOOM** and press Enter. From there type **Install** and press Enter. Follow the instructions that appear on-screen. You will be prompted to choose your destination drive (your hard disk is probably C:) and destination path (C:\Games\DOOM or C:\DOOM—or whatever directory you want). From there, select your controller preference (keyboard, mouse, or joystick) and sound card preference. After completing those steps, highlight Save parameters and Launch DOOM option, and away you go! Additional information and technical help is offered in the Dmfaq.txt files.

Installation Instructions for Windows 3.x

Insert the CD into your CD-ROM drive. Go to the Program Manager window, choose Run and type **D:\doom\install**. You will be prompted to choose your destination drive (your hard disk is probably C:) and destination path (C:\Games\DOOM or C:\DOOM—or whatever directory you want). From there, select your controller preference (keyboard, mouse, or joystick) and sound card preference. Once completed, highlight the Save parameters and Launch DOOM option, and away you go! Additional information and technical help is offered in the Dmfaq.txt files.

Another installation method is to go to File Manager, click on your D: drive icon, and double click on Install from the DOOM directory.

Installation Instructions for Windows 95

Insert the CD into your CD-ROM drive. Click on the Start button, and select Run. In the window type **D:\DOOM\install** (assuming your CD-ROM is the letter D:). You will be prompted to choose your destination drive (your hard disk is probably C:) and destination path (C:\Games\DOOM or C:\DOOM—or whatever directory you want). From there, select your controller preference (keyboard, mouse, or joystick) and sound card preference. Once completed, highlight the Save parameters and Launch DOOM option, and away you go! Additional information and technical help is offered in the Dmfaq.txt files.

There are two other ways to install DOOM from Windows 95. You can go to Windows Explorer and select your D: drive and double click on Install.bat in the D:\DOOM directory. Another method is to double click on My Computer and then double-click on D: Drive (there should be a picture of a CD-ROM). Double click on DOOM and then double-click on Install.

Quake

To run Quake, you will need an IBM PC or compatible machine; Pentium processor or better; VGA Compatible Display or better; MS-DOS 5.0 or higher or Windows 95; 8MB RAM minimum (16MB required for running under Windows 95); CD-ROM drive; and 30MB of hard-disk space for Shareware or 80MB if it's registered.

Installation Instructions for DOS

Insert the CD into your CD-ROM drive. If using DOS, simply change to the letter of your CD-ROM drive (most likely D: or E:), then type **CD QUAKE** and press Enter. Then type **Install** and press Enter. Follow the rest of the instructions that appear on screen. You will automatically launch Quake, but once you see the demo running, hit the Esc key and select Options. Here is where you can tweak the game, including customizing keys and video resolution. Additional information and technical assistance are offered in the README.TXT file.

Installation Instructions for Windows 3.x

Insert the CD into your CD-ROM drive. Go to the Program Manager window, choose Run and type **D:\Quake\install**. You will be prompted to choose your destination drive (your hard disk is probably C:) and destination path (C:\Games\Quake or C:\Quake—or whatever directory you want). You will automatically launch Quake, but once you see the demo running, hit the Esc key and select Options. Here is where you can tweak the game to your liking, including customizing keys and video resolution. Additional information and technical assistance are provided in the README.TXT file.

Another installation method is to go to File Manager, click on your D: drive icon, and double click on Install in the Quake directory.

Installation Instructions for Windows 95
Insert the CD into your CD-ROM drive. Click on the Start button, and select Run. In the window type **D:\Quake\install** (assuming your CD-ROM is the letter D:). You will be prompted to choose your destination drive (your hard disk is probably C:) and destination path (C:\Games\Quake or C:\Quake—or whatever directory you want). You will automatically launch Quake, but once you see the demo running, hit the Esc key and select Options. Here is where you can tweak the game to your liking, including customizing keys and video resolution. Additional information and technical assistance are offered in the README.TXT file.

There are two other ways to install Quake from Windows 95. You can go to Windows Explorer and select your D: drive and double click on Install.bat in the D:\Quake directory. Another method is to double click on My Computer and then double-click on D: Drive (there should be a picture of a CD-ROM). Double click on Quake and then double-click on Install.

MechWarrior 2 Demo
To run the MechWarrior 2 demo, you'll need an IBM PC or compatible machine, 486DX2/66 MHz processor, 8MB of RAM (7MB of free extended memory), 2x CD-ROM drive (although not required for the demo, you will need this for the full product), 22MB of hard-disk space (uncompressed space), VESA Local Bus (VLB) or PCI video, 256 color SVGA (640 x 480), MS-DOS 6.0, 100 percent Microsoft compatible mouse and driver, 100 percent Sound Blaster compatible sound card (digital and FM/MIDI audio), and a dedicated game card is highly recommended for joysticks.

Installation Instructions for DOS
Create a temporary directory called MW2DEMO on your hard drive. Insert the CD into your CD-ROM drive. If you're using DOS, simply change to the letter of your CD-ROM drive (most likely D: or E:), then type **CD MECH2DEM** and press Enter. Copy the MECH2DEM.EXE file and paste it in MW2DEMO directory on your hard drive. (**Note:** You can rename it or move it later). Double-click MECH2DEM.EXE to decompress the file. Open the README.TXT file and follow the instructions.

Installation Instructions Windows 3.x or 95
You can only install the game through DOS. Create a temporary directory called MW2DEMO on your hard drive. Insert the CD into your CD-ROM drive. Once at the C: prompt, change to your CD-ROM directory letter (D: or E:) and then type **CD MECH2DEM** and press Enter. Copy the MECH2DEM.EXE file and paste it in MW2DEMO directory on your hard drive. (**Note:** You can rename it or move it later). Double-click MECH2DEM.EXE to decompress the file. Open the README.TXT file and follow the instructions.

You can play the game in Windows, but you will experience a slowdown in performance. For Windows 95, go to Windows Explorer, and double click on the MECH2DEM.EXE file in the C:\MW2DEMO directory. Similarly, for Windows 3.x, go to File Manager and double click on the MECH2DEM.EXE file in the C:\MW2DEMO directory. Additional information is available in the README.TXT file.

INDEX OF WEB SITES